100 Natural Disasters

100 Natural Disasters

Spectacle and Tragedy

REBO
PUBLISHERS

© 2006 Rebo International b.v., Lisse, The Netherlands

Main redaction: Jordi Vigué
Text on pages 8, 10, 12, 14, 18, 24, 26, 28, 30, 32, 34, 38, 44, 46, 52, 56, 58, 62, 66, 70, 78, 80, 82, 84, 86, 88, 92, 94, 100, 104, 106, 108, 110, 112, 116, 118, 120, 122, 124, 128, 130, 132, 134, 136, 146, 148, 150, 154, 156, 158, 160, 162, 164, 168, 172, 176, 182, 184, 186, 188, 190, 192, 194, 198, 200: Joan Vaccaro

Text on pages 16, 20, 22, 36, 40, 42, 48, 50, 54, 60, 64, 68, 72, 74, 76, 90, 96, 98, 102, 114, 126, 138, 140, 142, 152, 166, 170, 178, 180, 196, 202, 204, 206: Frans Glissenaar, Aida Grovestins, Carien Reinking, Annemieke van Roekel, Marianne Wilschut for Studio Imago, Amersfoort, The Netherlands

Text on pages 144, 174: Marek Křížek, Zbyněk Engel

Photographs: Airphoto - Jim Wark, Arxiu Gorg Blanc, ANP - Algemeen Nederlands Persbureau ANP/AFP, ANP/EPA, AP – The Associated Press, Corbis, Earthquake Engineering Research Center, Berkeley, FEMA - U.S. Department of Homeland Security, Forest History Society, Inc., Getty Images, Jack Ives, KM.Krafft-CRI-Nancy-Lorraine, NASA's Earth Observatory NOAA - National Oceanic and Atmospheric Administration, Ogoniok Archives Reuters/WFA, Sigurdsson H., University of Rhode Island, Spaarnestad, State Historical Society of Missouri, Columbia, US Geological Survey, Wesson R.L.,/US Geological Survey, Xinhua/Landov/WFA Bohdan Dlouhý (144), rkfoto (145 both), Kateřina Davidová (174), Zdeněk Macháček (175), Borek Lupoměský (175), Fotobanka.cz

Layout and maps: A.R. Garamond, Prague, The Czech Republic
Typesetting: A.R. Garamond, Prague, The Czech Republic
Cover design: A.R. Garamond, Prague, The Czech Republic
Translators: Matthew Clarke, Jennifer Forbes (Spanish language), Guy Shipton (Dutch language), John Newton (Czech language) for First Edition Translations Ltd, Cambridge, UK
Editor: Sally Heavens for First Edition Translations Ltd, Cambridge, UK
Proofreading: Sarah Dunham

ISBN 13: 978-90-366-1892-2
ISBN 10: 90-366-1892-4

All rights reserved. No part of this publication may be reproduced, stored in a retrievalsystem, or transmitted in any form or by any means, electronic, mechanical, photocopying, recording or otherwise, without the prior written permission of the copyright holder.

100 NATURAL DISASTERS

Like all the heavenly bodies that make up the Universe, planet Earth is constantly changing. The plates that compose it, the strata of which it is formed, the materials of which they are made, the atmosphere in which it moves are subject to multiple, varied, and constant changes. One fine day, life appeared on this planet in a huge variety of forms. Thus began the evolution of humankind. Although the human race has adapted in order to survive, there is a constant struggle to find suitable habitats and a tolerable way of life. The word "disaster" is usually linked to the concept of a great misfortune or fatal event that inflicts great harm and loss on people and/or their environment. When we refer to natural disasters, we should bear in mind that they are actually the various ways in which the evolutionary process governing Earth manifests itself, often causing substantial changes in the geological and geographical morphology of the planet—and often seriously afflicting the human beings that inhabit it.

This work presents a selection of some of the many disasters humanity has suffered as a result of these telluric episodes. Earthquakes and volcanoes, hurricanes and tsunamis, are part of a range of disasters whose magnitude sometimes pits itself against the essential powerlessness of humankind. Spectacular events combine with tragedy, and ruin and slaughter and precede a new burgeoning of life. Before such displays of might, the human race can do little but acknowledge its limitations and vulnerability. These events are as impressive and transcendent as life—and the future of the Universe itself.

Jordi Vigué

Hurricane Carol

Bahamas, USA, Canada – 1953

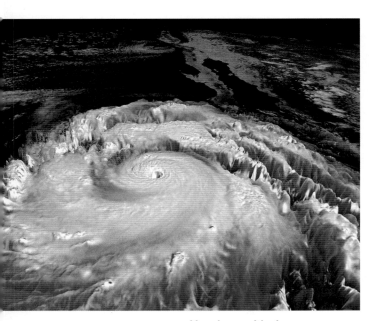

Hurricane Linda

United States – 1997

Typhoon Pongsona

Guam (Micronesia) – 2002

Index

Soufrière Hills eruption

Island of Montserrat – 2001

Texas tornado

United States – 1949

Hurricane Katrina

United States – 2005

Yellowstone eruption

If the crater of this volcano were to empty its contents, millions of people would die and Earth would undoubtedly suffer irreversible damage.

United States

650,000 years ago

For some years now, natural catastrophes have inspired numerous magazine articles, websites, movies, etc. Many display the fruit of meticulous research, but others are little more than science fiction or pseudo-science. One of the most popular topics is the volcanic megaeruption. This may sound like fantasy, but we all know that truth can be stranger than fiction. The event that took place in the distant past in Yellowstone has given rise to farfetched hypotheses that hopefully will never be put to the test.

Many thousands of years ago...

Yellowstone is the name of the first, and most famous, National Park in the United States. It is associated with expansive, untouched landscapes and dense forests, spectacular geysers, crystalline waterfalls, and even a popular cartoon character, Yogi Bear, who drives visitors to the park crazy in his search for food. With its surface area of 3,367 sq. miles (8,980 km²), Yellowstone is also the site of the biggest volcanic crater on Earth, stretching over an area of 34 x 45 miles (55 x 72 km). This volcanic formation is the most active in the United States, but it is only recently that its full size has been appreciated, as space technology and NASA satellites have been required to verify it.

The Yellowstone crater rests on what was once an old volcano. A large number of internal movements caused an explosion 650,000 years ago that was 2,500 times more powerful than that of Mount St. Helens. The ashes released in the eruption covered virtually the whole of North America. A series of further violent eruptions occurred at intervals of 20,000 years, leaving in their wake the crater that is visible today. The last of these gigantic explosions took place 70,000 years ago.

Nowadays, the only signs of volcanic activity are the hot water springs, domes of boiling mud, the surreally colored pools, and the famous geysers. Magma deposits lying just beneath the surface cause the latter, with the upward pressure of successive layers of magma creating jets of vapor like the Old Faithful Geyser. If a series of circumstances were to coincide in the subsoil of the crater, all the stored magma would be thrust into the air in a hugely violent eruption, more in keeping with overheated imaginations than scientific facts. This is not the only such caldera on the planet, as similar formations can be found in Toba (Indonesia) and Aso (Japan), but the one in Yellowstone National Park has attracted the most attention.

In addition to its current volcanic activity, the subsoil of the caldera and its surrounding area are lined by active geological faults. The combination of these faults and the movement of magma triggers numerous earthquakes. In 2002, for example, 2,300 were recorded, the majority imperceptible to the human eye. In the past, however, some have had serious consequences, such as the Hebgen Lake earthquake in 1959, which reached 7.5 on the Richter scale.

The Yellowstone caldera is sometimes called a supervolcano, although this is not an accepted scientific term – it was coined by a BBC program devoted to this type of volcano and its possible eruptions. It is, however, used in a generalized way to define volcanoes capable of producing colossal explosions beyond any recognized measurement system. A single eruption could cover an entire continent with several inches of ash and cause major climatic upheavals. As no conventional volcano could behave in this way, the expert view, led by the above-mentioned program, is that a giant caldera like this would be the most likely instigator of such a disaster.

Fact or fantasy?

Whenever there is talk of supervolcanoes, huge eruptions, and global crises triggered by such eruptions, the Yellowstone caldera is invariably used as a model. If this caldera were to empty all its magma content, the effects would be horrendous, with millions of deaths and climatic effects that could be almost irreversible in the short term, like a radioactive winter, but on a much greater scale. Eruptions like those of Pinatubo and Tambora would pale in comparison to an eruption of Yellowstone. The plant species of the entire continent would be threatened and millions of animals would perish, although some insects might perhaps survive this Apocalypse. The United States and its neighbors would be shrouded in a layer of ash a couple of inches thick, with any return to normal life an impossibility for several generations to come. It would be a cataclysm on a par with those that saw the formation of the Earth.

Fortunately, we need not be alarmed. There are no signs that anything like this can occur in the near future. Geologists still do not fully understand the functioning of the caldera and its possible actions, however, so they have to learn as they go along, by making exhaustive observations and analyses. In the last few years, a greater number of preventive measures have been applied and there has been an increase in the number of specialists studying the caldera, along with a host of different opinions on how to prevent a megaeruption.

Some experts advocate making holes to allow the magma and gases contained in the subsoil to escape, while others suggest dynamiting certain areas. The magma in Yellowstone is not very mobile, however, so such actions could be pointless (or have unpredictable consequences). The destiny of the caldera is ultimately in its own hands, or rather in its own subsoil. All we can do is study it, and hope – hope that alarmist theses, fuelled by sensationalist magazines and TV movies, will never become reality.

Left:
One of Yellowstone's spectacular natural pools. Note its internal formation, clearly of volcanic origin.

Terraces formed by erosion and volcanic activity.

The Castle Geyser in full eruption. Phenomena like this thrill the thousands of tourists who visit the National Park every year.

The Last Ice Age

During this period, ice covered 35 percent of the land above sea level (as opposed to 10 percent today).

100,000 years ago

The last Ice Age was rather more than a natural disaster. It is not possible to understand life on planet Earth without taking into account the Ice Ages. Life clearly flourished in the intervening periods (known as the interglacial periods), but it was substantially – although not entirely – extinguished during new episodes in which the ice relentlessly advanced. Every new Ice Age represented a struggle for life, as well as a global climate change, and the last of them gave rise to the species that would go on to dominate Earth: man.

The Ice Ages

The Ice Ages were geological periods characterized by a cooling of the Earth, during which ice covered large expanses of its surface. They were marked by humidity and – of course – extreme cold, as well as the lowest sea levels known to modern science.

There is no commonly accepted theory about the causes of the Ice Ages, although various explanations have been put forward since the 17th century. The current thinking is that there was more than one reason for the phenomenon, and that it could be the result of a combination of the following three factors:

- A change in the composition of the atmosphere, due to the ratio of carbon dioxide and methane, which would prompt huge drops in temperature. This is similar to what we now call global warming, but the other way round, and evidently in far greater proportions.
- The movement of the continents, which would have been brought about by cyclical changes in the Earth's orbit around the Sun; these may have been complemented by changes in the angle of the planet's orientation to the Sun.
- As it was receiving less sunlight, the Earth's mass would cool, leading to glaciation.

Ice Ages have affected the Earth on several occasions. The biggest glaciations took place around 950-600 million years ago, during the Precambrian era. Then came those of the Ordovician period, about 450 million years ago; those of the Permian period, 290-280 million years ago; and those of the Miocene epoch, 15 million years ago.

The traces of glaciation visible today are a legacy of the last two million years, during what is known as the Quaternary geological period. This Ice Age is the one best understood by scientists, who have divided it into four phases: Günz, Mindel, Riss, and Würm. The latter corresponds to the period of the last Ice Age.

The last Ice Age

The Würm period began some 100,000 years ago and reached its maximum intensity 18,000 years ago, before diminishing 8,000 years later. During this time, ice attained a thickness of 200–250 miles (350–400km) and covered one third of the land above sea level, or three times its present extension. If we take into account the amount of ice now covering the planet, we can get some idea of its appearance during this period: today's glaciers cover some 5.75 million sq. miles (14.9 million km²), almost 10 percent of the Earth's surface, but during the Ice Age they accounted for 15.4 million sq. miles (44.4 million km²), or 30 percent of the surface area. The ice in northern Canada, for example, was thought to have stretched over more than 5.1 million sq. miles (13.3 million km²), whereas it now occupies 56.85 sq. miles (147.25 km²). A similarly discrepancy can be found in Scandinavia; between 2.58 million sq. miles (6.7 million km²) then, and 1,470 sq. miles (3,810 km²) now.

The last Ice Age simultaneously afflicted both hemispheres, although the ice was more widespread in the north. In Europe it covered most of the British Isles, northern Germany, and Poland, while in North America, where

The Rocky Mountains covered in snow. Large parts of Europe and the American continent looked like this.

The sea of ice on Tigvariak Island in Alaska resembles the seas during the periods of glaciation.

The Ice Age came to an end as part of a slow process. The arrival of spring in Alaska gives an idea of what these days could have been like.

In the last Ice Age, the seas in places where snow and ice were not generalized could have resembled this one.

10

the Würm glaciation is known as Wisconsin, the layer of ice that descended from the North Pole shrouded the whole of Canada and extended further south than the Great Lakes. Like those in Patagonia and the Alps they formed on the hollows left by the melted mass of ice.

The sea level dropped by nearly 400 ft (120 m) such that, during this period, large tracts of land that are currently covered by seawater were dry. This fact is of great significance, as it permitted the large-scale human and animal migrations that were the starting point for life as we know it today, with the hominids walking from Siberia to Alaska and from mainland Europe to England. It is probable that the two largest masses of ice on Earth – in Antarctica and Greenland–remained during the interglacial periods and have undergone few modifications in comparison to the rest of the planet.

At the height of glaciation, the mean temperature reduction varied enormously from place to place: 50 °F (10 °C) in Alaska, 43 °F (6 °C) in England, 36 °F (2 °C) in the Tropics, and virtually no change on the Equator. Studies carried out on the last great glaciations of the Pleistocene epoch in North America and Europe yielded identical dates for the glaciations of this geological area, spanning (approximately) the last two million years.

The last 100,000 years are crucial to our understanding of human development. The Ice Ages posed a severe challenge to the Earth's inhabitants. Each time a glaciation ended, they had to adapt once again and learn how to survive in the changed scenario: higher temperatures, higher sea levels, fast-running rivers, new woods, new plants, and land that had risen once it was free of the weight of the ice.

The hominids were best equipped to adjust to these changed conditions. They were somehow capable of migrating to regions with the most resources and, once there, evolving slowly, but unremittingly–we are talking in terms of thousands of years and not of our period of history – into what we are today.

Eruption of Vesuvius

The earthquake of 83 B.C.E. was undoubtedly a bad omen, but nobody accorded it the least importance.

ITALY
Rome · Vesuvius
Mediterranean sea

Pompeii
and Herculanum
Campania
(Italy)

August 24, 79 B.C.E.

3,000 dead

Aerial view of Pompeii, brought back to life after excavations in the 18th century. The city had remained buried under lava since 79 B.C.E.

One of southern Italy's not-to-be-missed tourist sites is the city of Pompeii, in the bay of Naples; along with its neighbor Herculanum, it is one of the best-preserved ancient cities. This state of conservation would not have been possible without the eruption of Vesuvius on August 24, 79 B.C.E.

Vesuvius has given its name to a type of volcano that alternates eruptions of pyroclastic material with expulsions of lava, giving rise to successive strata that account for the great size of such volcanoes. Mount Fuji (Japan) and Teide (Canary Islands, Spain) are other examples of Vesuvian volcanoes. Another shared characteristic is the enormous strength of their eruptions, as can clearly be seen in the case in question.

Pompeii and Herculanum were two prosperous cities at the time of the eruption. Set in a strategic enclave of the Bay of Naples, they were key trading centers, as well as vacation getaways for the Roman emperors and patricians. Both cities were, however, situated in Campania, one of the most seismically active regions of Europe. Earthquakes were frequent, as they are today. Contemporary chroniclers described how the locals regularly moved house on account of this phenomenon. These tremors were caused by the movement of lava inside Mount Vesuvius, which was reflected in the exterior in the form of an earthquake. This chain of events is common knowledge now, but for Roman science it was an unfathomable mystery. Despite this seismic activity, the residents of both cities went on with their everyday lives, even after a major earthquake in 83 B.C.E. After this upheaval, both cities set about making improvements and investing in greater luxury, taking advantage of the flourishing trade that fuelled their economies.

The end of prosperity

Many commentators have expressed surprise that the Romans – who were much given to soothsaying and finding positive or negative auguries in the workings of Nature – did not foresee that something dreadful was going to happen. Earthquakes were a bad omen, but in this case the fateful signs were ignored. Between the earthquake of 83 B.C.E. and the eruption of 79 B.C.E., the volcano remained at rest. Unfortunately, however, in volcanoes of this type, the greater the period of lethargy, the greater the virulence when they awaken.

Although centuries have passed since this eruption, we have an excellent chronicle of the event from the pen of Pliny the Younger, who told the story of the disaster in a series of letters to the famous historian Tacitus. Pliny, who lived 20 miles (30 km) from Pompeii, tells how, on the morning of August 23, an enormous dark cloud in the shape of a pine emerged from the peak of Vesuvius, covering the sun and quickly turning day into night. Shortly afterwards, the cloud began to pour down the slopes and cover the sea. The phenomenon described by Pliny was an enormous formation of pyroclastic material — ash, gases and rocks — which advanced at a speed of over 60 miles (100 km) per hour. Pliny's hometown of Misenum, situated on the shore opposite Pompeii and Herculanum, was evacuated. His uncle, Pliny the Elder, the most prestigious naturalist of ancient times, was in charge of the garrison in Misenum. When he saw what was happening above Pompeii and Herculanum, he set sail with his fleet to evacuate the two cities. Fate was against him, however: along with hundreds of sailors and citizens, he was killed by the gases emanating from the cloud.

In the early hours of August 24, Vesuvius spewed tons of lava, ash, and igneous rocks with unprecedented force. It is not hard to imagine the panic that took hold of the two cities. In the dead of night, they found themselves caught up in a disaster that defied comprehension. The ash and lava engulfed them both, along with various towns on their outskirts. How many people were killed? Little is known in this respect. It has been calculated that both cities had around 20,000 inhabitants at the time of the eruption. Bearing in mind that the evacuation of Pompeii and Herculanum was ineffective and that both were important trading centers (and thus played host to countless visitors), it is believed that a total of around 3,000 people lost their lives.

The eruption lasted only a few hours, but it displayed immense destructive power, leaving not a trace

of these two thriving cities. The significance of the disaster to the Romans can be seen by their reluctance to repopulate the sites that were devastated by the eruption.

Recovering the past

Pompeii and Herculanum remained hidden from view for almost 1,700 years. In 1550, the architect Fontana discovered their remains while undertaking excavations to change the course of the River Sarno. It was not until 1738 and 1748, however, that Herculanum and Pompeii were respectively excavated on a more systematic basis, with the fruits of these digs remaining today, in the form of two petrified cities that remained unaltered after the eruption of Vesuvius.

This discovery was of immense importance to archeologists and historians, giving them a complete picture of everyday life in a Roman city with its houses, stores, inhabitants, food, and hundreds of other elements that have proved vital to our understanding of the classical world. During the excavations, hollows that had once contained human remains were found in the

ash. These were filled with modeling paste to yield statues that recorded with great precision the last moments of the citizens who were unable to escape the eruption. In some cases, their terrified expression is clearly apparent.

Far from being dormant, Vesuvius has continued to show signs of its vivacity: in 1906 and 1944, several nearby towns were evacuated as it was becoming increasingly

active. The eventual eruptions were less significant than that of 79 B.C.E., but nevertheless left 5,000 people homeless, destroyed entire towns, and killed many people. These were only warnings, however. According to recent studies, Mount Vesuvius may yet prove to be even more destructive than ever.

The summit of Vesuvius, now calm. Its violent eruption destroyed two jewels of antiquity: Pompeii and Herculanum.

The Bay of Naples, with Vesuvius in eruption. Although impressive, the eruption in Roman times was far more devastating.

Eruption of Tsurumi

This eruption was so violent that the top of the volcano was thrown into the air, with its height being reduced from 6,560 ft (2,000 m) to the 4,507 ft (1,374 m) visible today.

Kyushu Island
Oita District
(Japan)

867 A.D.

One of the mud fountains. Bubbling mud gushes out of these small cones – one of the many natural curiosities provided by the volcano to the city of Beppu.

The spa city of Beppu amidst the steam of its hot springs. The water is heated by the internal activity of Tsurumi.

Not all volcanic eruptions cause damage to the immediate environment. In Latin America and Indonesia, for example, lands ravaged by ash and other materials have become superb farming land only a few years later. Japan, where eruptions are often very destructive, has also reaped long-term benefits from the actions of its volcanoes. The most outstanding example of this is the city of Beppu, close to Mount Tsurumi.

A giant brought down to size

Mount Tsurumi is located in the northeast of the island of Kyushu, in the district of Oita. It is surrounded by the National Park of Aso-Kuju, one of the most beautiful natural areas in the country, renowned for its expanses of cherry trees and the spa waters of the city of Beppu, which are derived from Tsurumi itself. This volcano is complemented by Mount Yufu, which is of a similar geological age. Of the two, Yufu is higher, at 5,197 ft (1,584 m), while Tsurumi stands at 4,508 ft (1,374 m) above sea level. On the north slope of the two volcanoes, which appear to form a single mountain from some angles, there are three small, smoking volcanic cones that register significant activity. Geologists, who estimate that both mountains have been active for over 35,000 years, monitor the cones from nearby observation posts.

Yufu has never erupted in modern times, but it is known that its last signs of life were marked by strong explosions and a massive outrush of pyroclastic material, which caused the dome to cave in and form a crater. The ash deposits that have been analyzed by paleogeologists suggest that a substantial column of tephra was formed.

Tsurumi has been rather more active, although only three eruptions have been recorded, all in ancient times. The first was in 200 AD, with two more in 771 and 867. The latter was by far the most significant, although that of 200 had a high explosive component, being characterized by expulsions of pyroclastic material as well as emanations of ash and gases. The eruption in the middle of 867 was much longer, lasting a full two months! Over the course of this period, the volcano was shaken by several explosions that ejected huge amounts of ashes and other residues, particularly pyroclastic material. In one of the periods of greatest activity, the peak of Tsurumi itself was thrown into the air. According to contemporary poems, the mountain had once soared to 6,560 ft (2,000 m), but the explosion reduced it to its present height.

The impact of the disaster must have been considerable, as there are reports of the extinction of most of the fish in the nearby lakes and rivers on account of the downpour of pyroclastic fragments and lava. No data is available, however, with respect to the loss of human life and property.

Tsurumi has not erupted since then. Its activity has been confined to fumes from the crater and the heating of the spa waters in the city of Beppu. Even though it presents no imminent risk to the local population, five observation posts have been established on the volcano, under the auspices of the Aso Volcanic Laboratory, founded in 1928 and now one of the most prestigious departments in Kyoto University. Its work consists in keeping watch over the volcano's activity to warn of any eruptions and studying all the geological aspects of the mountain.

Beppu, a spa city

If Mount Tsurumi is famous for anything today, it is for its contri-

bution to Beppu. In fact, if it were not for the volcano, the city would not exist. Thanks to the internal activity of Tsurumi, the waters of Beppu can reach temperatures of up to 392 °F (200 °C), although these are obviously reduced for water used for curative or pleasure purposes (to 104–107 °F/40–42 °C). The fumeroles and hot water springs attract countless visitors, making Beppu one of the most famous spas in Japan. The area covered by the various geysers, fumeroles, and natural pools amounts to almost 15.45 sq. miles (40 km²).

Some of the springs have been popular for hundreds of years, especially the so-called *jigokus* (infernos): for example, the turquoise Umi Jigoku, the reddish Chinoike, and the Tatsumi Jigoku, a geyser that spurts water to a height of 80 ft (25 m). These are just some of the many natural attractions offered by Beppu.

The inhabitants of the city, faithful to time-honored traditions, celebrate two festivals in

which the volcano and the hot springs are the focal points. Beppu Onsen Matsuri expresses gratitude for the gift of the waters heated by the bowels of Tsurumi by means of a week of dances, religious ceremonies, and other activities. Mount Tsurumi itself provides the setting for the Tsurumi-dake Ikki Tozan Taikai,

a race that starts in the spa and ends on the summit of the volcano. The runners cannot step on asphalt, only the soil of the mountain itself, which has thus evolved from a source of destruction into a symbol of healing.

One of Beppu's most popular hot springs: Chinoike, notable for its reddish-colored water.

Lisbon earthquake

The Lisbon earthquake was one of the most destructive events of its kind in history, its effects reaching as far as the Caribbean and Finland. The scale of the disaster led to the first serious research into seismology.

Lisbon, Portugal

November 1, 1755

100,000 dead

Engraving depicting the earthquake of 1755: burning buildings and capsizing ships

The epicenter of this earthquake lay in the Atlantic Ocean approximately 125 miles (200 km) southwest of Cape St. Vincent, which marks the most southwesterly point of Europe. The effects of the quake were colossal, particularly in Lisbon and its immediate surroundings, but also elsewhere in Portugal as well as in Spain and Morocco. The observation of effects as far away as Finland suggests to modern geologists that the quake approached magnitude 9 on the Richter scale.

It began at around 9:30 a.m. on November 1, the Catholic holy day of All Saints. It was a perfect fall morning with beautiful weather, and the residents of Lisbon—whose then population of 275,000 made it one of the largest cities in Europe—were preparing for a day of celebrations. Three shocks were felt one after the other, which altogether lasted for approximately six minutes and caused thousands of

homes and buildings to collapse. Most of the survivors of this initial devastation fled toward the banks of the Tagus, the river that flows into the sea at Lisbon and divides the city into two. At that time, Lisbon was a major port and the capital of Portugal's great colonial empire, whose interests embraced Latin America, Africa, and Asia. Consequently, the harbor was bustling with ships in transit, and many people sought refuge on board these vessels.

Tidal wave

Approximately 30 minutes after the earthquake, these refugees witnessed the waters of the Tagus recede almost entirely into the sea. This was followed immediately afterward by an enormous wave, several feet in height, which swept many people away and sank all the ships. This tidal wave, or tsunami, was not confined to Lisbon. The

entire coast of Portugal was assailed, in particular the Algarve in the south of the country where many towns and villages were devastated. The tsunami later struck northern Europe as well, where waves measuring 10 feet (3 meters) in height ravaged the coasts of countries such as England and Finland. Unusually rough conditions were reported even in the Dutch lagoon of Haarlemmermeer. To the south of the epicenter, the tidal wave inflicted major damage on the Spanish coastal cities of Huelva and Cadiz and even affected the inland city of Seville, where the River Guadalquivir burst its banks.

The coast of Morocco was also hit, with fatalities in many cities including Tangier, Rabat, and Agadir. The earthquake itself had already caused death and destruction in Meknes, Fes, and Marrakech. Elsewhere, people were killed as a result of tidal waves hit-

ting the Caribbean islands of Martinique and Barbados.

Fires broke out throughout Lisbon almost immediately after the earthquake, many of them caused by abandoned cooking pots and burning candles. As homes were fled in panic, fires quickly took hold, with nobody able or willing to fight them. It was five days before the conflagration burnt itself out, with the flames destroying many of those buildings that had somehow managed to withstand both the earthquake and the tidal wave. The final death toll of the quake was later estimated at 100,000, of which 90,000 were in Lisbon and 10,000 elsewhere. In view of the far-reaching nature of the quake and the subsequent tsunami, however, the number of casualties beyond Lisbon was probably much greater than this.

Cultural disaster

The earthquake was also a cultural disaster. Churches and museums were razed together with, for example, the Phoenix Opera House, built barely six months earlier. The Royal Palace at Terreiro do Paço was lost and with it the royal library, which together contained more than 70,000 books and hundreds of paintings by famous artists such as Titian, Rubens, and Correggio. The royal archives, which housed such items as the logbooks and accounts of explorers and navigators including Vasco da Gama, were also destroyed. Despite this, the royal family itself was miraculously spared, having followed the desire of one of the princesses to spend the feast day in the hills outside

Lisbon. Following the disaster, the court took up residence in an encampment in the outlying district of Ajuda. For the rest of his life, King Joseph I refused to live indoors and, until his death in 1777, continued to be housed with his family in tents and pavilions.

Immediately after the earthquake, the Prime Minister, Sebastião José de Carvalho e Melo, later better known as the Marquis of Pombal, set energetically to work on reconstruction. In response to the king's inquiry on what was to be done, he is said to have replied: "Now? Bury the dead and feed the living." Against the wishes of the Catholic Church, as many of the dead as possible were cremated. Looters were punished immediately by hanging and all roads out of the city were closed off: anyone who was fit to escape was deemed able to help with reconstruction. Although Lisbon was quickly rebuilt through a combination of these measures and the steely resolve of the Marquis of Pombal, the earthquake is still seen by many as marking the beginning of the end for Portugal as a flourishing, colonial power. Over the course of the eighteenth century, the country lost much of its colonial territory and was outstripped in terms of maritime supremacy, by Great Britain and the Netherlands in particular.

The beginnings of seismology

The earthquake suffered by Lisbon—an important economic and cultural center—sent emotional shockwaves through Europe. Writers, painters, artists, and philosophers took it as a source of

inspiration. As one example, it plays a role in the novel *Candide* by the French writer Voltaire, who also devoted a special poem to it entitled *Poème sur le désastre de Lisbonne* (Poem on the Lisbon Disaster). The German philosopher Immanuel Kant published various texts in response to this calamitous event, while also developing a theory to explain the cause of earthquakes in general. Although this theory was later proven to be false, it nevertheless constitutes the first attempt to account for the phenomenon of earthquakes from a scientific approach; as such, it can be considered the first step in seismology. In Portugal itself, on the orders of the Marquis of Pombal, every municipality was issued with a checklist containing a number of practical questions concerning the events surrounding the earthquake, such as the number of aftershocks that had been felt, and observations made relating to springs and wells. All answers to these questionnaires have been preserved to this day; over the intervening centuries they have proved an important source of information to seismologists and other scientists.

Lisbon at the time of the disaster, as viewed from the sea

Illustration of the tidal wave, on land and at sea

Eruption of Papandayang

The materials expelled into the air covered an area measuring 12 x 5½ miles (20 x 9 km), caused the death of 3,000 people and the disappearance of 40 towns.

Western Java
(Indonesia)

August 11–12, 1772

3,000 dead

In the past, volcanic eruptions were seen in some parts of the world as violent punishment meted out by the gods. One such disaster occurred in what is now Indonesia, a group of islands dotted with volcanoes that have caused several major catastrophes over the course of time. The eruption of Papandayang was one of the earliest of these – and also one of the most destructive ever to hit the region.

A lethal avalanche

The island of Java is clearly of volcanic origin, as indicated by the presence of nearly forty extinct cones scattered over its territory. Just a few decades ago, some of these volcanoes were still rumbling ominously, instilling fear in the island's inhabitants. Although many are now inactive, others are still full of life and have been known to cause severe material damage and even fatalities in the past. Such was the case with Merapi in 1849 and Galoen-Gong, which erupted with enormous violence in 1822, but did not lead to any loss of life – quite amazing, if we consider the absence of the warning systems available today.

Of all the volcanoes on the island, however, Papandayang is a case apart. This mountain in western Java is a stratovolcano 6,560 ft (2000 m) high, and forms part of a ring of volcanoes. It has two separate peaks – Alun-Alun, which is virtually flat, and Gunung Putang, which is pointed – making it appear incomplete when seen from a distance. It was in fact originally one single peak, but over time eruptions have caused the walls of its main crater to collapse, leaving this curious sight.

Papandayang's main crater is flanked by a lush forest that stretches down its steep northeastern slope before reaching a river at the foot of the mountain. This can prove fatal to the local inhabitants if lahars form, although the risks have been reduced over time. The volcano's crater, characterized by its intense activity, contains sulfurous pools and fountains, fumeroles, geysers, and jets of mud, making it a noisy and picturesque spectacle. The presence of sulfur has stained much of the opening and the surrounding areas a strange yellow color, which slightly unreal look has turned Papandayang into a tourist attraction, although it must be pointed out that, however striking these formations may appear, they can still cause problems. Many of the residues of this sulfur end up in the river, making it dangerously polluted.

All this activity is paltry, however, in comparison with the eruption of 1772, which has been by

far the most destructive of those experienced by Papandayang. We owe our knowledge of this awesome event to the Dutch merchants in the region and the information gleaned by travelers after the event.

On the night of August 11, 1772, the summit of Papandayang seemed to be lit up by a cloud. The locals were accustomed to the noises emanating from the mountain, but they considered this phenomenon abnormal. They sensed that something bad was going to happen and, just a few hours after the appearance of the cloud, decided to abandon their villages. It was already too late, however; in the early hours of the morning, strong tremors shook the summit of the mountain, accompanied by fearsome roars. In just a few minutes, part of the peak collapsed. Eyewitness accounts state that the noise was so loud that in other parts of the island it was assumed to be the sound of an artillery bombardment from a warship. The eruption was brutal, as the volcano hurled all types of pyroclastic material, lava, pumice stone, rocks, and ash around its vast bulk, forming gigantic avalanches that caused immense dev-

astation and enshrouded an area some 12 miles (20 km) long and 5½ miles (9 km) wide.

Two months later, the inquisitive souls who approached the sight declared that the ground and rocks were still hot enough to burn at the slightest touch. It proved impossible to reach the mountain or the remains of the devastated villages for several more months. In all, forty settlements were destroyed and three thousand people died, many instantaneously, as a result of this brutal eruption.

Subsequent episodes

Fortunately, Papandayang has never again been so destructive, although it has erupted since. The last two eruptions with a high index of activity took place in 1942 and 2002, but as we have seen, this volcano is a site of constant activity and small explosions can occur at any time.

The last eruption that caused anxiety in the towns close to the volcano took place three years ago. After a few days in which minor earthquakes were noted, the vol-

cano rumbled fiercely and intensified its activity for almost two months, from November 11, 2002 to January 13, 2003. During this period it ejected enormous quantities of lava and a column of ash and smoke nearly 4 miles (6 km) high. Several towns were evacuated and the levees, which had been built on the rivers and sides of the volcano to prevent any possible lahars, were severely damaged. Avalanches of lava, debris, and ash decimated hundreds of acres of crops. The eruption attracted photographers and geologists from all over the world. Luckily, there were no victims, but the incident has led to increased vigilance and improved safety systems.

A stream on the slopes of the volcano. Its high sulfur content is clearly apparent.

This mouth of the volcano emits sulfur, which has formed deposits all round the mountain.

A sulfurous cloud emanating from the depths of Papandayang.

New Madrid earthquakes

A series of destructive earthquakes took place that would change the course of the Mississippi River.

Missouri, Kentucky, Tennessee, Arkansas, United States

December 1811–February 1812

Major gully in the Chicksaw Bluffs in Tennessee, caused by a landslip

Extremely high waves in the Mississippi River in the state of Missouri

Wooden houses jolted and panic among the population

In the winter of 1811–1812, a series of earthquakes equivalent to magnitude 8 on the Richter scale began in the early morning of December 16, 1811 and was followed by two further waves of quakes that occurred the following January and February. The epicenter was close to New Madrid, a town on the Mississippi River located between the two major river cities of St. Louis and Natchez.

At the beginning of the nineteenth century, the western frontier of the New World was the Mississippi, which, together with the Missouri, forms the largest river system in North America; it was a busy shipping channel even then. The areas affected were thinly populated; contemporary estimates of the population of New Madrid vary in the archives from 400 to a few thousand. Roughly 4,000 Americans must have experienced the disaster locally, a figure that does not include the native population.

Fountains, craters, and sulfurous fumes

Survivors reported how the earth split open, the ground visibly rippled, and plots of land sank into depressions, while, in other places, the ground rose up. Some fissures in the ground continued for several miles. This natural disaster was accompanied by an enormous roaring like thunder and a nerve-shredding whistling. "My horse stood rooted to the spot, lame with fear," recalled an eyewitness.

"The trees broke like matchsticks, groves of them falling to the ground. The air was filled with sulfurous fumes."

"All about me, water spurted from the earth in fountains many feet high," reported another survivor. "The ground shook so mightily that it was with great difficulty I was able to keep my footing and stay upright. Miniature volcanoes appeared, while water and sand were forced from the water-saturated riverbed under great pressure. For as far as my eyes could see, the landscape was covered in craters, some of which were some 15 ft (4.5 m) deep." Apart from New Madrid, the small towns of Little Prairie and Point Pleasant also took their share of the assault. Little Prairie was so severely hit that it was entirely abandoned.

The bed of the Mississippi river subsided, causing the river to flow backward for a brief while. Thousands of miles away in Boston, Massachusetts, church bells began to ring of their own accord due to the ground vibrations. The disaster, which became the subject of serious geological study only in the second half of the twentieth century, occurred as the first steamboat to travel the Mississippi, the New Orleans, was making its maiden voyage from the Ohio River to New Orleans. Its crew reported how the island to which the vessel was moored had disappeared underwater by the following morning.

The three series of quakes and thousands of aftershocks took place within the space of eight weeks. These seismic movements would change the landscape and course of the Mississippi forever. Forests were drowned or laid waste and new lakes appeared, such as Reelfoot Lake in Tennessee and St. Francis and Big Lake in Arkansas.

Failed rift

Historically, despite its mid-continental location, the area surrounding New Madrid (Missouri) has had to deal with countless earthquakes. The upstream segment of the Mississippi, better known to geologists as the New Madrid seismic zone (NMSZ), forms part of a "failed rift," a fault line that runs for hundreds of miles and which, in ancient geological history, was several times at the point of splitting the North American continent into two. The possibility was finally eliminated when the Atlantic Ocean began to form. This failed split, known today as the Reelfoot Rift, created a depression, later to become the river basin of the Mississippi. Many other great rivers of the planet flow through such failed rifts.

Most of the earthquakes in the United States to the east of the Rocky Mountains occur in the NMSZ. Although this type of natural disaster occurs much more frequently in the west of North America, the impact of an earthquake in the Midwest is experienced over a far greater area. The reason for this is the great depth of the underlying faults, which enables tremors to travel much further. Damage was even reported in Washington D.C. and South Carolina, with the shocks being felt as far away as Quebec. Later earthquakes in 1843 and 1895, estimated at magnitude 6.5 on the Richter scale, were also felt at great distances.

The "scar tissue" of faults and fissures under the ground surrounding New Madrid remains a point of weakness. According to seismologists, new earthquakes could occur in the region at any time, with a 7–10 percent likelihood of an earthquake registering a magnitude of at least 8 on the Richter scale occurring within the next 50 years.

Nowadays, the Mississippi basin is heavily populated. Memphis, Tennessee and St. Louis, Missouri, have grown into cities that are home to millions. Compared with other parts of the United States (California, for example) modern buildings in this region remain inadequately prepared for serious earthquakes. The midwestern states of the USA have therefore united to form the Central United States Earthquake Consortium (CUSEC), which provides information on, and conducts research into, earthquakes in the region. Regulations have also been drawn up for architects in designing earthquake-proof buildings.

Enigma

Seismic activity has been recorded in earnest since 1974. Thousands of earthquakes, many of them minor, have been recorded since that time. The force of the 1811–1812 quakes has never been equaled, however, and remains an enigma to scientists. Uncertainty also surrounds the tectonic forces the faults in the NMSZ have the potential to unleash.

Island of Sumbawa,
Indonesia

April 5–12, 1815

12,000 dead
(direct causes)
80,000 dead
(indirect causes)

Eruption of Mount Tambora

The eruption of the Tambora volcano in Indonesia in 1815 is the greatest ever recorded. Its effects were still being felt a year later: 1816 was referred to worldwide as "the year without a summer."

On the evening of April 5, a loud explosion was heard in Batavia–present-day Jakarta–780 miles (1,250 km) from Tambora. The British Governor-General, Stamford Raffles, thought that revolutionaries were attacking the city and dispatched army units to Batavia. In the harbor of Makassar, the captain of a British naval vessel thought that fighting must be in progress somewhere at sea. What nobody knew at the time was that a natural disaster of unimaginable proportions was announcing itself to the world: the eruption of the Tambora volcano.

There have almost certainly been greater eruptions in the history of mankind, but such events took place so long ago that no records of them exist. Tambora has been rated a VEI magnitude 7 eruption: the Volcanic Explosivity Index runs from magnitude 1 through 8. Consequently, this was an eruption of greater severity than that, for example, of Krakatoa in 1883, classed as magnitude 6. Mount Tambora is referred to as a "stratovolcano," sometimes also known as a "composite volcano." These are symmetrical, cone-shaped volcanoes composed of various layers of lava, fallen rock, and ash. Famous stratovolcanoes include Mount Fuji in Japan, Cotopaxi in Ecuador, and Mount Hood in Oregon.

Tambora, located on the island of Sumbawa, had been restless for years prior to 1815. Its crater disgorged thick, black clouds of smoke, rumblings were heard, and the earth regularly shook. Many eruptions followed the explosion of April 5. A steady rain of ash had begun to fall on Java that day and numerous earth tremors were felt, but nobody knew the exact cause. The major eruption occurred on the evening of April 10. The volcano spewed out over 62 cubic miles (100 cubic km) of magma and rock, creating a crater measuring some 4 miles (7 km) in diameter. Huge blocks of rock landed more than 25 miles (40 km) from the volcano. Before the eruption, the height of the volcano had been approximately 13,800 ft (4,200 m). Afterward, it measured a mere 9,350 ft (2,851 m). For three consecutive days, the island of Sumbawa and its immediate surroundings were shrouded in a thick cloud of black smoke, the sea around the island littered with driftwood from uprooted trees and floating islands of pumice stone ejected from the volcano. For days there were earthquakes, tidal waves, and tornados, and it is estimated that 12,000 lost their lives: those who lived either on, or in the neighborhood of, the peninsular where Tambora lies.

Famine

A major part of the island of Sumbawa, where it is estimated that 140,000 people then lived, was covered with a layer of ash and mud 20 inches (50 cm) thick, which smothered all plant life. No food could be grown on the island for years afterward. Consequently, those who had survived the disaster now faced famine. Moreover, this famine was not restricted to the island of Sumbawa. The neighboring islands to the west, Lombok and Bali in particular, were also swamped with a rain of ash and there, too, all harvests failed. It is estimated that these famines, together with a cholera epidemic on Sumbawa due to

Even now, clouds of smoke still sometimes emerge from the volcano

At the edge of the crater

a lack of clean drinking water, claimed another 80,000 lives; however, experts agree that the actual death toll cannot be confirmed and that it could have greatly exceeded this number.

On April 18, Governor-General Raffles dispatched Lieutenant Owen Philips to the disaster area with a ship laden with rice, to distribute aid and discover precisely what had happened. The report with which Philips returned in September 1815, including the eyewitness account of a village chief at a distance of 25 miles (40 km) from Tambora, remains one of the most important sources of knowledge about this eruption today.

The repercussions of the eruption were on a worldwide scale. As a result of the volcanic ash rising high into the atmosphere, average global temperatures fell by approximately 5.4 °F (3 °C). The results of this were largely felt in the year *following* the eruption. Throughout North America and Europe, people had to contend with lower temperatures and too little sunlight, which is why 1816 was referred to as "the year without a summer." Many harvests failed due to ground frosts during the spring and summer, resulting in famine in many places. Some historians consider that the uprising against Emperor Napoleon in France was a consequence of food shortages that year.

Europe also experienced a shortage of oats—the most important source of feed for horses. Horses were the most important means of transport at the time, and inventor Karl Drais (1785–1851) is said to have thought of a solution to this problem when he developed the velocipede in 1817, the forerunner of the bicycle.

Light quality

The ash-laden skies were plain for all to see worldwide. Sunrises and sunsets in 1816 were particularly spectacular, due to a special type of glow in the sky. It is said to have inspired the unique quality of light portrayed in the landscapes by the English artist J.M.W. Turner (1775–1851). Meanwhile, in Switzerland, the 18-year-old Mary Shelley and her husband Percy were on summer vacation at the country house of Lord Byron in Geneva. They endured constant rain and, to dispel the tedium, Byron proposed

a competition to see who could write the best horror story. Mary Shelley won with her tale of Frankenstein's monster, which has since become world famous.

Tambora itself remained restless for several years after 1816. Rumblings could still be heard in August 1819, with boiling lava continuing to overflow the crater. It was only in 1847 that a scientific expedition first dared to climb Tambora. The peak of the volcano was reached under the direction of the Swiss botanist Heinrich Zollinger and a variety of investigations were made. Much of what we now know about the eruption of Tambora is due to that first expedition.

New discoveries continue to be made, however, both at and in the vicinity of Mount Tambora. In the

summer of 2004, a team led by Professor Haraldur Sigurdsson of the University of Rhode Island in collaboration with the Indonesian Vulcanological Institute discovered the remains of a centuries-old town under a 10-ft (3-m) layer of ash. Bowls, pots, and bronze objects were found there, as well as the bones of two adults. According to Sigurdsson, the objects found bore similarities to the Khmer cultures of present-day Vietnam and Cambodia. A new expedition has been planned for 2007 as, according to Sigurdsson, there must be much more awaiting discovery in what he describes as "The Pompeii of the East."

Satellite image of part of the island of Sumbawa, with Mount Tambora clearly visible

Quito • Cotopaxi
ECUADOR

PACIFIC

ATLANTIC

Cotopaxi
(Ecuador)

June 26, 1877

1,000 dead

Eruption of Cotopaxi

Some towns, such as Latacunga, have been destroyed more than once by the mudslides produced by this volcano, one of the highest in the world.

Cotopaxi has become a legend among volcanoes. Its summit is a coveted prize for hundreds of climbers throughout the world, so the ascent to its highest point has become a lucrative business for dozens of small establishments devoted to climbing and adventure sports. Nevertheless, the volcano has given unpleasant surprises to the people of the region in the form of powerful eruptions.

A giant in Ecuador

Cotopaxi is a very high volcano. Its 19,346 ft (5,897 m) dominate the province that bears its name. It is not, however, the highest volcano in Ecuador. Chimborazo, at 20,701 feet (6,310 m), exceeds it. The volcano stands 31 miles (50 km) from the country's capital, Quito. Cotopaxi has a base of some 10 x 11 miles (16 x 19 km) and above 16,400 ft (5,000 m) is covered in glaciers with an estimated volume of a third of a cubic mile (0.5 km³). These glaciers are the subject of many photographs taken by the daring climbers who attempt the summit. The activity of the fumaroles in the volcano's crater and on its slopes, together with the recent historical eruptions, confirm that the volcano is active although its most recent periods of wakefulness have not caused the local inhabitants serious problems.

Cotopaxi has experienced several large eruptions since 1534, the episodes of the years 1742, 1744, 1768, and 1877 being outstanding. They generated extensive falls of ash and pumice, lava, pyroclastic flows, and destructive lahars that severely affected the surrounding areas. Due to the mud and rubble that flowed for hundreds of miles along the routes of the rivers that rise on the volcano, Cotopaxi's eruptions caused severe damage to property, much loss of life both human and animal, and a serious economic crisis throughout the region.

During the various eruptions that have struck the immediate area, some towns such as Latacunga have been destroyed more than once by the mudslides triggered by the pyroclastic flows surging from the volcano's crater. In some cases, these lahars traveled more than 62 miles (100 km), penetrating to the Pacific Ocean and even Amazonia.

Cotopaxi's most catastrophic eruptions occurred throughout the eighteenth and nineteenth and centuries. The worst were those of 1768 and 1877. The eruption of April 4, 1768 has been catalogued as the most harmful of all. According to reports at the time, its ashes and destructive power reached as far as the coast of Ecuador. The earthquake that caused the eruption was intensely felt in Quito and other more distant cities. The eruption was so powerful that

darkness reigned at 9 o'clock in the morning in Quito. Darkness persisted in many parts of the country until the early evening. Meanwhile, jets of lava and pyroclastic materials surged out of the gigantic mountain. When approaching Cotopaxi, there was no need to carry any light; the tremendous splendor of its eruption gave more than enough. After the violent episode in that year, the Latacunga valley, one of most fertile parts of Ecuador, was devastated.

The eruption of 1877

The eruption of June 26, 1877 was very similar to the one just described. In December 1876, Cotopaxi had begun its preparations for this new eruption. The day before, an eruptive column of steam and ash had risen to a height of some 26,200 feet (8,000 m), but did not cause serious problems in the fields and rivers. It is possible that the direction of the wind played a part in that. Suddenly, at 6:30 a.m., a towering column of smoke and ash burst out of the crater, casting much of the country into complete darkness to the point that, in Quito at 4 o'clock in the afternoon, people said that they could not see their hands in front of their faces. The same thing happened in Guayaquil and all along the southern coast, where a loud explosion was heard, like a cannon shot.

A picture of the glacier at the summit of Cotopaxi. Its snow was the cause of the mudslides that destroyed several villages and cities two centuries ago.

Between 9:00 a.m. and 1:00 p.m. in distant provinces, the cannon-fire could be heard very clearly. Of course, it was not cannon-fire, but the explosions of the eruption, which accompanied the terrible lahars sliding down the sides of Cotopaxi until they reached Latacunga.

The destruction it caused in the three main valleys was terrible, and nearly 1,000 people lost their lives. The scenes of panic were heartrending. No one was prepared for such a situation. The volcano had appeared calm. This was the last of Cotopaxi's big eruptions, especially as regards the number of fatalities. The people of the region live under a serious threat. A big eruption would rep-resent a great danger, especially due to the formation of the lahars that can be generated by lava or pyroclastic flows, which partially melt the thick cover of ice and snow on the volcano's summit. These lahars can be enormous, covering large areas and affecting infrastructure and densely popu-lated areas within a few dozen miles of the volcano.

The risk that something similar to the eruption of Nevado del Ruiz (see pp 118–119) will be repeated is in the minds of many geologists, who fear for the future of the region. The towns of Lata-cunga, Sangolquí, San Rafael, and Tumbaco lie in this area, all of them with many inhabitants, and, due to the country's impoverished economy, there are few resources for confronting an eruption of such proportions.

At present, Cotopaxi is quiet and its future eruptions will prob-ably be moderate in extent. In view of the size of the population living in the danger zones, how-ever, the damage could be very great, particularly along the river beds where the fateful mudslides are likely to flow.

A picture of the Cotopaxi crater. It is hard to believe that such a beautiful volcano could have been the author of so much misfortune.

The impressive mass of Cotopaxi, one of the world's biggest and most active volcanoes.

Krakatoa (Indonesia)

August 27, 1883

36,000 dead

Eruption of Krakatoa

The eruption was heard over 3,000 miles (4,800 km) away – the loudest explosion ever experienced in the entire history of the planet – and caused unparalleled destruction.

The eruption on the island of Krakatoa is one of the most famous of all time. Its violent explosion was one of the most significant in human history and is still the subject of research, over a century after the event. The phenomenon not only influenced the Indonesian archipelago, of which Krakatoa forms part, but affected the global climate for many years.

A unique eruption

Krakatoa is set in what is now Indonesia, 25 miles (40 km) to the west of Java, in the Sonda Strait. Local chroniclers have reported the existence of this volcano being known as early as the 5th century B.C.E. The next we hear about it comes from European adventurers, mainly from Holland and Germany, who traded in these seas.

The name "Krakatoa" has itself been subject to some controversy. Where does it come from? There are a host of theories. One is that it is derived from an English account of the eruption in 1883 that incorrectly transcribed the local name for the volcano (Krakatua), which was in turn an onomatopoeic interpretation of the cackling of the parrots that lived on the island. Another theory traces the name back to the Sanskrit word for lobster (*karkataka*), a common species on the shores of the island.

Unfortunately, all this is mere speculation, as there is no proof either way.

Whatever the correct explanation, it is certain that a group of three volcanoes – Danan, Perbuwatan, and Rakata – is popularly known by the name of the island, Krakatoa. At the time of its eruption in 1883, the volcano had been inactive for over two centuries, but in the preceding years a series of events took place that may have some causal link. In 1878, both Java and Sumatra were rocked by a series of earthquakes, with north Australia being similarly hit two years later. In 1880 and early 1883, further earthquakes ravaged parts of Java, destroying the lighthouse that guided sailors to the west of the island.

On May 20, 1883, the first eruptions took place in Perbuwatan, which continued to expel ash and steam for three months; by August 11, all three cones were in eruption. This activity caused continuous tremors on the nearby islands, causing damage to buildings. On August 24, the eruption began to intensify, sending out ash and steam for miles around, to the amazement of European travelers on the seas of Indonesia.

Two days later, on August 26, the eruption reached its critical phase. The column of volcanic material rose to a height of 22 miles (36 km), threatening the populations of Java and Sumatra. On the morning of August 27, four eruptions took place: at 5.30, 6.42, 8.20, and 10.02. The last of these opened a series of fissures on the slopes of the volcanoes. This had a decisive effect, as seawater entered into the chamber of magma. The contact between the two elements produced a brutal explosion that was heard over 3,000 miles (4,800 km) away, in places such as Sri Lanka, Mauritius, and eastern Australia. It is believed to have been the loudest sound ever heard by human ears.

The explosion did not just cause a fearsome din, however, but also threw two-thirds of the island into the air and wreaked unparalleled destruction. Pyroclastic materials, lava, igneous rocks, and ash spanned a radius of 50 miles (80 km), killing some 5,000 local people. Even worse was the tsunami detonated by this intense explosion. Its waves, over 140 ft (40 m) high, swept away over 150 towns and submerged entire islands. More than 30,000 people lost their lives on account of this giant wave.

The ships that normally plied the Sonda Strait could not approach the area for months, as they could not break through the pumice stones and volcanic material covering the water. Residues reached the Indian Ocean and, in September 1884, one large fragment was even spotted in Durban, South Africa, over 5,000 miles (8,000 km) away. For months after the catastrophe, the captains of ships in the seas around Indonesia were describing scenes worthy of any disaster movie, complete with floating volcanic masses strewn with corpses.

Global change

The only vestige of the eruption was an inactive caldera. In 1927, however, a group of fishermen noticed that it was emitting steam and hot rocks under the water. This activity continued

The crater of Krakatoa. The violent eruption of 1883 destroyed the original one, which was replaced by this formation.

and, in 1928, the cone that was being formed emerged from the sea. A year later, a small island had formed, christened Anak Kakatau: Son of Krakatoa.

Ever since, this new volcano has been incessantly active and the island has continued to grow – at a rate of 5 inches (13 cm) a week, according to experts on the spot. Scientists have discovered that this island and the surrounding waters are devoid of all life.

The 1883 eruption had consequences for the entire planet. The gases released into the atmosphere accumulated in the stratosphere, where they remained for over three years. This layer of sulfur dioxide reduced the supply of sunlight, creating a drop in temperatures for an astonishing three years, during which strange optical phenomena, lunar and solar halos, orange dawns, and unusually colored dusks became commonplace in many parts of the world. Artists such as William Ashcroft depicted these effects in landscape paintings that are arguably the best record of the impact of this extraordinary event.

Anak Krakatoa emitting a column of smoke. The activity of this young volcano is monitored by volcanologists from all over the world.

Spectacular image of Anak Krakatoa expelling pyroclastic material, commonly known as volcanic bombs.

Johnstown
Pennsylvania
(United States)

May 31, 1889

2,200 dead

Johnstown flood

This was not only one of the worst floods to hit the United States in the 19th century, but also the one with the highest death toll in its entire history.

The length and volume of the numerous rivers that flow through the United States have often led them to burst their banks in periods of torrential rain. Nowadays, they are kept in check to a certain extent by means of dams, locks, and canals controlled by modern technology, but the situation was very different in the late 19th century: the infrastructure was in a poor state, creating unnecessary risks and possibly contributing to disasters like the Johnstown flood.

The South Fork Dam and the rains

Johnstown, a town in the state of Pennsylvania, was founded by European colonialists in 1794 and subsequently experienced a boom with the arrival of the railroad in 1834. The Cambria Iron Company established a steel foundry there in 1850, which soon gained a national reputation for the quality of its products. Fortune seemed to be smiling on the (mainly German and Welsh) inhabitants of the young town; at the time of the disaster, it boasted a population of 30,000.

Johnstown was situated in the Conemaugh Valley, surrounded by high hills and the Allegheny Mountains. The river was the source of much of the town's wealth, but it also made Johnstown vulnerable whenever excessive rain caused it to break its banks. Furthermore, the winters were extremely hard, as Johnstown was often cut off by the snow in the mountains. Despite these setbacks, its industrious citizens had succeeded in creating a prosperous and hospitable place in which to live.

The floods prior to the historic event of 1889 had never had unduly serious consequences. The first to be recorded by the European immigrants in their personal diaries took place in 1808. Subsequently, Johnston was struck every ten years or so by a significant swelling of the Conemaugh, but the town was not anticipating any problems in 1889 and, more than this, it had never even considered the possibility of a disaster of this magnitude. It was not only one of the worst floods to hit the United States in the 19th century, but also the one with the highest death count in its entire history. On May 28, a storm that formed over the states of Nebraska and Kansas started to move eastward. Two days later, when it descended on Johnstown and the Conemaugh Valley, the rainfall broke all known records: 6–10 inches (150–250 mm) of water fell in barely 24 hours. The situation became desperate during the night of May 30, as the surrounding streams gradually turned into turbulent rivers that uprooted trees and telegraph posts. The following morning, the railroad lines were under water and the Conemaugh was on the point of overflowing. Throughout the morning of May 31 the water level went up and up, even before the Conemaugh itself burst its banks, and in the early afternoon the situation grew even worse. The South Fork Dam, 14 miles (23 km) upstream, could no longer take the strain and the water from Lake Conemaugh rushed into the river, causing it to overflow. The torrent entered Johnstown at more than 40 miles (60 km) per hour, sweeping aside everything in its path and brutally dashing debris against the buildings until few were left standing. In just a few minutes, some parts of the town were under 60 ft (18 m) of water. The residents who survived the deluge had to wait for hours, if not days, either on roofs or floating adrift, clutching doors, windows, or tree trunks — anything that offered a chance of living through the flood.

This family from Washington D.C. goes down a street Venetian style. In the background, horses laboriously pull carts; their efforts created a degree of mobility in flooded areas.

A street in Williamsport, Pennsylvania, after the flood. Days have gone by but the scene is still macabre.

Inhabitants of Johnstown in front of ruined buildings in the town center.

The town's industry was very badly hit. This photograph shows a foundry.

The collapse of the South Fork Dam was subject to fierce controversy after the disaster. Built between 1838 and 1853 as part of the state's canal system, it had been sold to private companies shortly after opening. Its facilities were allowed to deteriorate, even when it came to be surrounded by elegant homes and restaurants, not to mention a club for hunting and fishing, built for the benefit of local magnates. The inhabitants of Johnstown complained to the mayor and the owners of the dam about cracks on its surface. Repairs were made, but it is questionable as to whether they were of a sufficiently high standard. The subsequent investigations divided public opinion. For some, the lamentable state of the dam had been responsible for the seriousness of the floo-

ding, while others argued that the rainfall had been so intense that no dam could have withstood. Whatever the cause, the damage had been done.

Innovations in disaster relief

The flood was remorseless in its ferocity, killing 2,200 people, of whom 750 were never identified, and destroying 10,600 buildings. Some 4 sq. miles (10 km²) were totally devastated, including the bridges and railroads so vital to the economy of Johnstown. The cost of the damage was calculated at more than 17 million dollars, an astronomical sum at that time.

Aid was not slow to arrive, with volunteers from all over the country coming to lend a hand. For several months, more than 7,000 people worked to rebuild Johnstown and

help the afflicted. Russia, Turkey, France, Great Britain, Australia, Germany, and twelve other nations sent money, food, clothes, and construction materials to Johnstown. One particularly noteworthy aid worker was Clara Barton, the president of the American Red Cross. The Johnstown flood marked the organization's first intervention in the aftermath of a disaster; Barton and her volunteers stayed in Johnstown for five months, offering medical assistance to thousands of inhabitants of the battered city.

Johnstown was rebuilt, but the risk of flooding remains. The most recent, and most serious, incident took place in 1977, when the water reached a height of 10 ft (3 m) and killed 80 people.

USA
Washington D.C. ●
Galveston
PACIFIC   ATLANTIC

Galveston
Gulf of Mexico, Texas
(United States)

September 8, 1900

6,000–12,000 dead

Galveston hurricane

A merchant ship sent a message to the Governor: Galveston had been reduced to ruins. The city was nothing more than a pile of rubble and corpses.

In the summer of 1891, the United States took the still rudimentary science of meteorology to a new level by creating the U.S. Weather Bureau, which would make weather forecasting a reality. One of its additional functions was the detection and possible prevention of natural disasters, including hurricanes. This service proved useless, however, on September 8, 1900, when a hurricane devastated the city of Galveston, Texas. This was to prove the most significant natural catastrophe in the history of the United States up to that time.

The pride of the South

The turn of the century arrived during a golden age for the United States. It had won the war against Spain and established total control over the affairs of its southern neighbors. Its expansionism and industrial growth seemed unstoppable. The city of Galveston, on the Gulf of Mexico, was a showcase for this thriving nation. It had been founded in 1839 on a sandbank in the bay that bears its name, and in only a few years had established itself as the most important port in Texas, the most important cotton

port in the country, and the third most important overall. Cotton production and trade provided the basis for its prosperity. By the end of the 19th century, the 38,000 inhabitants could boast more millionaires living in their midst than any other American city.

A few months after the creation of the U.S. Weather Bureau, a representative was sent to Galveston. The city had been buffeted by several storms of considerable magnitude and some of its inhabitants had appealed for the construction of a wall on the coast to obstruct the large waves and winds caused by hurricanes. The delegate from the Weather Bureau issued a report stating that such a wall was unnecessary – a decision much regretted in years to come. It now seems incredible that this wall was not built, as the neighboring city of Indianola had been completely destroyed by two hurricanes in 1875 and 1886. Galveston had in fact benefited from these incidents, as Indianola had been its main commercial rival, but lost many prosperous citizens to its competitor in the aftermath of these events.

On September 1, the U.S. Weather Bureau received news of a major storm that had spent several days to the southeast of Cuba. It was considered a mere tropical storm of little significance. Three days later, the Galveston bureau received notice from its headquarters in Washington D.C. of a storm that had left Cuba and was approaching the country's southern coast. Unfortunately, the meteorologists of the time could not ascertain the exact position of this storm as first-hand information was lacking.

On September 6 and 7, the storm reached the Keys of Florida and Louisiana respectively, but no news of this could be transmitted because the telegraph lines had been destroyed. On the evening of September 7, cloud movements and strong gusts of wind boded ill. The meteorologists issued an alert: a hurricane was approaching. The citizens of Galveston received this warning with some indifference. Some were seduced by the still magnificent weather into turning a deaf ear, but more cautious souls attempted to leave the city via its bridges or the railroad. By the early afternoon of September 8, the prospects were alarming: the winds were becoming increasingly stronger, reaching speeds of over 95 miles (150 km) per hour in some areas close to the city. Soon, the water being swept from the Gulf by the force of the wind started to invade the streets. The telegraph stopped working at 3.30 p.m. There was no news of the city until the next morning, when a merchant ship sent a message to the State Governor in Houston: Galveston had been reduced to ruins. At first, this message was assumed to be an exaggeration, but when the first rescue workers reached the area they were horrified: the city was nothing more than a pile of rubble and corpses.

It is now thought that the hurricane that devastated the city would have registered 4 on the Saffir-Simpson scale. The storm waves crashed almost 16 ft (5 m) high against the city, whereas the island of sand on which Galveston stood

Until hurricane Katrina, the Galveston hurricane was the worst ever experienced by the United States. This image shows the damage caused by the wind and subsequent floods.

was only 10 ft (3 m) high and was completely flat. If the city had built the much-discussed coastal wall, the result would have been very different. As it was, more than 3,600 houses, mostly made of wood, were totally destroyed. In the railroad station, cars full of people attempting to flee were hurled off the tracks and dashed against the ground. The bridges collapsed, preventing all means of escape, and the telegraph posts were swept away, hence the news blackout.

Between 6,000 and 12,000 people lost their lives. Hundreds died amidst the ruins of their homes, after waiting in vain to be rescued. There were so many corpses that it was decided to throw them into the sea, as there was a high risk of epidemic on account of their decompositions and there was no time for funerals – but the currents in the Gulf returned this macabre flotilla to the beaches of Galveston. It was

finally decided to burn the bodies in giant pyres, which stayed alight for days.

The reconstruction

The survivors were provided accommodation in army tents. On September 13 the water supply was restored and three weeks later cotton was leaving the port once again. The inhabitants of Galveston resolved to rebuild their city. Its foundations were raised to a height of 20 ft (6 m), new buildings and bridges were constructed with more resistant materials, and a protective coastal wall some 20 ft (6 m) high was finally put up in 1902.

In 1915, Galveston was attacked by another fierce storm, which unleashed waves 13 ft (4 m) high. Thanks to the wall and the measures taken, there were just 275 fatalities. The reconstruction had been a success, as can be seen from the sight of the city today. Galveston has become a leisure zone for the inhabitants of Houston, with magnificently preserved, early 20th-century buildings, beautiful hotels, and tourist attractions for all ages.

Galveston, Texas. The water level dropped after the floods. These historic images bear witness to the worst hurricane that had ever hit the territory of the United States.

The city, devastated by the force of the hurricane, with only a few buildings still standing.

A cart carries corpses to an unspecified part of Galveston. Between 6,000 and 12,000 of the inhabitants of this prosperous city were killed.

Eruption of La Soufrière

The eruption caused more damage than any other from this volcano, as the northern part of St. Vincent was almost totally destroyed.

St. Vincent
West Indies
Caribbean Sea

May 7, 1902

1,681 dead

Dome formation on La Soufrière.

Lahars and burning clouds caused most of the havoc wreaked by La Soufrière.

The West Indies has become a popular tourist destination on account of the idyllic beaches, exotic wildlife, and wide range of leisure activities. Like many chains of islands, those of the West Indies are of volcanic origin, and some of their mountains are still active. One such volcano, La Soufrière, on the island of St. Vincent, was responsible for one of the worst eruptions in the region in 1902. Even today, its activity has made it a major tourist attraction, on account of its fumeroles and sulfur springs.

A coincidence

St. Vincent, one of the biggest islands in the West Indies, is divided into two distinct parts, christened by British colonialists as Windward (to the east) and Leeward (to the west). This earthly paradise, with untouched beaches and beautiful valleys dotted with plantations of sugar cane, bananas, and coconuts, provides the setting for La Soufrière, one of the many stratovolcanoes in the region.

The peak of this volcano is the highest point in St. Vincent, at a height of 4,048 ft (1,234 m). The interior of its crater, over 1 mile (1.5 km) in diameter, contains a lake that has experienced great changes during the volcano's active periods. La Soufrière may be relatively small, but it is powerful: its eruptions have always been extremely destructive, despite long periods in which it has seemed completely inactive. In fact, as in the case of many of the world's volcanoes – Mount Merapi in Indonesia, for example – the longer its rest periods between eruptions, the more devastating those eruptions are likely to be.

Ever since the first arrival of European colonialists in the West Indies, La Soufrière has experienced a series of eruptions that have caused huge problems to the local population. The first of these occurred in 1718, but unfortunately little is known about it. The next one took place in 1821, when fearsome explosions shook the peak of the volcano and created burning clouds that devastated the land around the mountain. The next eruptions occurred in the 20th century (in 1902, 1971–72, and 1979) and, of these, the first was by far the most violent.

On May 7, 1902, La Soufrière came to life again, after eighty years of tranquility. The eruption was almost a carbon copy of the one that would rock Martinique on the following day – one of the worst eruptions ever known, as Mount Pelée ravaged much of the island and killed 30,000 people. For a long time, geologists thought that the two volcanoes were interconnected by extremely deep channels, a theory reinforced by the fact that the two eruptions occurred within 24 hours of each other, with similar phenomena being observed in both cases, such as burning clouds. Today, however, this hypothesis is losing credence.

The eruption in May 1902 had severe consequences for St. Vincent. The northern part of the island was almost completely destroyed. The clouds of ash, igneous rocks, and pyroclastic material hurled at great speed from the crater of La Soufrière destroyed most of the crops in the vicinity. The financial impact was tremendous: the damage has been calculated at the equivalent of several hundred million dollars today. The speed and intensity of the eruption gave the terrified islanders no time to react and, not knowing what to do, they succumbed to panic and despair. In total, 1,681 people died as a result of the eruption of La Soufrière; hours later, 102 miles (165 km) to the north, another 30,000 lost their lives. These two days rank amongst the most ill fated in Caribbean history. The ash spewed by the volcanoes formed a blanket half an inch (2 cm) thick in the island of Barbados, 75 miles (120 km) to the east.

The trials of St. Vincent

The disaster of 1902 was the most damaging of all La Soufrière's eruptions, but it was not the last. That of 1971 left a dome of lava in the crater of the mountain, but the next, in 1979, was more alarming. The lava in the crater was thrown through the air, only to be replaced by another dome that suffered the same fate. This activity took the islanders completely by surprise, there having been no prior warning, and for the next two weeks La Soufrière expelled steam and tephra in columns reaching heights of 12 miles (20 km). Fearing the worst, the authorities were swift in evacuating most of the population to neighboring islands. Fortunately, the situation did not deteriorate any further, with damage being limited to the destruction of plantations, a few nearby houses and little else, although the region around La Soufrière underwent significant geological modification.

This eruption of St.Vincent's famous volcano was not the last trial for the local population, however. In 1980 and 1987, a series of hurricanes devastated the coconut and banana plantations, which numbered among the most important in the world, volcanic ash being an excellent fertilizer. This pheno-menon was repeated in 1998 and 1999, when hurricane Jenny destroyed many of the tourist complexes on the west coast of the island.

Another view of the dome formation. Burning clouds are also visible.

Eruption of Mount Pelée

The deaths caused by this eruption were instantaneous and horribly extensive: of the 30,000 inhabitants of the city of Saint-Pierre, only two managed to survive.

Martinique
The Caribbean

May 8, 1902

30,000 dead

Mount Pelée was responsible for one of the biggest volcanic eruptions in history, killing around 30,000 people.

Deposits of ash expelled by Mount Pelée, photographed in 1929.

The remains of the church in Saint-Pierre, destroyed by the violent awakening of Mount Pelée in 1902.

The Mount Pelée disaster marked both a beginning and an end in the history of volcanology. This eruption was not only the most deadly of the 20th century, but also brought to light a series of phenomena previously undiscovered by scientists. Even now, over a century after the event, it is still a subject of study by volcanologists and geophysicists worldwide.

Cataclysm in Martinique

Mount Pelée is set on Martinique, one of the most beautiful of all the Caribbean islands. Its capital, Saint-Pierre, built on the slopes of the volcano, was considered the Paris of the West Indies, the French colonialists having labored to create a model for the whole Caribbean. In the official census of 1894, the population of the city stood at 20,000, most of whom were native to the island. Despite being in a minority, the French and Creoles constituted the dominant social class. The comfort and vitality of Saint-Pierre gave no hint of the disaster that would befall it. Mount Pelée was part of the landscape and nobody paid it much heed. It never showed any signs of life, so there was no reason to worry.

Even when fumes began to emerge from the peak of the small mountain in January 1902, it was barely a matter of curiosity to local residents; on April 23, however, the capital was surprised by a series of explosions in the volcano, followed by increasingly strong tremors over the following days. With every new tremor, the volcano ejected significant amounts of ash and sulfurous gases.

The concern of the islanders intensified when Saint-Pierre was invaded by thousands of poisonous snakes, fleeing from the upper slopes of Mount Pelée on account of the explosions. The reptiles killed 50 people, many of them children, and almost 300 animals: dogs, horses, pigs, and other livestock. The volcano continued to spew ash and gases over the following days. The water in a lake close to the crater started to boil and, on May 5, overflowed to create a lahar mixed with the pyroclastic materials flung out by the crater. The lahar then flowed down the slope to the north of the city at over 60 miles (100 km) per hour, destroying a distillery in its path and killing 23 people before finally creating a wave 10 ft (3 m) high that crashed against the sea front of the capital.

By now, the residents of Saint-Pierre had grown nervous. Some argued in favor of evacuating the city and heading for a safer place, but the governor of the island ruled against this measure; elections were due to be held on May 11 and the voters had to be on hand. He issued a statement written by the city's schoolmaster (and only scientist), assuring the citizens of Saint-Pierre that there was no danger to them or their city. This had the desired effect: the people stayed put (although, as a precaution, the police force was ordered to prevent anybody from attempting to abandon the city). Unfortunately, however, at 7:50 a.m. on May 8, a tremendous explosion generated a cloud of ash, gases, and incandescent material that poured full pelt down the slopes of Mount Pelée, engulfing the little paradise of Saint-Pierre in a minute or less, pulverizing its houses and uprooting its trees.

The burning cloud caused several explosions when it encountered rum warehouses and distilleries, further intensifying the destructive power of the eruption; it even reached the ships in the harbor, sinking some of them, including sizable liners such as the Grappler and the Roraima, which lost all their passengers. In the city itself, rivers of lava swept away whole streets, melting metal and

demolishing stone houses until nothing remained standing.

Curious sequels to the disaster

Of the 30,000 inhabitants of Saint-Pierre, only 2 survived, and hundreds of the residents of nearby towns were also killed. In Saint-Pierre, death was almost instantaneous. Many were asphyxiated by the toxic gases emitted by the eruption, while others were burned and buried by the pyroclastic materials.

The two survivors became celebrities. One was Léon Compère-Léandre, a cobbler who managed to escape the destruction by taking refuge in his house. Somehow he avoided death, although he did suffer severe burns on his legs. His excellent physical condition and, of course, his good luck, saved him. The other case is even more curious. Louis-Auguste Cyparis, alias Samson, was a delinquent renowned on the island for his frequent escapes from prison. At the time of the eruption, he was locked in his cell, where he survived for four days with serious burns. He was rescued and subsequently pardoned, before being recruited by the Barnum & Bailey Circus, which presented him all over the world as the only survivor of Saint-Pierre.

There was another curious sequel to this eruption. Weeks after the disaster, a column of lava formed in the crater of Mount Pelée and gradually solidified. On some days, it even grew by almost 50 ft (15 m), eventually reaching a height of over 820 ft (250 m). Known as the Pelée Tower, it is undoubtedly the most spectacular outcrop of lava recorded in modern times. In March 1903, the base of this bizarre obelisk could no longer support the weight and, after 11 months of continuous growth, the structure collapsed.

The eruption of Mount Pelée alerted contemporary volcanologists to the existence of pyroclastic flow – also known as a burning cloud or incandescent avalanche – and its immense destructive power. This phenomenon had been previously unknown, as had the eruptive potential of an apparently dormant volcano like Mount Peleé. Since then, violent eruptions of this type have been classified as Pelean.

Yacolt Burn forest fire

The great Yacolt Burn forest fire destroyed nearly 400 square miles (100,000 hectares) of forest. This disaster created the impetus for better forest fire management in the western United States.

Yacolt, Washington, United States of America

September 10–13, 1902

38 dead

People lost their lives in a wide area surrounding the Yacolt fires, due to the huge pall of smoke

In North America, forest fires had been a continually recurring phenomenon since the beginning of the nineteenth century. They had almost always been the result of human actions: an inadequately extinguished campfire, a fallen candle, or, worse still, trees set deliberately ablaze to liberate land for cultivation or grazing. The actual circumstances surrounding the great Yacolt Burn have never been conclusively established.

In the months preceding this forest conflagration, there had been several smaller such fires in Washington and its neighboring states. At the time, people considered these to be largely unavoidable events, and little or nothing was done to combat them.

The Yacolt Burn probably started due to a lumberjack lighting a fire to clear the remnants of an area of felled forest. The only forest ranger in the area, one Horace Wetherall, did see the initial blaze, but did nothing about it. Shortly before, he had received a caution from his superiors for spending money on putting together a band of men to fight an earlier fire.

Easterly winds

Stoked by strong, dry, easterly winds, the fire covered more than 30 miles (50 km) in 36 hours. A major part of the area surrounding Yacolt and Stevenson in the southwest of Washington was in flames. Burning embers fell to the ground as far away as Portland, 25 miles (40 km) to the south of Yacolt on the other side of the Columbia River. The little town of Yacolt itself was miraculously spared, but the flames engulfed all the villages, lone houses, and farms in the neighborhood.

Though families living in isolated farms within the forest tried to flee to nearby rivers or creeks, the flames still overtook them. Barely a hundred yards from the Speelyai Creek were later found the remains of 11 members of the Smith and Hartsuck families, who had tried to reach the water in a covered wagon. The local mailman, Newhouse, made the same attempt in his fast, lightweight delivery carriage, but one of his two horses stumbled over a log toppled by the blaze. Newhouse was found dead, propped up against a tree stump with the metal portion of his riding crop still in his hand. A certain Mrs. Schmidt in Dole territory sought shelter with her three children in the cellar under her house. But the house caught fire and collapsed into their refuge, turning it into a furnace.

Approximately 40 people who lived along the banks of the Lewis River managed to reach the Speelyai plain, which was without trees and largely overgrown with grass and clover. Here there was one farmhouse, to which everyone fled. People slept in the house, the barn, and even in the fields in the immediate vicinity, while the fire raged all about them. They were forced to remain there for four days before the blaze had passed and they could return to the charred remains of their own homes. As they did so, they saw numerous forest animals that had also fled from the forest to the plains, including six bears, eight deer, and a lynx.

With rafts on a lake

A group of some 60 farmers, traders, fishermen, and hunters managed to survive by reaching Trout Lake just in time. They built rafts from the timber of fallen trees, spending two days and nights afloat on the lake, while the forest burned all around them. Walter Dugan, together with the other men from his team of lumberjacks, hid in an old mine tunnel close to the small community of Washougal, where they lived for two days until the fire had passed.

The smoke from the fire was so thick and dense that, according to witnesses, it was almost as dark during the day as it was at night, the only light coming from the leaping flames. Even in neighboring districts where the fire itself had not taken hold, people were troubled by the smoke. A railroad engineer related how his train had to travel with its headlamps lit during the day and in the surrounding area people had to light their premises in what should have been daylight hours. Chickens became so confused they settled down to roost in the afternoon. Pregnant women are said to have miscarried spontaneously as a result of the heat and smoke, with elderly citizens dying because of breathing difficulties.

In total, it was estimated that nearly 400 square miles (100,000 hectares) of forest were destroyed. Given the fact that this occurred in an area where lumber production was the major industry, it was

calculated that timber worth $30 million (at contemporary prices) had been lost to the flames. Thirty-eight people were recorded as having burned to death, but it is suspected that more may have perished this way, as it was a region populated by many adventurers who traveled the area hunting and fishing with no fixed abode.

Subsequent measures

Not long after the Yacolt Burn, serious work to combat forest fires began for the first time in northwestern America. In 1909, the Western Forestry and Conservation Association was set up and, in 1911, Congress in Washington D.C. promulgated new laws to grant the federal forest service far-reaching powers to institute measures throughout the whole country against forest fires.

Nevertheless, many such fires still occurred, even in Yacolt and its surroundings. Up until 1952, 24 minor and larger-scale fires were recorded, each of which again destroyed large areas of forest. The fires were usually able to spread quickly as the trunks of trees half-burnt in previous major fires had been left standing. This dead, dry timber was always quick to catch alight. Even in 1992, 90 years after the Burn itself, clusters of

these stumps could still be found amid the younger trees. Measures were taken from 1950 onward, however, which have proved effective to this very day: fire corridors have been dug out, water reservoirs have been built, and over 750,000 old stumps of burnt trees have been uprooted.

Devastating forest fires, such as those at Yacolt in 1902, leave behind them a desolate, blackened landscape

According to reports, these fires began in an area of cleared forest

San Francisco earthquake

The magnitude and circumstances of this tragedy greatly expanded the scope of scientific research into seismic phenomena.

San Francisco
(United States)

April 18, 1906

3,000 dead

The San Francisco
City Hall in ruins.
The humble
materials used
in its construction
contributed to its
lamentable state.

The City Hall in
Santa Rosa, close
to San Francisco.
Santa Rosa suffered
significant damage
as a result of the
earthquake. More
than eight blocks
were totally
flattened.

At the beginning of the 20th century, geology and seismology were nowhere near as developed as they are now. Very little was known about movements in the Earth's crust or the causes of earthquakes. These sciences progressed in leaps and bounds as a result of phenomena like the San Francisco earthquake in 1906. If knowledge of such matters had been more extensive at the time, the effects of the disaster could possibly have been mitigated.

The fateful night

In the early hours of April 18, 1906, the city of San Francisco changed completely. At 5.12 a.m., the first seismic movement was noted; 25 seconds later another, far more violent, tremor shook the city for 47 seconds. The earthquake, whose epicenter was on the San Andreas Fault, was so brutal that its effects were felt in the neighboring states of Oregon and Nevada.

The primitive seismographs of the time registered an earthquake of 7.9, but current thinking is that it would have registered 8.2 on the Richter scale (created in 1935). If it is considered that a mark of over 8.9 – the highest recorded to date – is the equivalent of a hundred hydrogen bombs, we can gain an idea of the impact of this earthquake.

The earthquake caused visible fissures 290 miles (470 km) long (the longest ever seen in the United States), as well as horizontal landslides of up to 21 ft (6.4 m) and vertical ones of over 3 ft (1 m). Rocky areas withstood the onslaught better than more fragile land made up of various sedimentary layers, as was the case in the city center. Trees, even entire hill slopes, were swallowed up in the cataclysm, while in the city the consequences were deadly. Broad avenues were transformed into winding alleyways, while bridges either vanished entirely or appeared to have been twisted by giant hands.

A city in the grip of terror

The earthquake sparked various fires, which spread with unusual speed due to explosions in the gas mains, while many water pipes and fire hydrants were damaged, further hindering the firefighting effort. Attempts were made to use water from the nearby Lake San Andreas, but the pipes that channeled it to San Francisco had also been destroyed. A few hours after the last tremor, panic overtook the city.

The houses in San Francisco had not been built to withstand natural disasters like earthquakes or fires. Materials such as wood and flammable textiles were widely used, undoubtedly enhancing the destructiveness of the fires. There was an additional factor that proved decisive, however: many fires were the work of arsonists, in the form of property owners whose insurance policies covered losses due to fire, but not those caused by an earthquake. Contemporary reports include eyewitness accounts from firemen, police officers, and soldiers of people burning their own homes to take advantage of this loophole.

General Frederick Funston, who had been entrusted with the evacuation and relief of the city, had no alternative but to impose martial law; the looting that followed the fires had turned the city into a veritable inferno. Funston dynamited whole blocks to create firebreaks, a drastic measure which proved successful. Four days after the first fire, the situation was under control.

Out of a total population of 400,000, around 3,000 were killed; a further 225,000 lost their homes, as 28,000 buildings (over 80 percent of them made of wood) were destroyed. The effects of the earthquake were felt over 30 miles (50 km) away, in towns like Santa Rosa and San José, where over 100 people were killed.

A few months after the catastrophe, the report of an investigation calculated the material losses to be in excess of 400 million dollars.

The legacy of the earthquake

During the reconstruction of San Francisco, various regulations were introduced for the construction of buildings and infrastructures, the layout of streets, and public safety. San Francisco is situated in a seismic zone, where the Earth's crust is weak and thus highly susceptible to earth-

quakes. The San Andreas Fault is a prime example of a seismic zone, and therefore subject to study by scientists across the globe.

The disaster of April 18, 1906, has not been the most powerful earthquake to rock North America, nor was its death toll as high as in some other disasters that have struck the United States. It was nevertheless of fundamental importance, for various reasons.

Firstly, it was the first natural disaster of this magnitude to be recorded in photographs, leaving an unforgettable testament. Secondly, it entered into the collective American consciousness, to such an extent that Hollywood made a movie about it in 1936, called *San Francisco*, directed by W.S. Dyke and starring Clark Gable and Spencer Tracy. It proved a smash hit, winning an Oscar for the best special effects of that year. The movie brought to life what many spectators had seen and read in the newspapers.

Such anecdotes apart, the cataclysm was of enormous benefit to geology. In 1910 the geologist H.F. Reid formulated the elastic rebound theory on the basis of his research into the San Francisco earthquake. This is still applied today to explain the cycle of an earthquake. The tremor revealed the great importance of the San Andreas Fault in the geological formation of North America, to the astonishment of many experts. Studies of the disaster, in particular the 1908 Lawson Report, went a long way toward unraveling some of the causes of such phenomena.

Half a century would pass, however, before the exact origins of the disaster could be understood through the theory of plate tectonics and in the light of new research, particularly on the ocean beds. Nevertheless, despite the host of scientific and technical advances made since 1906, earthquakes like that of San Francisco never cease to confound experts. They have learnt from this experience and other fateful events like it that, while it is possible to provide warnings about these disasters, there is no means of preventing them.

Many buildings such as this one withstood the impact of the tremors, only to be completely destroyed in subsequent fires.

House on Howard Street, where most of the buildings were tilted to the left by the unstable terrain.

Messina earthquake

The earthquake that struck southern Italy in 1908 was one in a long series of such events. On this occasion, however, its destructive force was exceptionally great.

Straits of Messina, Italy

December 28, 1908

160,000 dead

A ruined church in Messina

Italy is extremely susceptible to earthquakes, as it is located where the Eurasian and African plates collide. Every year, the African plate inches northward. There have been reports of serious earthquakes since Roman times, with the south of the country often being particularly badly affected. In 1693, an earthquake was responsible for an estimated 150,000 fatalities on the island of Sicily and in Naples. In 1783, the loss of some 50,000 people was mourned in a quake in Calabria, the region that forms the southwestern "toe" of the Italian mainland. A further earthquake in the same region struck in 1905, destroying 25 villages and resulting in the deaths of approximately 5,000 people.

The 1908 earthquake caused so much devastation as its epicenter lay in the Straits of Messina, a channel approximately 2 miles (3 km) across at its narrowest point between the mainland and the island of Sicily. The coasts on either side of these straits were densely developed and populated. The northeastern point of Sicily is the location of Messina, a city of 150,000 people at the time of the earthquake. Opposite Messina, on the mainland, is the town of Reggio di Calabria, which then boasted a population of 45,000. In addition to this many other ports, large and small, dotted the coastline of the straits.

Caught unawares in their sleep

This natural disaster occurred at 5:20 a.m. on December 28, registering a magnitude of 7.5 on the Richter scale. The quake caught people unawares in their sleep and many perished as their homes collapsed. There were two brief movements: first, a gentle, pre-liminary shock that lasted approximately 20 seconds, then the major shock, which continued uninterrupted for 30 seconds.

The fish market in Messina was swallowed up, the train station completely collapsed, and the cathedral toppled in ruins into the great square it faced. In Reggio di Calabria, countless buildings also crumbled, with not a single one left standing over a 25-mile (40-km) stretch of the Calabrian coast. The quakes were followed by a tidal wave. In Messina, its height was no greater than 9 ft (2.7 m), but elsewhere it towered to 40 ft (12 m). Destruction was total and all communication with the outside world lost. The earthquake and tidal wave had, however, spared a few naval vessels in the port of Messina. Following the disaster, the captain of the ship *Serpente* set off in search of a place where the telegraph cables were still intact. He had to travel 44 miles (70 km) north before he was able to send a distress call to the world, from the Calabrian coastal resort of Marina di Nicotera.

It was almost 48 hours before the first ships carrying aid reached the disaster zone. Sailors later told of the difficulty they had in finding their bearings, because the appearance of the coast had completely changed. In many places, huge tracts of land had disappeared into the sea. Meanwhile, the survivors and local Red Cross workers had already begun to set up emergency hospitals in the open air and to collect the bodies of the dead. One of the ships arriving from Rome brought with it King Victor Emmanuel III who, in shocked tones, telegrammed the court: "The devastation is complete: fire, blood, and death; send ships, ships, and yet more ships!"

As time passed, increasing numbers of vessels were indeed sent, not only from Italy itself, but also from other European countries and the United States. Ten thousand inhabitants were evacuated, many of whom were never to return to their homes again. This was the case for several thousand Sicilians, for example, who were taken on board cargo ships to America. Some of them were destined never to arrive, however, because the ship on which they were traveling, the *Florida*, ran into another ship in thick fog close to New York. The 850 refugees panicked, and 3 of them drowned. Fortunately, the rest were rescued in time.

More earthquakes

After the earthquake, both Messina and Reggio were rebuilt. Both have been spared from natural disasters since then, though the restlessness of the earth's crust has continued to make itself felt. In 1968, Sicily again experienced an earthquake, in which there were some 400 fatalities and the town of Gibellina was completely destroyed. In 2002, a quake occurred in the vicinity of Palermo, causing some damage, but taking no lives. The shock was felt across the island and thousands of people ran into the streets, heedless in their panic of its being the middle of the night.

It is not only Sicily and Calabria that regularly have to contend with earthquakes. In 1915, an earthquake that left 30,000 dead destroyed the town of Avezzano in central Italy. In 1976, Friuli in northeastern Italy was assailed, with a death toll of nearly 1,000, and in 1980 over 2,700 were killed in an earthquake at Eboli to the south of Naples. A series of earthquakes occurred in the region of Umbria in 1997, rendering 40,000 people homeless and leaving 13 dead. It also caused major damage to the world-famous Basilica of St. Francis in Assisi.

Nevertheless, over the past few decades Italians have become increasingly better prepared for possible earthquakes and volcanic eruptions. Much scientific research is being done into causes and early warning systems and the construction of roads, houses, and offices takes the danger of seismic tremors into greater account. All the same, there has been much

debate in recent years concerning the planned construction of a suspension bridge across the Straits of Messina. The bridge needs to extend over 2 miles (3 km) in length, with supporting towers on either side taller than the Eiffel Tower in Paris. The bridge would have to be able to withstand earthquakes up to 7.1 on the Richter scale, but the question is whether that would be enough in practice. After years of discussion, the Italian parliament approved the plan in 2005 and tendered it to an international construction consortium at a budget of 4 billion euros. This budget has proved problematic, however: due to a shortfall, the new administration that came to power in 2006 has for the time being put the plan on hold.

To the left, the ruins of the Duomo, the cathedral of Messina dating from 1160; to the right, in the foreground, seriously damaged fountains; in the background, collapsed houses on Via 1 Settembre

Devastation at Via Cavona, Messina

Wellington
USA Washington D.C.
PACIFIC
ATLANTIC

Stevens Pass,
Washington,
United States

March 1, 1910

96 dead

Avalanche at Stevens Pass

The avalanche at Stevens Pass in the state of Washington on March 1, 1910 caused the worst disaster of its kind in the history of North America. Ninety-six people were killed when a gigantic river of snow carried off the two trains in which they were traveling.

In the early morning of March 1, 1910, an avalanche over 1,300 ft (400 m) wide tore down the mountainside close to Stevens Pass, in the Cascade Range. On its way, the huge river of snow took with it two trains operated by the Great Northern Railway. Six locomotives and fifteen cars were thrown down the slope as though they were toys. After a fall of around 130 ft (40 m), the trains came to rest, partly because of a large tree. The area was littered with railroad cars, trees, and boulders. The miracle was that rescuers were able to dig 23 survivors from the snow; 96, however, died.

Even before the avalanche hit them, people traveling in both the passenger and mail trains heading for Seattle had already endured a number of hardships. The violent blizzards raging at that time had already caused a delay of several days to passenger train No. 25, at Leavenworth in the eastern part of the mountain range. Blizzards were commonplace in the region at that time of year, so it was usually the case that the railroad tracks could soon be made passable again. In the preceding 17 years that the railroad had been in use, the snow had never caused a delay of more than 24 hours.

In good spirits

This may account for the railroad staff being in good spirits. In any event, on February 23, 1910, the No. 25 was given the signal allowing it to depart westward. The train had only just got going, however, when it was again forced to call a halt, this time due to a severe blizzard just outside the small railroad depot of Wellington at Stevens Pass. Mail train No. 27 came to stand alongside the passenger train in a siding. For six days in a row, neither the trains nor those within could go anywhere.

According to glaciologist Erin Petit, the great-granddaughter of one of the conductors on train No. 25, the passengers were not all that concerned at first. "After all, the slope above Wellington was not so very steep—a gradient of 1:20 or 1:25. Not one that would make you make you really think twice about avalanches," comments Petit. "However, when the blizzard continued unabated, people did start to wonder whether the train might not be better off sheltering in a nearby tunnel. Rumor had spread that a small cabin had been smashed to smithereens at a spot further back along the track. Nevertheless, because the railroad staff were concerned that either an avalanche might block the tunnel or the passengers might suffocate in the fumes emitted by the steam locomotives when inside it, it was decided to keep the trains at Wellington. In any case, an avalanche had never been recorded there before."

During the six days that train No. 25 was at a standstill, only a few passengers and crew actually left it. Joseph Petit, great-grandfather of Erin, was among the crew who undertook the dangerous trek through the snow to the small town of Scenic further ahead. He and his colleagues braved this rigorous journey to fetch

Salvage workers next to the wreckage of one of the trains hit by the avalanche

Stevens Pass and the surrounding Cascade mountains, seen from above

supplies and round up new passengers. On the night of February 28, that the blizzard turned into a lethal cocktail of downpours and lightning storms, increasing the risk of avalanches. The critical point was reached just after midnight on March first: the storms and the rain became too much for the mass of snow perched on the mountain above Wellington. The deluge of snow, overwhelming all in its path, caught the sleeping passengers unawares.

One of the survivors interviewed after the disaster described it as follows: "Just before the avalanche, a huge thunderstorm bellowed above us. There were violent bolts of lightning and a biting wind howled through the ravine. Suddenly, there was a muffled roar, and the sleeping men and women felt the train being picked up and dragged away."

White wave of death

Charles Andrews had just left the train to walk to Wellington. When he heard the din, he turned around. "I saw the white wave of death coming downhill from the mountain slope above the trains. It charged ahead mercilessly, thundering, crushing, exploding. It was a crescendo of noise that could just as well have been made by ten thousand goods trains smashing into each other. The avalanche approached the tracks and picked up the cars as if they were snow-covered toys, swallowed them up, and disappeared like a huge, great, white monster into the gorge below."

There are two main types of avalanche: loose snow and wet snow. The latter was the culprit in Wellington. A wet-snow avalanche is triggered, as its name might imply, by rainfall or melting snow. A surface layer of waterlogged snow forms on the underlying bed and can easily start to slip. This type of avalanche moves more slowly than its loose snow counterpart, but the mass dislodged and ensuing destruction are often extreme in scale. Logging and forest fires, had already contributed a great deal in preparing a path for the deluge. As a result of deforestation, there was little traction for the snow on the bare inclines.

It took the Great Northern Railway Company three weeks to repair the track. In 1913, to protect trains from future avalanches, a section of railroad running 9 miles (14.5 km) between Scenic and Wellington was at first covered with snow roofs. This notorious section of track became superfluous once a new tunnel through the Cascades was opened in 1929. The former railroad is still in use today for hiking and is known as the Iron Goat Trail. The name derives from the mascot of the Great Northern Railway: a mountain goat, standing atop a boulder.

Since the name of Wellington held such unpleasant associations for people, the small train depot was renamed Tye after the Tye River nearby. However, Tye was not blessed with a long life. Its residents abandoned the small town following the completion of the 1929 tunnel. Nowadays, Stevens Pass is a popular ski resort. Since 1952, an avalanche research station has been located there.

Deforestation due to excessive tree felling increases the risk of fatal avalanches

The Great Flood

The water that passed through the river in Dayton in three days was the equivalent of the normal flow through the Niagara Falls in thirty days.

Midwestern
United States

March 1913

428 dead

Troy, New York. The
flood devastated
the factory to
the right, which
belonged to Cluett,
Peabody, and Com-
pany, then the
world's foremost
shirt manufacturer.

The floods in the Midwest of the United States in 1913 were the worst that have ever hit this part of the country, but nowadays they are not remembered as often as those of Mississippi in 1927 or Johnstown in 1889. The Great Flood is usually considered a local phenomenon, despite the fact that it affected four states and took the lives of hundreds of people, as well as provided the basis for federal legislation on flooding.

An Easter to remember

The origins of the floods of March 1913 can be traced back to a few months earlier. According to private diaries and newspaper reports, the New Year had brought heavy rain to the state of Kentucky and its neighbors. A combination of low pressure and abnormally high temperatures created the ideal conditions for such weather. The front moved through Kentucky for several weeks, before reaching Ohio, Illinois, and Indiana at the end of January.

It was not until mid-March, however, that the heavy rains began to cause concern. The inhabitants of Ohio were accustomed to their rivers overflowing in spring, but it was clear that something exceptional was happening this time. The rain that had been falling for weeks was obviously going to swell the traditional floods: during East-er week 1913 the rivers finally burst their banks. The exact date varies according to the area, in some places it was March 21, in others March 23. The floods even affected towns normally immune from this phenomenon, such as Akron, which is situated on a plateau and seemingly out of reach of rivers that have overflowed.

The rainfall in Kentucky and Ohio was three times higher than the average for that time of year. The Ohio River caused the most damage in its eponymous state, although the problems were compounded by the overflowing of tributaries like the Great Miami and the Muskingum. The authorities failed to react promptly and, in some cases, the measures taken proved to be misguided. At this time, few canals had been con-structed, but those that did exist were dynamited in an attempt to check the rising water – to no avail. Furthermore, these dynamited canals later proved to be beyond repair. The flooding was the worst ever to affect the states of Ohio and Indiana, as well as parts of Illinois and New York.

In the prosperous city of Day-ton, the few dams and levees in place were powerless to resist the advance of the waters, which floo-ded the city center to a height of 20 ft (6 m). The force of the overflowing rapids destroyed the city's gas mains, causing several fires that raged out of control, the fire service being unable to app-roach them. Dayton was thrown into chaos, although one of the city's most eminent figures, John Patterson, deserves special men-tion for his decision to open his factories and banks as refuges, as well as for organizing rescue and healthcare teams. People like Pat-terson played a key role during the days in which the official response to this challenge proved woefully inadequate.

The fact is that the disaster overwhelmed not only the rivers, but also the authorities; they were incapable of responding to the appeals of thousands of residents, particularly in Ohio and Indiana. In the valleys of the Rivers Muskingum and Great Miami, the situation was worse than in Dayton, as fewer resources were available. Muskingum Valley was lashed by torrential rain for four whole days and, when the river finally breached its banks, it caused havoc throughout the valley, sending thousands of people fleeing into the surrounding hills. There was no electricity supply or drinking water in the local towns, and, as in Dayton, the firemen were helpless in the face of the rushing water. In Zanesville, the Muskingum rose an unprecedented 50 ft (15 m), submerging 3,400 buildings in the process. Similarly, Coshocton saw much of its historic center disappear under 10 ft (3 m) of water. Eight people lost their lives in the valley, with material damage amounting to several million dollars.

The Great Miami also wreaked destruction in its valley. The rain did not stop for three days. In previous years, much of the flooded area had been iced over, but on this occasion the unusually high February temperatures had prevented the formation of ice. This was fortunate for, if the land had been frozen, it would not have absorbed the water, and the effects would have been even worse. To give an idea of the amount of water that engulfed the area, it has been estimated that the water that passed through the river in Dayton in three days was the equivalent of that which flows through the Niagara Falls in thirty days.

Meanwhile, two-thirds of Indiana was underwater. In the city of Indianapolis, the waters of the White River reached a height of 30 ft (9 m), with a similar situation in the nearby towns. Cincinnati registered the record for water levels, with no less than 62 ft (19 m) covering its center and many buildings completely submerged. The dams that constrained the White River and its tributaries also proved unable to fulfill their function.

Perspectives for the future

The floods officially caused 428 deaths, although the actual figure is thought to have been closer to 1,000. More than 300,000 people lost their homes. The overflowing rivers destroyed 30,000 buildings, hundreds of bridges, and much infrastructure. The loss of crops in Indiana severely afflicted local farmers. The material losses were substantial – around 100 million dollars in 1913, or some 2 billion in today's money. The disaster did have one positive effect, however. Thanks to pressure exerted by the governors of the affected states, in particular Ohio, the federal government agreed to introduce a series of legislative measures with respect to flooding, along with the grant of subsidies for the construction of dams, locks, and canals, the responsibility for which had previously been a subject of dispute between the federal government, individual states, and private companies.

Java
(Indonesia)

May 19–20, 1919

5,110 dead

An extinguished
fumarole on the peak
of Kelut.

Eruption of Kelut

Since the 1920s, various construction projects have been undertaken to reduce the amount of water in the lake inside the crater, in order to neutralize the action of the lahars.

Indonesia is a country that has often been afflicted by violent volcanic eruptions. This is hardly surprising, as it is comprised of a chain of islands that contain some of the largest volcanoes on Earth, which have been responsible for some hugely destructive eruptions. The case of Kelut is slightly different, as it is not particularly big; nevertheless, in 1919 it was the setting for one of the most awesome eruptions ever witnessed.

The power of the lahars

The island of Java, in Indonesia, is home to some of the world's biggest and most destructive volcanoes in the world. Kelut, also known as Gunung Kelut, is not one of the bulkiest or highest on the island, but it is one of the most feared. Its mass, 5,679 ft (1,731 m) in height, conceals a lake in its crater that has been the main cause of death during an eruption.

Several smaller craters surround the peak of Kelut, lending it an irregular appearance. The east, west, and southwest flanks are marked by further small craters, which have also been highly active. Strangely, the eruptions from these openings have occurred in a clockwise direction, so after one eruption it is possible to predict where the next one will occur.

The accounts of Chinese merchants who traded in the area and the tales of the islanders themselves indicate with some certainty that the eruptions of Gunung Kelut date back to 1000 B.C.E., although the first one recorded took place in the 14th century. In the last two centuries, fifteen eruptions have occurred in the peak, with most of them leading to a significant number of casualties, especially in 1919. The destructive force of Kelut is derived from the lake inside its

main crater, but what has this got to do with the eruptions? The explanation is that, when the volcano awakens and starts to expel pyroclastic material through its main crater, this material mixes with the water in the lake, so that it, too, is ejected with enormous ferocity. The conjunction of these two elements plunges down the mountainsides at terrifying speed, pulling in rocks and soil to form spectacular lahars or lava-mud flows, which have caused countless deaths and wreaked incalculable destruction. In addition, secondary lahars are formed by rain and sometimes feed the main lahar. Another of the latent dangers of Kelut's eruption are the fiery clouds; admixtures of ash, gases, and incandescent material that also rush down the sides of the mountain toward the unfortunate inhabitants below. The combination of these two factors had

Deposits of petrified lava left by an earlier eruption.

An advancing lahar destroys any building in its path, as proven by this image from the foot of Kelut.

devastating consequences in the dreadful eruption of 1919.

In the first weeks in May, fumes and mild, but worrying, tremors were noticed. At noon on the 19th, Kelut exploded violently. In the following hours, until nightfall on May 20, the pyroclastic material flung out of the main crater was accompanied by water from the lake. It was calculated that the water in the lake at the time of the eruption amounted to some 1.4 billion cubic feet (40 million m³). The gigantic lahar – formed, on the one hand, by water and red-hot matter from the lake and, on the other, by stones, sand, and debris from the slopes of Gunung Kelut – destroyed the town of Blitar as well as 104 villages, flattening over 9,000 homes.

The eruption killed 5,110 people and devastated 52 sq. miles (135 km²) of farmland. The lahar traveled over a distance of 22 miles (35 km). One of its branches reached the River Badak, with fatal consequences for most of those who lived on its banks; the watercourse only served to ease the path of the deadly concoction. The European expatriates who came to see what had happened could barely believe their eyes. The landscape that only hours before had been lush and fertile was now a pitch-black wasteland. No resources were available to rescue the victims of such a catastrophe.

Continued activity

This was not the last of Kelut's lethal eruptions. In 1951, 1966, and 1990, the mountain stirred again to sow panic in the towns of northern Java. After the tragic events of 1919, attempts were made to mitigate the effects of the lake. If this contained little water, it was reasoned, the lahars would be smaller and therefore less destructive. Over the course of a few years, the water level was reduced by some 160 ft (50 m), but the eruption of 1951 annulled this progress by sinking the crater by a further 228 ft (70 m), leaving some 1.75 billion cubic feet (50 million m³) of water. The next eruption, in 1966, took the lives of over 200 people.

The efforts to dry the lake via tunnels and artificial openings had met with little success, although the velocity and length of the lahars were less than in 1919. In 1951, they were 4.5 miles (7 km) long, and in 1966, 19 miles (31 km), while their speed dropped from 15 miles (25 km) per hour to 13 miles (22 km) per hour.

The 1966 disaster spurred engineers to construct more tunnels, dams for the lahars, and diversion canals for both the lahars and the River Badak; they also installed a warning system. The most recent major eruption put all these measures to the test. In 1990, the volcano hurled igneous rocks and pyroclastic material over a distance of 44 miles (70 km). The fiery clouds buried 50 schools and over 500 houses under tephra and 30 people were killed. The lahars were not of a significant size, however. The volume of water in the lake a few months before this incident amounted to only 35 million cubic feet (1 million m³); the work begun in the 1920s had borne fruit, but the battle has by no means been won, as Kelut is still active.

Drought and famine in China

Around 1920, drought and an accompanying famine claimed a great many lives in the northern provinces of China. Nor was it the first time such an event had taken place.

Northern provinces of China

1920–1921

500,000 dead

A mother and child from Shantung during the famine of 1920

Every year, a number of regions in China have to deal with periods of extreme drought

China seems to suffer almost constantly from natural disasters. Over the past 2,000 years, there have been a total of 1,092 major floods and 1,056 periods of drought, which means statistically that somewhere in China every year there will either be extensive flooding or else a period of extreme drought.

The consequences of this are often large-scale and devastating, in part due to the size of the country and its enormous population. For example, the extreme drought in the years from 1876 through 1879 virtually wiped out food production across 9 provinces and an area of 386,000 square miles (1,000,000 square km). This disaster cost the lives of 9,000,000 people. Thirty years later, due to excessive rainfall and the failure of the harvest, an estimated twenty million people died in the famine of 1907.

When we consider these tragedies, it should be remembered that at the beginning of the twentieth century food shortages and famines were virtually intrinsic to life in the north of China. Local authorities were also extremely reticent about reporting serious famine and food shortages. As a result, the actual severity of a situation would be poorly documented, so that often there seemed no reason to provide for any relief efforts.

Extreme drought and failed harvests

The famine that affected large parts of China's northern provinces in 1920 and 1921 did succeed in attracting the attention of relief workers. Nevertheless, hundreds of thousands of lives were lost to this famine, the cause of which was extreme drought and failed harvests.

China's northernmost provinces lie in the catchment basin of the Yellow River, which flows from the Tibetan plateau through the Ordos Desert into the Gulf of Bohai. The soil is fertile due to large quantities of loess (a fertile, sandy, calcium-rich loam, pale-yellow in color), which the river carries away from the desert and deposits in the lower reaches of the river.

The hardworking farmers who scratched a living from the soil were the main inhabitants of this area, living with their families in thatched mud huts or small, wooden cabins. The farmers grew millet, sorghum, and wheat on small plots of land, both to feed themselves and to sell. Harvested produce was taken to the cities on poorly navigable roads.

In 1920, as a result of the persistent drought, the harvest was so poor that appalling situations began to develop in the area. The peasant population was living in conditions of abject poverty. People fed themselves with whatever they could find. In villages, starving people scrabbled in the dust of the dry streets looking for any waste scraps of food or a single grain of wheat. Exhausted people slept on the street, and many others—estimated at one million—abandoned their homes to travel

to other areas in the hope of a better life. Whole communities became ghost towns as a result.

Out of sheer desperation, tens of thousands of children were sold by their parents, for little in return. For example, in a settlement numbering 250 inhabitants, close to the city of Handan, between 40 and 50 children were sold, most of them girls. They were sold for various purposes, sometimes as concubines, prostitutes, or as second wives. Due to the lack of food, epidemics broke out. So it was that this famine grew into a terrible disaster that affected 20 million people and cost 500,000 lives. At the beginning of the twentieth century, international relief efforts for areas affected by famine were not as large scale or well coordinated as they are nowadays. A great deal of the foreign aid for this famine came from the American Red Cross. In collaboration with the Chinese authorities and the Chinese Red Cross, the Americans provided the northern provinces of China with food, clothing, and temporary shelter. In 1920, the Red Cross granted more than a million dollars in aid to the north of China.

Not the last famine

In 1928, another severely extended period of dry weather affected millions and claimed many victims. During a major famine in 1936, millions starved, with the province of Sichuan being particularly badly hit. Probably the most gruesome famine disaster of all, however, affected China in the period from 1959 through 1962. The famine was caused or, at the very least, seriously worsened by the economic policy that the then communist government was pursuing under the leadership of Mao Tse Tung. In 1958, Mao launched a plan under the name of "The Great Leap Forward." The objective was to make a collective advance in agriculture and industry by creating communities in which industrial workers and agricultural laborers would work together. Farmers had to surrender their plots of land, which were amalgamated into large areas that had to be managed collectively. Food shortages actually increased rather than diminished, partly because a considerable amount of the harvest had been sold to the Soviet Union in order to pay for the industrialization program in China. In some agricultural areas, too little manpower was available to harvest the crops, because many farmers had been encouraged to work in factories in the cities. The result was that large amounts of the crops to be harvested were left to rot in the fields. It is estimated that this famine ultimately cost thirty million people their lives between 1959 and 1962.

Measures

Given that the climate has been becoming increasingly dry in the northeast of China since the 1970s, the Chinese Minister for Agriculture took measures in 2001 to combat drought and failed harvests in northern agricultural regions. For example, the ministry offers assistance through providing artificial fertilizers, diesel, and cereal seed to these areas. Flood-control dams have been introduced to rivers in order to manage water more efficiently. Whether these measures will be able to eradicate drought and famine, however, remains to be seen.

Parched and cracked ground at Hengyang in the province of Hunan

The Ukraine
and Volga region,
(former) Soviet Union

1921–1922

Estimated
5,100,000 dead

Drought and famine in the Ukraine and Russia

Drought at the beginning of the 1920s led to a major famine. This ranks it among the worst disasters in terms of the number of lives it claimed, not only as a direct result of the drought, but also through associated circumstances.

In the summer of 1921, a major drought afflicted the south of the Ukraine and the Volga delta. The Volga is the longest river in Europe, rising in the hills to the northwest of Moscow and running in a southeasterly direction to discharge into the Caspian Sea. The Ukraine lies to the south of Russia and borders the Black Sea. From 1918 through 1922, the southern Ukraine was an independent republic, principally reliant for its economy on the vast quantities of grain it produced.

The definition of a drought is a long period with less than average rainfall. The spring of 1921 in Russia happened to be a relatively mild one. Proof of this comes from records for the average temperature of the Baltic Sea for the months from November through March, when it was around 25 °F (-4 °C). This was seven degrees warmer than in 1917, for example, when the entire Baltic Sea had frozen solid during the winter. Normally speaking, the south of the Ukraine has hot summers, but in the summer months of 1921 the little rain it should have received never came. The rest of Europe was also suffering from a seasonal drought. Only 14.5 inches (370 mm) of rain fell in the Netherlands in the months from September 1920 through August 1921, while in England a drought of 100 days was finally broken on June 26, 1921.

Cannibalism

Massive crop failures afflicted the south of the Ukraine as a result of the lengthy drought, which began in the spring of 1921 and endured for the entire year that followed. Grain yields were 10–25% below normal that year. The consequence of these poor harvests was a major famine, which claimed a huge number of lives. Although estimates of the number of victims vary, there is now general acceptance that approximately five million people died at that time, both from starvation and

from the epidemics such as typhus and cholera that broke out due to the desperate conditions. Large numbers of children in particular succumbed to starvation, disease, and even the cannibalism that, as a grotesque consequence of the food shortages and utter desperation, assumed ever-greater proportions.

The starving population attempted to survive by eating grass, leaves, earth, and emaciated domestic pets. It was largely the stricken peasants who left hearth and home to traverse the country in search of food and aid. Many people gathered together in temporary encampments or loitered about railroad stations in the hope of

boarding a train to the north to escape the famine. They stowed away in empty cars and, if there was no room inside, sought refuge on the roof instead. Suzanne Ferriere, who was working for the International Save the Children Fund that visited the town of Poltova in 1922, was told about just such an instance in which 400 children died because, during the space of 48 cold winter hours, they had frozen solid to the roof of a freight wagon.

Drought or politics to blame?

The huge number of victims of this particular disaster cannot, perhaps, be attributed to the drought

Peasant families journey through the country in search of food and help

October 1921: refugees affected by famine in a temporary encampment

alone. Many say that there could have been fewer victims if politicians had been less concerned about other issues and taken action sooner. Other factors also played a role. The First World War, the October Revolution of 1917, and the Russian Civil War (1918–1921) had together decimated agriculture. Poverty reigned throughout Russia, with major food shortages being suffered in urban areas. The Soviet government forced farmers from the Ukraine to hand over food to the population in big cities such as Moscow and Petrograd (St. Petersburg), and to the Red Army. This let to peasant riots and discontent among the populace.

Lenin realized that something had to be done to improve the poor economic situation and launched the New Economic Politics (NEP). This was intended to win back the support of the peasants for his party; he also hoped it would translate into the recovery of agricultural and industrial production. For the peasants, it meant that they were allowed to keep the remainder of their harvest for themselves, after paying a certain sum of money. Despite the introduction of NEP, however, the returns for the peasants were so meager that the food shortages, and thus starvation, continued unabated.

When foreign powers made it clear to Lenin that something had to be done about the famine and its disastrous consequences, he consented to their assistance.

Foreign food aid

During her journey through the region in the summer of 1921, Dutch writer Henriëtte Roland Holst met with the Russian author Maxim Gorki. Gorki spoke openly with her about his concerns regarding the massive famine that was breaking out in the area surrounding the Volga. He foresaw that the Russian government would not be sufficiently able to provide help in dealing with the food shortages. On July 13, 1921, Gorki and Tikhon, the patriarch of the Russian Orthodox Church, petitioned for help from abroad.

The United States responded positively to this plea. The American Relief Administration (ARA) was founded under the leadership of Herbert Hoover. The ARA was the largest aid organization to operate in the affected areas. In terms of scale and quality, it was the ARA that gave the greatest assistance in terms of food, medical aid, and clothing, and without interference from the Russian government.

Additional assistance from abroad came from the League of Nations in Geneva, Switzerland. The Nansen Committee (named for the Norwegian Fridtjof Nansen) was formed specifically for this purpose. In addition to financial resources, it also provided food aid. A committee representative, who visited the affected area in February 1922, stated: "The situation in the province of Katerynoslav is appalling … at present, it is estimated that 520,000 people here have no food, including 200,000 children."

Unfortunately, the famine of 1921 would not be the last the country would suffer. In 1932 and 1933, the Soviet Union was again hit by a famine of biblical proportions, in which an estimated further five million people lost their lives. In this case, too, it was thought that the death toll was higher than it should have been, probably due to the actions of the Soviet leadership (at that time, Stalin was in power).

Hunger-driven migrants from the country in a refugee camp

USA

Washington D.C.●

PACIFIC

ATLANTIC

United States

January 27–29, 1922

100 dead

Knickerbocker snowstorm

In some areas 32 inches (82 cm) of snow accumulated in a mere 24 hours – a catastrophe for cities totally unprepared for such falls.

New York Avenue and 14th Street, almost impassable during the storm.

For many hours, trams found it extremely difficult to circulate on Pennsylvania Avenue.

Nature, with all its primal power, can turn even the most inoffensive element into a serious threat. We only have to think of seawater and its transformation by tsunamis or, in the case in question, snow. The fluffy white flakes that delight both young and old can represent a severe hazard in excessive falls. Snowstorms are common in many parts of the world, but they can still take even the best-protected countries by surprise. This was the case with the snowstorm that descended on Washington in 1922.

White January

As its name implies, a snowstorm occurs when the precipitation accompanying a storm consists of snow rather than water. Although this phenomenon is associated with winter, it can often occur during spring in areas where temperatures remain low. The intensity of a snowstorm is very different to that of a rainstorm – at least as regards its consequences. If, for example, there is rainfall of 4 inches (10 cm), we consider this a light precipitation that will not cause any problems; if this level is extrapolated to snow, however, the situation becomes very different. Clearly, in regions such as the Alps and Scandinavia, 4 inches of snow on a winter's day is nothing out of the ordinary, but in urban areas the same amount can create a host of problems: blocked roads, traffic lights out of action, and other inconveniences that can create emergency situations. A major snowstorm, however, can cause much more serious problems and result in cities and towns being cut off for days, if not weeks, on end. Furthermore, it can lead to a range of life-threatening mishaps: falling trees, telephone posts, and electricity pylons; traffic accidents; disruptions to the electricity supply—extremely dangerous in cold weather – and, in mountain regions, avalanches capable of burying entire villages.

Snow is a common sight in much of the United States, especially in the inland and northern regions. Some snowstorms have paralyzed cities for days, as in the case of the most recent major snowfalls in 1996. Of all the snowstorms to hit the country, however, the one that occurred in 1922 stands apart, not only for the amount of snow that fell but also for its tragic consequences.

In the last week of January 1922, a front approaching from the northeast was bringing with it intense blizzards. On January 26, the temperatures started to plummet, reaching minimums of 12 °F (-11 °C) in Washington. The air from the Artic was growing colder and colder, and on the following day the snow started to fall in the northeast. Cambridge, College Park and other cities in the state of Maryland received 24 inches (62 cm) in a mere 24 hours. (These levels were so exceptional that they would not be surpassed until the late 1990s.) By January 29 the snow had reached 32 inches (82 cm) in the district of Columbia and various parts of Baltimore, Howard, and Prince George. The minimum levels recorded, in the mountains of Allegany or the city of Washington, were a remarkable 14 inches (35 cm).

Moreover, the blustery, icy winds exacerbated the perilous conditions by felling trees, blocking roads and turning them into veritable lumberyards. The trams in Washington could barely circulate, even though small teams from City Hall diligently cleaned the lines. The city's hospitals were kept busy by patients who had slipped and fallen over, often breaking limbs in the process. The shelters of organizations like the Salvation Army were full to bursting. Many of Washington's most disadvantaged inhabitants were trapped in their homes.

The last picture show

On January 29, the storm seemed to be retreating, even though snow was still falling. Those who ventured outdoors tried to resume their normal lives – this included having fun. The Knickerbocker, previously a theater and now one of the city's most modern movie houses, continued with its program. As usual, it was full for the evening show, and everything proceeded as normal, despite the thick snow outside. At 9 p.m. there was an intermission, and just at that moment a loud noise came from the ceiling. A terrifying crack appeared and rapidly increased in size, before, in the blinking of an eye, the ceiling caved in over the stalls, no longer able to support the weight of three days' snowfall.

It is thought that around 900 people were inside the movie theater; 98 were killed and 133 seriously wounded. Panic set in, as terrified spectators tried to flee, while others stayed to help those crying for help from below the rubble. Order was not restored until the arrival of the police and fire brigade. Five hours after the disaster, some 200 members of the emergency services and 600 volunteers were working amidst the debris. The rescue operation involved grueling effort, hindered by the precarious state of the remains of the roof, the low temperatures, and the primitive equipment available. The building had been well constructed, but the weight of the snow had overwhelmed it.

The disaster was a test of the city's solidarity. The Knickerbocker snowstorm – so called after the tragically famous movie theater – caused material damage of over half a million dollars and killed nearly one hundred people.

All thoughts of entering the Capitol were mere fantasy during the storm.

Accidents liked this caused a host of injuries.

Great earthquake of Kanto, Japan

The Kanto earthquake was one of the most severe in the history of Japan. The cities of Tokyo and Yokohama were totally devastated. Many lives were lost in the fierce fires that broke out following the quake.

Kanto, Japan

September 1, 1923
140,000 dead

On September 1, 1923, just before midday, a major earthquake struck Japan. The first two shocks did not appear too serious to most of the natives, who were used to such phenomena; the third one, however, was massive. It later emerged that this shock had registered 8.4 on the Richter scale. The epicenter of the quake lay close to the volcanic island of Oshima, some 63 miles (100 km) to the south of Tokyo and the Kanto plain. While the quake was felt in Hiroshima, Osaka, and Kobe, the cities on the Kanto plain were much more severely affected due to the lower ground density in that region. Evidence of its magnitude can be seen from measurements taken in Misaki, near Kobe, where the earth's crust rose by 23 ft (7 m) and the entire coastline changed. The ground level remained at this height for three days, thereafter slowly dropping by roughly 24 inches (60 cm) a day until it settled finally at a height approximately 5 ft (1.5 m) greater than it had been before the earthquake.

Lunchtime

The time of the earthquake—noon—had devastating repercussions. Many residents of Tokyo and Yokohama were preparing lunch, traditionally cooked over charcoal fires. The result of this was, not only did countless buildings collapse immediately after the quake, but fires also broke out on all sides, the flames of which were fanned by whirlwinds and the explosions from oil and gas storage facilities. People who had fled onto the streets after their homes had crumbled found themselves having to escape the fires. This led to dramatic scenes, such as at a bridge crossing a water feature in Tokyo's Ueno Park, where people literally fought with each other to reach sanctuary as the sea of fire advanced ever closer. The quays and piers in the harbors of both cities were overwhelmed with refugees seeking shelter aboard the ships in dock.

A major depot for military uniforms in Tokyo, where thousands had congregated with the few possessions they had managed to salvage, was consumed by an inferno that claimed the lives of an estimated 40,000 people.

The severity of the earthquake was also demonstrated elsewhere in Japan, through massive tremors and tsunamis with waves some 33 ft (10 m) high. These caused hundreds of deaths. The total loss of life was afterward estimated at some 140,000. Nearly 600,000 dwellings were destroyed and approximately 2 million people

rendered homeless. The cost of the damage was estimated at a billion dollars at the time. Famine ensued, lasting for weeks, as well as shortages of clean drinking water and medical supplies.

All communication between the affected regions and the rest of Japan and the outside world was for a long time impossible. At one point foreign vessels in the harbors of Tokyo and Yokohama were temporarily requisitioned, not only to provide accommodation for refugees, but also to take advantage of their telegraph systems.

Massacre of Koreans

Martial law was declared on the affected region, the police being tasked with maintaining public order and preventing looting and robbery. Official directives cast particular blame on Korean residents in Tokyo for these offenses, which led to all manner of rumors that, not only were Koreans the perpetrators of looting, they were also committing arson and poisoning well water. The resulting witchhunt involved the deaths of hundreds, if not thousands, of Koreans. They were not the only ones to be victimized, however; many whose

accents differentiated them from the norm, such as Chinese immigrants and even native Japanese who spoke regional dialects, also suffered.

The Japanese army and police had to guard large numbers of Koreans against the murderous masses. Eyewitness accounts, however, speak of police officers and army units that were themselves actively involved in the slaughter. Numerous Korean historians later asserted that the Japanese government of the time had consciously encouraged the murder of Korean civilians. Japan had occupied Korea since 1910 (a state of affairs that lasted until 1945), with Koreans considered second-class citizens. The fact is that there were a number of nationalist activists among the Korean victims whom the Japanese were relieved to be free of. Furthermore, during the chaos that followed the earthquake, many Japanese opponents of the regime, including some well-known socialist, communist, and anarchist leaders, were also arrested and killed.

To this day, Koreans consider Japan to be in denial over the massacres of 1923. In Korea, the death toll is estimated at some 6,000, while official Japanese records refer to 231 dead and 43 wounded. Charges were eventually brought against 362 Japanese citizens for their involvement in the slaughter, although only a few were sentenced and even these were shown clemency.

Tokyo and Yokohama were rebuilt only slowly following the earthquake. New and tighter regulations were introduced for the foundations of tall buildings and many parks and open spaces were created to serve a double function as places of refuge. The plans that

were prepared after the quake were never executed in full, however, due to the outbreak of World War II. In 1960, September 1 was proclaimed "Disaster Prevention Day" and, since then, the populations of Tokyo and Yokohama have been reminded on an annual basis of the need to prepare for the possibility of another earthquake.

Tokyo lies close to the fault line below the Izu peninsula, where the Pacific and Philippine tectonic plates slide slowly beneath the Eurasian plate. Every year, this causes around a thousand minor tremors; geologists estimate, however, that an earthquake may occur on average once every 70 years. In 1995, one struck the city of Kobe, around 280 miles (450 km) west-southwest of Tokyo, claiming more than 6,000 lives.

Even stricter building regulations have been in force since 1981, but more than 1.5 million houses had been erected in the meantime; according to research, these would be unable to withstand an earthquake of magnitude 7 or more on the Richter scale.

Devastation in one of the main city streets

Panorama of the havoc caused at Hongokucho Street and Kanda District, Tokyo. Photograph taken from the Yamaguchi Bank building

Scarely a single building survived undamaged at the epicenter of the earthquake

USA
ILLINOIS INDIANA
MISSOURI
Washington D.C.
PACIFIC
ATLANTIC

Illinois, Missouri,
and Indiana
(United States)

March 18, 1925

695 dead

Tri-State Tornado

Due to the severe material damage and the number of deaths caused in only three and a half hours, this ranks as the most destructive tornado ever to have occurred in the United States.

Few natural disasters have so deeply affected the population of the United States as the Tri-State Tornado of 1925. Its intense passage through a series of small towns left a veritable trail of death and destruction from which many of them never recovered. Unfortunately, in the early 20th century the modern detection and alert methods that might have saved many lives did not exist.

Fatal tornado

The Tri-State Tornado of 1925 claimed more victims than any other such storm in the United States, doubling the number of deaths caused by the worst tornado recorded in the country, that of Grand Natchez of 1840, which formed part of a series of storms that had started in Tennessee, Kentucky, and Indiana. Some of these were also highly destructive, but none came close to the Tri-State Tornado.

The first sign of the storm was recorded at one o'clock in the afternoon of March 18, to the northeast of Ellington, Missouri. It soon changed direction, blowing to the northeast toward Annapolis and the mining town of Leadanna. Two people died in the

former town and the damage caused was assessed at more than half a million dollars. When it reached Leadanna, its size made many of the townsfolk think that it was in fact two storms, not just one, that were approaching. Before entering the state of Illinois, the storm left its imprint on the towns of Redford, Cornwall, Biehle, and Frohna in Bollinger county. Eleven people died and nearly forty schoolchildren suffered serious injury. The school was destroyed. The tornado crossed the Mississippi and entered southern Illinois. At half past two in the afternoon it struck Gorham. Little of that small town remained standing and 34 of its inhabitants died.

Advancing at about 63 miles (100 km) an hour with wind speeds approaching 190 miles (300 km) an hour at its core, leveling all structures, the tornado changed direction again and moved north. If the Fujita-Pearson measuring scale had existed then, it would have registered as an F5 tornado without doubt, and a special classification might even have been introduced. The cities of Murphysboro, De Soto, Hurst-Bush, and West Frankfort were

the next to be hit by the storm, Murphysboro suffering the worst damage. The mining installations on the city's outskirts simply ceased to exist. Eight hundred workers were found 500 ft (150 m) below ground, cut off without electric power or an elevator to enable them to escape. Long hours passed before they were rescued. Many of them had lost wives and children. One of the city's witnesses said that many of the houses were lifted up like toys and exploded in mid-air, which is what happened to three of the town's schools. Their weak structures, lacking reinforcements of any kind, could not withstand the approach of the storm and were blown to pieces in minutes. Twenty-five children lost their lives in those schools. Next, the towns of Zigler and Crossville and the farms in Hamilton and White counties received a thrashing. The farmers of the area, who were fully acquainted with local meteorology, were taken completely by surprise by the brutal storm. They had never seen anything like it. This tornado did not behave like other phenomena of the kind, but appeared as a gigantic dust cloud. The classic sleeve of wind was hid-

The Baptist church in Murphysboro. A few of its parishioners survived the tragedy.

den in its midst. The particular form of the storm misled even those best informed on the subject. The total number of victims in Illinois was 613, the highest count of the 3 states. The Tri-State Tornado left Illinois after crossing the River Wabash, arriving next in Indiana. Griffin, Owensville, Princeton, and Petersburg suffered the most in this state, where 71 people died. At 4.30 p.m., to the southeast of Petersburg, the tornado finally dissipated. It had been three and a half hours of absolute hell.

A macabre trajectory

In a short space of time, the tornado covered about 220 miles (350 km) – the longest journey by a tornado in history – visiting the 3 states of Illinois, Missouri, and Indiana as well as 19 surrounding counties. It holds the infamous record of being the natural disaster that caused the greatest number of deaths in the shortest time: 695 victims in barely 3½ hours. The material damage was estimated at 16 million dollars, which equates to 1.5 billion dollars today. More than 15,000 homes were destroyed, leaving tens of thousands of people homeless. More than 2,000 of the injured were treated in places far from their homes or in field hospitals set up by the army.

Re-housing the people who had lost their homes and establishing places of refuge was a huge challenge for the United States government. Unfortunately, the army and the police force had to act to stop the looters and thieves who started rushing to the cities and towns hit by the tragedy. The newspapers of the day emphasized in particular the deaths of the many schoolchildren in the three states. In total, nine schools were destroyed and sixty-nine children killed. As already noted, the installations did not have any safety measures, nor was there any great concern about the matter at the time.

The tornado left in its wake a string of ghost towns, which have never been reconstructed or inhabited again, and tragic accounts of lost friends and relatives that have endured until the present day.

Great Mississippi Flood

The dams defied Nature, but Nature had the last word.

USA
Washington D.C. ●
Mississippi River

PACIFIC   ATLANTIC

Mississippi, Arkansas,
Illinois, Kentucky,
Louisiana,
and Tennessee
(United States)

April–August 1927

246 dead

The Mississippi is the most legendary river of the United States. Its various floods throughout history have always been highly destructive. The worst of them, and possibly the most serious the country had suffered until the arrival of Hurricane Katrina, was the flood of 1927, known as the Great Mississippi Flood.

An indomitable river

The Mississippi, with its vast length and massive volume of water, has been one of the main preoccupations of the engineers of the United States, its course forming an obstacle to the building of highways, railroads, and other centers of communication. From the beginning of the 20th century, a series of dams and locks were built to try to control its surges. But the Mississippi was having none of that. At the beginning of 1926, the rain kept falling and the level of the river kept rising. Never before had such conditions prevailed. In the spring, the Army Corps of Engineers gave the assurance that the dams, dykes, and locks that had been built would withstand the Mississippi. What could anyone say, if they had indeed raised the containment systems?

In mid-April, when it became clear that the dams could not withstand the waters and the rainfall continued, errors committed in the efforts to contain the river were noticed. Only the elements mentioned had been constructed. At no time had anyone thought of creating artificial canals and channels to divert the course of the river's flow. Even some of the civil engineers who had taken part in these infrastructure works criticized this lack of foresight. The military engineers believed these measures were not necessary. In the state of Mississippi, however, the threat was real.

As well as being a natural disaster, the flood exacerbated the shameful racial policy of the time. In Greenville, a town famous for its numerous cotton plantations and the source of the wealth of most of the southern states, the governor, Leroy Percy, forced the black plantation workers and convicts, likewise black, to shore up the dams at police gunpoint. Meanwhile, the white population who had the means to do so, fled to the north of the country. In the days that they were working on the dams, 30,000 plantation workers were crowded into a form of concentration camp.

At eight o'clock in the morning of April 21, the Greenville dams said "enough." Water flooded into the area with the force of Niagara Falls. The tide was unstoppable. With enormous speed, the water advanced through several states: Mississippi, Arkansas, Illinois, Kentucky, Louisiana, and Tennessee. At some points, it was up to 33 ft (10 m) deep. Highways, bridges, and railroads were submerged beneath the powerful waters of the Mississippi. At the river's delta, which had become a veritable stormy sea, some 13,000 black men, women, and children tried to flee. The son of Senator Percy, Will Percy, who was in charge of the Red Cross, suggested transporting these people by steamboat to the northern states where there was no danger. Both his father and the plantation owners refused. If they moved up there, they would not return. The cotton industry needed cheap labor, which is what the wretched

descendants of the African slaves were. The whites who lived on the delta were, however, transported.

Along the river, some 150 dams burst, unable to contain the mighty waters. At some points, the Mississippi grew to a width of nearly 80 miles (125 km). The actions carried out by the authorities were mistaken, such as dynamiting a series of dams near New Orleans to prevent its flooding. In the end, the torrent did not reach the city but, the dams having been destroyed, neighboring towns and fields of crops were flooded. In mid-August, the rain ceased and the water level fell. During those terrible weeks, 43,500 sq. miles (70,000 km²) of land were under water; 246 people, most of them black, died; 700,000 found themselves displaced; 130,000 homes were destroyed; and the material damage was assessed at over 400 million dollars.

Controversy after the floods

In Greenville, the waters receded and the time came to remove the rubble and corpses and commence reconstruction. Again, the suffering workers of the cotton plantations, compelled by the governor and the armed forces, did the work. Complaints soon reached the person heading the commission for the assistance of flood victims. Many analysts believe that news of the governor's actions reached the President, Herbert Hoover. Although he knew what had happened in Greenville, how-

ever, and of the existence of the 154 camps for black people in which some 30,000 people had been held, Hoover tried to hide the fact. It was not until the arrival of Franklin D. Roosevelt that the matter was given some attention, although the injustice had already been done and little action was taken to remedy it.

The Great Flood of 1927 demonstrated that whatever humanity might wish, the mighty waters of the Mississippi are not to be dominated. Attempts were made to ensure sufficient restraint through the new containment works, but the risks remained. On the other hand, the episode caused

the first step in the great migration of black people northward. This movement crystallized in 1942, during the Second World War, when cities such as Detroit and Chicago seemed to offer a chance of happiness and freedom to those who had worked in the southern plantations.

In Junior, Louisiana, this steamboat broke through the containment dykes, exacerbating the appalling situation.

Okeechobee Hurricane

The hurricane that tore across Lake Okeechobee in Florida in September 1928 caused massive flooding.

Lake Okeechobee, Florida, USA

September 16, 1928

2,500 dead

Trail of devastation in West Palm Beach

Flooded streets and damaged buildings in Lake Worth

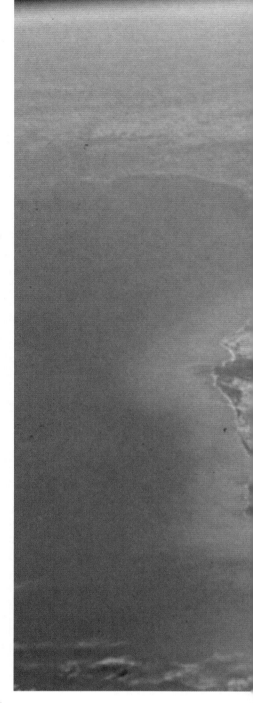

It was in the evening of September 16, 1928, when residents on the southern shore of Lake Okeechobee in Florida were taken by surprise by a hurricane that resulted in an immense flooding of the lake. It was not the first time that the south of Florida had been affected by severe storms. In 1926, the Great Miami Hurricane had also spent some time rampaging around Lake Okeechobee. Due to its location, the "Sunshine State," as Florida is known, is vulnerable to storms that arise in the Atlantic Ocean, the Caribbean, and the Gulf of Mexico.

Lake Okeechobee, which means "great water" in the native Seminole language, lies in the south of Florida. It is a relatively shallow lake, but one with a large surface area (730 square miles/1890 square km), located in a subtropical climate zone. The lake is a catchment pool for rivers (particularly the Kissimmee River) as they flow north to south through the state toward their mouth in the Everglades, an area of swamp that runs to the southern tip of Florida.

On September 10, 1928, messages were received from ship radios at sea that a hurricane to the east of Guadeloupe was on its way. Three days later, it reached Puerto Rico. With wind speeds over 160 miles (260 km) per hour, this hurricane was considered to be the first in history to achieve category-5 status. Category 5 is the highest possible classification on the Saffir-Simpson Hurricane scale.

After leaving its mark on the Caribbean islands, the hurricane rushed onward in the direction of mainland America. On September 16, at around a quarter after six in the evening, the hurricane reached southern Florida; it was now classified as Category 4. With immense power, it tore over West Palm Beach on the east coast in the direction of Lake Okeechobee, leaving a trail of devastation in its wake.

Black Sunday

Many of the black migrant workers who lived on the southern shore of Lake Okeechobee had come from the Caribbean to work the fertile farmland of Florida. Vegetables, sugar cane, fruit: almost anything would grow in its rich, dark soil. With justification, the land in the area was dubbed "black gold." Most agricultural laborers lived in poor conditions in small mud huts, with a few roads of mud and sand linking together villages such as Belle Glade and South Bay. Following the disastrous storm of 1926, and to protect the farms and villages, the government had caused a "dike" of mud to be raised around the lake, to a height of approximately 8 ft (2.5 m). This barrier afforded adequate protection as long as it did not rain too hard and the wind was not too strong. On this "Black Sunday" in September,

however, the dike proved no match for the enormous force of the wind. It had also rained a great deal in the weeks leading up to the storm, causing a sharp rise in the level of the lake. On top of this, water levels rose by a further few

SCENE NEAR DIXIE COURT APARTMENT, WEST PALM BEACH

STREETS FLOODED IN LAKE WORTH AND BUILDINGS WRECKED

inches during the first few hours of the storm.

At a wind speed of approximately 140 miles (225 km) per hour, the southwesterly wind passed over the lake and breached the dike on the southern side. Land to the south of the lake was flooded: an area of hundreds of square miles under water, to a depth of 30 ft (9 m) in some places. Houses were torn from their foundations and broken apart; streets became impassable.

Earlier that day, residents surrounding the lake had been warned that a hurricane was on its way, and had sought shelter on higher ground. Because the hurricane did not come at the expected time, however, many people had returned to their homes by the time it struck.

After the disaster

Roughly 75 percent of the victims were black immigrant workers who had not been officially registered. This made it difficult to give a precise figure of those who had died. In 1928, the Red Cross recorded a death toll of 1,836. In 2003, the National Weather Service adjusted this number upward to 2,500, which ranks the Okeechobee hurricane as the second worst hurricane in American history in terms of the number of fatalities.

The black laborers who had survived the disaster were mainly responsible for recovering the dead, pulling corpses from the swampy, muddied flood waters that stood for several more weeks in the Everglades. There were not enough coffins to go around; those available were used for the bodies of white victims. Due to the heat,

the bodies could not be kept long, which is why many vanished into mass graves or were burned. The mass graves for white victims were later given a memorial; others were "forgotten." Arguments concerning racial discrimination arose as a result and continued for a long time afterward.

The Okeechobee Flood Control District was set up following the floods of 1926 and 1928. In collaboration with the U.S. Army Corps of Engineers, the Herbert Hoover Dike was built around the lake to prevent such a disaster from ever happening again.

Satellite image of Florida and its neighborhood, with Lake Okeechobee clearly visible in the Florida peninsula

Eruption of Mount Merapi

In spite of being one of Indonesia's most active volcanoes, Merapi is an inexhaustible source of wealth, which is why so many people live in constant danger on its slopes.

The island of Java (Indonesia)

November 21, 1930 through September 1931

1,396 victims

General view of Merapi, one of Indonesia's most destructive volcanoes.

At present, Indonesia has more than 500 volcanoes. Of those, at least 129 are considered active. Throughout its history, both its extinct volcanoes and those that are still active have caused terrible disasters. In spite of that, the inhabitants of this Asian archipelago continue to live under the skirts of its volcanic giants. The appeal of the rich fields of crops in their vicinity is too strong to resist. An example of this dangerous tendency is Mount Merapi, Indonesia's most active volcano.

Clouds of fire

Merapi is in southern Java. Although a young volcano, geologically speaking, it has erupted 68 times since 1548. It has certainly never rested. The danger posed by this volcano is increased because it is in an area inhabited by around 1,500,000 people. The city of Jogjakarta is only a few miles away, so each time Merapi awakes, the danger becomes more apparent. Although this 9,550 ft (2,911 m) giant represents a great threat, it is also a blessing for those who live beneath it. The ash expelled from its summit is an excellent fertilizer for crops, which can yield up to three harvests a year. In an area of economic hardship, how can the people reject what Merapi and other volcanoes have to offer?

Red Fire, the translation of the name Merapi, is the youngest volcano in the southern part of the island. Situated in the subduction zone of the Indo-Australian plate and the Euro-Asian plate, it has been constantly active for 100,000 years. The intense geological activity under its surface has caused the large number of eruptions. Although its first eruptions were dominated by the expulsion of basaltic material, pyroclastic fluids have now taken over. Explosive eruptions accompanied the pyroclastic materials, which were much more harmful than the previous effusive expulsions that occurred more than 100,000 years ago at the beginning of the volcano's long life. Merapi's activity follows a fairly well defined cycle, although there is no shortage of unexpected jolts. Every two or three years there are smaller eruptions, followed by larger ones every ten or fifteen years. These eruptions have caused many deaths. The most significant were those of the years 1006, 1786, 1822, 1872, and 1930, each of which was unique in some way.

The activity in the year 1006 was an historical watershed. It is thought that Merapi covered half of Java with ash. Combined with a series of social factors, this put an end to the Hindu Mataram civilization, which was followed by Muslim domination. Islam remains the predominant religion today, in a case similar to the disappearance of the Minoan civilization following the eruption of the island of Santorini.

The eruption of 1822 left a broad crater 1,970 ft (600 m) deep. Burning clouds are one of the recurrent phenomena of this volcano's eruptions. Many were formed in 1872, together with an eruptive column that rose to a height of over 29,500 ft (9,000 m).

The last significant eruption was the most severe. At the end of October 1930, seismographers installed in the city of Maron, 5.5 miles (9 km) from the volcano, detected a series of tremors within it. During the night of November 21, a strong jolt alerted the residents of the villages nearest to Merapi. A few minutes later, the first fountains of lava began to emerge at an altitude of 8,860 ft (2,700 m). On December 18 and 19, the climactic episode occurred: the most intense

period of the eruption. The explosions steadily increased in magnitude, as did the pyroclastic emissions. Burning material covered a distance of more than 9 miles (15 km), near the Blongkeng river. Then the forest began to burn. In desperation, the local inhabitants fled, but could find no refuge. The forest was on fire and the emissions of pyroclastic material and burning clouds seemed unending. Due to the powerful explosion, a depression 2,800 ft (850 m) deep formed in the main crater.

In January 1931, the effusive phase of the eruption began. Lava surged from the new depression, creating outflows that leveled whatever they encountered on the slopes of the volcano. In June and July of that year, avalanches repeatedly assailed the villages below the mountain. In mid-September 1931, the eruption ceased. The dead numbered 1,396 and 36 villages had disappeared. The economic repercussions were felt for many years. The cultivated land was devastated and more than 2,000 of the animals so vital to Indonesian farmsteads died.

Eruptions without end

The episode of 1930–31 was the worst ever experienced at Merapi, but not the last. We have already noted that Merapi is Indonesia's most active mountain. In 1976, a new eruption killed 28 people and

destroyed more than 300 homes. The volcano's most recent eruption occurred in 1992 and lasted ten years. The morphological changes in the volcano were profound and gave rise to yet another disaster. In November 1994, the dome formed in earlier years collapsed, emitting large quantities of pyroclastic material and forcing people to evacuate their villages. Forty-three people lost their lives.

The eruption ended in 2002. The monitoring stations set up in the area, which were severely punished by the activity of those ten years,

remain on watch 24/7. Merapi is a powerful enemy and cannot be trusted. The Indonesian government has initiated an internal emigration policy in favor of unpopulated areas. Its intention is to reduce the population living under the threat of the volcanoes. The result has not, however, been encouraging. In the case of Merapi, the nearby regions are a veritable hive of activity. The soil is rich and it will be hard to make people to leave. To the great majority of those living close by, it is a source of wealth. But for how long?

The active fumaroles on the volcano's summit. Note the landscape devastated by the activity of its crater.

A curious picture of the sulfur crystals that abound in Merapi's crater.

Flood of the Yangtze River

An estimated 3.7 million people died as a result of drowning, disease, and starvation.

Yangtze River, Huang He or Yellow River, Hwai River, China

1931

3.7 million dead

This aerial photograph, taken by Charles Lindbergh, shows various breached dikes and the area flooded at the city of Tunning

China's great rivers, the Yangtze and the Huang He or Yellow River, have a long tradition of flooding and calamity. When, in August 1931, both of them burst their banks together with the Hwai River, it led to a catastrophe of epic proportions in densely populated China.

In summer, when the southeasterly winds start to blow, humid air travels from the Pacific Ocean and amasses above China. Consequently, rainfall is considerable in the region, particularly in June, July, and August. In the summer of 1931, this monsoon was of an extremely severe type. Downpours and tropical storms ravaged the rivers' basins. The dikes that for weeks had had to sustain huge cloudbursts and tropical storms at last gave out, collapsing in hundreds of places. Approximately 825,000 acres (333,000 hectares) of land were swamped, at least 40,000,000 people were made homeless, and great sections of the harvest were lost. Large areas of land remained inundated with water for three to six months. Disease, lack of food, and absence of shelter were together responsible for the final death toll of 3.7 million.

The town of Gaoyou in the northern province of Jiangsu was one of the epicenters of this tragedy. On August 26, 1931, a powerful typhoon struck Gaoyou Lake, the fifth largest lake in China. The level of the lake water, which was higher than the surrounding buildings, had already risen to record levels as a result of excessive rain in the preceding weeks. Gusts of wind created high waves that buffeted the dikes. Just after midnight, the dikes lost the battle. They were breached in six places—the largest of which was a gaping hole of almost 2,300 ft (700 m). The water tore through the town and across the province. It is estimated that 10,000 people died in Gaoyou on that morning alone.

Famous relief workers: the Lindberghs

In September 1931, the famous American pilots Charles and Anne Lindbergh flew over the ravaged area and took a series of striking photographs. When landing their plane on water, on one of their relief missions, they were almost overwhelmed by a horde of people in their sampans, making for the aircraft. The starving masses thought the plane was transport-

ing food, but the cargo consisted only of medicines.

Help came only in piecemeal fashion. The focus of China itself was elsewhere, on a civil war between the Communists and Nationalists and an invasion by the Japanese in the north. The rest of the world was in the grip of an economic depression. An immense challenge awaited the relief workers who did leave for the area. In the end, two million people throughout China were set to work on repairing the dikes.

The survivors of this catastrophe were given little respite. Large-scale breaches of dikes have occurred time and again, including in 1938, 1954, and 1998. In 1938, the dikes were cut through intentionally in order to stop the advance of the Japanese. Wide-scale tree felling has also started to play an increasing role in the rapidity with which China's rivers swell. In the absence of tree cover on the hills and mountainsides, the ground is unable to absorb the rainfall, which instead flows

straight into the rivers, thereby increasing the volume of water they have to channel away.

River courses

The Yangtze and the Huang He are extremely susceptible to flooding. At 3,960 miles (6,380 km) long, the Yangtze is the third longest river in the world after the Nile and the Amazon. It is a fickle river. In its upper reaches, where the river twists through deep gorges, its water level can rise by dozens of feet in a short space of time. This happened to an extreme degree in 1871, for example. Once the water had receded, a steamboat was found atop a rock some 115 ft (35 m) above the water level. In the lower reaches of the river, its channel is actually higher than the land surrounding it. Thus flooding can have catastrophic consequences.

The turbulent Huang He or Yellow River is the largest in China after the Yangtze. This 3,395-mile (5,464-km) river follows a course every bit as capri-

cious as that of the Yangtze. Half way downstream, it takes with it the thick, yellowish sediment to which it owes its name. This sediment is responsible for the constant rise of the riverbed. In some places, the water flows as much as 65 ft (20 m) above the adjacent land. The river overflows its banks so frequently it is referred to as "China's sorrow."

The Chinese government is trying to curb these floods with the construction of the Three Gorges Dam. Apart from providing protection against high water levels, the dam is also intended to provide a considerable amount of electricity. The vast infrastructure of this project is controversial, however, because large amounts of land and natural landscape will disappear underwater as a result, and millions of people will be forced to relocate.

In December 2003, a memorial museum was opened in the town of Gaoyou, which was so severely affected by the great floods of 1931. Few of the sur-

vivors of the disaster are now still living, and the town felt it important to keep the memory of this catastrophe alive for residents today.

Deforestation of the riverbanks: according to some, a cause of the many floods in the area

Nuns acting as relief workers help people to saefty

USA
Washington D.C.
KANSAS
OKLAHOMA
TEXAS
PACIFIC
ATLANTIC

Oklahoma, Texas,
Kansas
(United States)

April 14, 1935

Black Sunday dust storm

The gravity of the Black Sunday Storm, combined with the country's economic situation, caused over 300,000 people to flee to California.

A wall of dust hundreds of feet high over a defenseless area in Texas. The Dust Bowl at its worst.

Farms and machinery buried under tons of sand.

The storm approaching Stratford. Not surprisingly, the streets of the town are deserted.

The dust storm approaching Stratford, Texas. The dimensions of the cloud are colossal.

Natural disasters never seem to occur in isolation. Volcanic eruptions, seaquakes, tsunamis, etc. often combine with existing social ills. During the 1930s, the United States experienced its worst economic recession. In mid western states such as Oklahoma, Texas, and Kansas, the continuous dust storms ended by destroying the lives of thousands of people already in desperate straits after the infamous crash of 1929.

A common phenomenon

So-called sand or dust storms are a fairly frequent meteorological phenomenon in large and normally desert areas of the planet: for example, the Gobi Desert in Mongolia, the Taklamakan Desert in China, and the Sahara in Africa. In the United States they are common in the west where there are large areas of desert or semi-desert. The storms occur when strong currents of hot, dry air impact on arid surfaces at high speed. The effect of the air, thanks to a series of meteorological factors such as variations in pressure and temperature between the two elements, lifts

the sand, forming veritable walls hundreds of feet high that become impenetrable. Storms do not always reach this magnitude, but they can be very damaging. Severe dust storms can reduce visibility to zero, making travel impossible and removing the valuable upper layer of the soil, depositing it elsewhere.

Several factors contribute to the appearance of these phenomena, which are particularly damaging to agriculture and livestock. Drought is one of them. As it lifts and removes the topsoil, the storm destroys things such as roots, seeds, manure, and fertilizers that are fundamental to a successful harvest, while the progressive disappearance of surface vegetation is fatal for livestock, as they will then starve. The dust raised by these storms can travel thousands of miles. Saharan sandstorms affect the growth of plankton in the western Atlantic Ocean and, according to some experts, are an important source of scarce minerals for plants in the Amazon rainforest.

As we have mentioned, these storms are frequent in the west-

ern and midwestern United States. During the 1930s, they were extremely serious. The era of dust storms that began in 1930 and ended in 1941 was inextricably linked with the area known as the Dust Bowl, an ecological disaster that had been caused by several factors. Firstly, the 1930s was a decade of long, hard drought for Kansas, Texas, Colorado, and Oklahoma, to name those most severely afflicted. The origin of the drought was meteorological, but also human. Since the mid-1910s, the territory had been cultivated intensively by successive grain harvests, which finally exhausted the soil. For years, the progressive hunting and near extinction of the buffalo had been a tragedy for the tribes of Native Americans. Now it was the turn of the white man to lament the loss of that animal. Thanks to the buffalo, the land in the states that were then suffering from drought had previously been fertilized. The absence of those great herds of animals was fatal for the farming economy. The First World War and the need for wheat in the international markets had stretched arable land to its limits. Farmers benefited in the short term, but in the 1930s they paid a high price. The land was dry and could support nothing. Thus,

when the wind blew, the storms escalated. On the great plains, droughts and storms were commonplace, but not to the extremes witnessed during the Great Depression. Three hundred dust storms were recorded during the era of the Dust Bowl. They became so great that, one in the winter of 1934 in South Dakota turned the snow in Chicago, Washington, and Boston red for several hours. Clearly, it was not snow, but sand.

The Black Sunday storm and its sisters, combined with the impoverished situation of west-

ern North America, triggered the migration of more than 300,000 inhabitants of the affected states, in particular Oklahoma, who traipsed along Route 66 toward hope–California. Here we should perhaps mention John Steinbeck's novel *The Grapes of Wrath*, as it depicted the people of that era as being without hope, yet at the same time prepared to make a new start.

Famine in India

India has had its calamitous events in which famine has been a recurrent factor. One such period of famine, during World War II, is less prominent in our consciousness, though it had a devastating effect on the easternmost areas of the region.

India and present-day Bangladesh

1942–1946

1.5–4 million dead

Construction of a road:boulders are excavated and broken up with pickaxes, and the rubble carried away in baskets.

Famines, frequently the result of drought and failed harvests, have been a recurrent phenomenon in India since the Middle Ages. Up until the end of British colonial rule in 1947, it is estimated that between 30 and 40 major famines ravaged the region. The most dramatic of these took place in 1770, a few years after the beginning of British rule, when an estimated 10 million people died from hunger through drought in Bengal (present-day Bangladesh)—a third of the population at that time. The new colonial masters were completely unprepared for a famine of such proportions.

The situation was aggravated on these various occasions by the fact that much of the food produced in the region itself was earmarked for export and to feed the army. It thus did not find a direct route to the people in afflicted areas. In the nineteenth and twentieth centuries, the region continued to be extremely susceptible to drought and poor harvests, with social and political factors exacerbating this instability. The explosive growth of the population meant that ever more people had to be fed from every available square yard of agricultural land.

The famine that began in 1942, but which actually lasted into 1946, occurred in the region of the Brahmaputra River and Ganges delta. Most sources refer to this as the Great Bengal Famine. According to some estimates, at least 4 million people fell victim to famine between the years 1942 and 1944. Some sources have profiled this famine as a manmade disaster, considering that sufficient food was available at the time, but not properly distributed. Circumstances surrounding World War II have also been cited as compounding factors. The British colony of Burma, for example, from which substantial amounts of food were exported to India, fell into Japanese hands, and the British lost control of the Gulf of Bengal, making it very difficult to transport resources by sea. The famine of 1942 and the following years is best defined as a chain reaction of events and factors, without being attributable to any one single cause.

Tidal surge

Like 1941 before it, 1942 was notable as a year of major drought, causing fears of disappointing harvests. On October 16, 1942, a tropical storm produced a tidal surge 16 ft (5 m) in height that caused a large part of the Ganges delta to flood, affecting an area of over 3,000 square miles (5,000 km²). The disaster claimed 14,500 lives and killed approximately 10 percent of livestock. The harvests that fall were largely destroyed, with inundation by the sea rendering agricultural land unusable for a long time due to the high saline levels created in the soil. A shortage of wood for cremating the bodies of the dead meant that human and animal corpses were left to rot and decay. This in turn contaminated the drinking water, with cholera and other illnesses becoming rife. Shortly after the tidal surge, a plant disease also appeared that affected the rice fields in particular and further diminished the harvest yield.

Food shortages drove up the price of rice and grain to twice their pre-war levels. Opportunist food traders saw their chance to make greater earnings and demanded extortionate prices for their wares. In the main, it was the agricultural workers who, having no property of their own, were unable to sustain themselves as a result of the famine. The authorities—both locally and in the United Kingdom—had their attention focused mainly on developments in the war and initially underestimated the situation in Bengal, which resulted in little or no aid or food relief being sent. Desperate, starving masses left the country for the big cities, such as Calcutta, in search of food. This led to chaos and overcrowding in the cities, where poor sanitation and public disorder took their toll. To illustrate this point, the refugees in Calcutta in October 1943 numbered over 100,000.

The mortality rate for this famine peaked in December 1943. Following the harvest of that year and the arrival of food stocks from other parts of India, rice prices fell and the intensity of the famine

declined somewhat. The death toll remained extremely high, however, and lasted through the whole of 1944. This was largely due to outbreaks of cholera, smallpox, and malaria. Hunger, social and economic unrest, and epidemics continued unabated in 1945 and 1946, albeit to a lesser extent.

In 1945, a national commission of enquiry investigated the effect of the famine and came to an official estimate of 1.5 million dead. Subsequently, various scientists have argued that this figure is far too low, the prevailing view nowadays being that the total number of victims was between 3.5 and 4 million. To this day, the causes of this disaster remain the subject of debate between two main camps: those who point largely to natural causes, and those who lay most of the blame at the feet of the authorities and their lack of emergency relief measures.

Self-administration

Mahatma Gandhi's independence movement ultimately resulted in the end of British colonial rule and the independence of the republic of India, from which Bengal took its own course as the independent state of Bangladesh. Even under its own administration, the region was to be affected many times more by drought, famine, and flooding. For example, large parts of India experienced periods of severe drought and famine in the years from 1965 through 1967. Bangladesh has had to contend regularly with flooding and tropical storms, as for example in 1970 and 1991. It is estimated that a million people died from famine in Bangladesh in 1974, largely as a result of natural causes such as cyclones, floods, and failed harvests.

Starving people wait for rations of rice and grain to be distributed

Employment creation project in a landscape as dry as sand

The Aleutian Tsunami

This tsunami led to the creation of an institution dedicated to studying and combating the consequences of such disasters.

Hawaiian Islands

April 1, 1946

165 dead

The headquarters of a political party in Kamehameha Avenue, Hilo, Hawaii. The wave brutally overturned the wooden building.

For decades, the Hawaiian islands had been a "lost paradise," the destination of travelers from all over the world who wanted to enjoy its dream landscapes. In April 1946, this paradise became a veritable hell. The worst tsunami that had ever reached an archipelago threw the island into chaos. Its effects, however, were not all negative. Thanks to this tsunami, an institution was set up that since then has been studying and warning of the possible arrival of these giant waves.

Without warning

To the English-speaking world, April 1 is April Fool's Day. On that day, a tremor to the south of the Aleutian Islands, west of Alaska, caused a tsunami that devastated part of the Hawaiian Islands. Some believe that, if a warning of its arrival had been issued on that day, it would have been treated as a joke. Regrettably, there was no such warning.

The seaquake, some 94 miles (150 km) to the south of Unimak Island, spawned the gigantic wave. Its epicenter was recorded at a depth approaching 16 miles (25 km), and even today is the subject of debate. When it occurred in 1946 it was given a value of 7.2 on the Richter scale, but subsequent research has raised its magni-

tude to 8.6, which explains the destructive behavior of the tsunami.

Another of the mysteries surrounding the seaquake is the question of what, exactly, happened to the subsoil. Was it a break in the fault line? Was it a slippage? Let us hope that the passage of time and technical progress will help elucidate the matter. At present, scientists remain divided as to the cause of the tremor. The wave generated by the quake scarcely disturbed Alaska, but it did affect the Aleutian Islands, which acted as a barrier to that distant territory of the United States.

The gigantic wave initiated by the telluric movement traveled southward through the Pacific Ocean toward the Hawaiian archipelago. Their geographical position renders these islands highly vulnerable to any tsunami originating in that vast ocean. In fact, since the early 19th century, 50 tsunamis have been recorded in Hawaii, 7 of which have caused major damage. The biggest were those of 1960 and 1946; the former caused by the sudden earthquake that devastated part of Chile, the latter being the one that now concerns us.

The wave reached the islands nearly five hours later, but not before causing damage in the Aleutian Islands. A lighthouse some 130

ft (40 m) tall had recently been built on Scotch Cape. Its base was a stout platform of reinforced concrete, with the signal being of metal construction. Five people were employed in its operation. In just a few seconds, the waves smashed it to pieces, killing the five lighthouse keepers. At that moment, the tsunami was more than 115 ft (35 m) high.

In 1946 there were no observation posts along the Pacific, so the arrival of the great wave was a complete surprise. The places that suffered most were Laupahoehoe, where the waves were 30 ft (9 m) high, Pololu Valley, with waves measuring 52 ft (16 m), and Hilo, which suffered the worst damage. A series of six or seven gigantic waves reached the city at intervals of 15 to 20 minutes. Most of these were 26 ft (8 m) high.

The waves completely destroyed the coastal fortifications of Hilo. The houses on the main street were torn from their foundations by the force of the sea and dragged along, crashing into other buildings as the water advanced through the city. In Hilo alone, 159 people lost their lives.

In Pololu Valley, waves 40 ft (12 m) high struck a school, killing some of the children inside. The local hospital was also unable to withstand the tsunami, and crumbled. In total, the tragedy caused 165 deaths, with material damage being assessed at 26 million dollars. The inhabitants of the islands were utterly terrified by the sudden and destructive phenomenon. It was not only Hawaii, however, which was punished by the tsunami. Its effects were felt the length and breadth of the Pacific. In Taholah, Washington, on the west coast of the United States, waves approaching 7 ft (2 m) in height damaged fishing boats. At Coo's Bay, Oregon, waves reached a height of nearly 10 ft (3 m). In California, the tsunami was somewhat more destructive. Waves 10 to 13 ft (3–4 m) high hit the harbor installations of Half Moon Bay, causing damage assessed at 20,000 dollars. In Santa Cruz, one person was drowned, dragged down by the force of the sea. Although weakened, the tsunami

could still make itself felt in Santa Barbara and the Los Angeles area. On the other side of the Pacific, the tsunami waves reached 26 ft (8 m) in height, appearing in the Marquesas Islands and some parts of French Polynesia, although they did not cause serious damage.

A warning system

As a result of this terrible tragedy on April 1, 1946, the Hawaiian authorities and United States government agreed to devise an early warning system for such fatal natural phenomena. The discussions bore fruit and, in 1949, the Pacific Tsunami Warning Center (PTWC) was set up as a tsunami alert center at Ewa Beach, Hawaii. Since its creation, the PTWC has been run by the National Oceanic and Atmospheric Administration (NOAA). This center's task is to collect information from the seismographers at the Pacific Ocean's various observation posts. When one of these posts detects a tremor that could cause a tsunami, the PTWC informs the authorities of the area at risk. If no news is heard within a determined time, no further measures are taken. Otherwise, evacuation measures are initiated.

The system is designed to warn of the possible creation of a gigantic wave hours before it reaches the coast line. It has operated since its inception to highly positive effect.

The leading tsunami reaches the Puumaile Hospital for tuberculosis sufferers in Hawaii. The giant wave was especially destructive in the area of Hilo, Hawaii, 2,360 miles (3,800 km) from where the phenomenon was generated.

The tsunami reaches wharf N° 1 in Hilo, one of the worst hit areas of Hawaii.

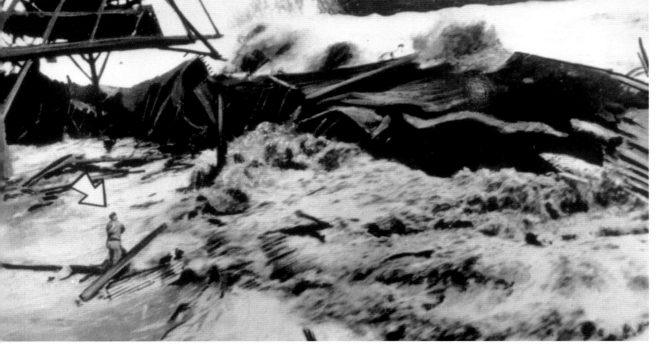

Great Fukui earthquake

The magnitude of the Great Fukui Earthquake of June 1948 was not, in fact, all that great. Because of the low density of the soil in the area, however, the tremors caused extreme havoc.

Fukui, Japan

June 28, 1948

4,000 deac

After the earthquake, fires broke out on a massive scale. Photograph by Carl Mydans, who captured the disaster at close range for posterity

In the 1940s, the inhabitants of the Japanese city of Fukui had to contend with a considerable amount of violence. Their city was destroyed three times in the space of three years: firstly as a result of Allied bombardments in 1945; subsequently, because the city was hit by a severe earthquake in June 1948; and, finally, a month later, due to the flooding of the Asuwa and Kuzuryu Rivers. Despite these disasters, Fukui managed to scrabble back to its feet again. It is not for nothing that the city chose the Phoenix as its symbol.

At 5:13 p.m. on June 28, 1948, the population of Fukui was shaken by an earthquake measuring 7.1 on the Richter scale. The epicenter of the earthquake was close to the town of Maruoka-cho. As far as Fukui itself was concerned, it was largely its northern district that was most seriously affected. Nearly 4,000 people died and almost 22,000 were injured. The force of the seismic movement destroyed more than 35,000 homes. The huge fires that ensued after the earthquake destroyed almost another 4,000 homes. The city's transport system also suffered major damage. Trains had been thrown from their tracks, and the damage to bridges and dikes was also severe. Because of the great havoc that it caused, it was not long before the earthquake was

dubbed The Great Fukui Earthquake.

Landslides and fissures

The Fukui quake registered an actual seismic intensity of 6 on the Richter scale. Owing to the fact that the area where the shocks were felt consisted of level, low-density soil, however, the damage was proportionately greater than might otherwise have been expected. As a result, the Japanese Meteorological Institute decided to assign the earthquake a recorded measurement of 7.1 on the Richter scale. The criterion for 7 on the Richter scale is notably that more than 30% of buildings collapse as a result of an earthquake. Moreover, there should be evidence of landslides and fissures in the ground. The Fukui earthquake more than satisfied these conditions.

Historical legacy

The area surrounding Fukui is famous for its many seventh- and eighth-century Shinto temples and castles. This historical legacy was severely affected by the quake. Maruo-

ka Castle, dating from 1576, was leveled to the ground. Eighty percent of its original structure was re-used in its restoration.

In 1998, Fukui played host to the World Urban Earthquake Conference as a tribute to the 50th anniversary of the quake. The municipality took the opportunity of this conference and memorial to provide additional information to its residents about earthquakes and to explain how best to respond to any future events. Information in Japan about earthquakes is extremely thorough and extensive, with many cities having disaster emergency teams and food rations on standby.

This high level of readiness is necessary, because earthquakes assail the Land of the Rising Sun on a regular basis. A minor tremor is felt each day somewhere in Japan and, every so often, there comes a major one. Japan is a volcanic archipelago that was brought into existence as a result of the movement of the earth's crust, in a phenomenon known as plate tectonics. Japan lies at the intersection of three of these plates, where the Philip-

pines plate and the Pacific plate slip beneath the Eurasian plate. The forces released in consequence discharge their energy in the form of earthquakes, tsunamis, and volcanic eruptions.

It is no surprise, therefore, that Japan has established a firm tradition of research into earthquakes. The Great Fukui Earthquake played a major part in this. After that disaster, scientists recognized that it was time to start making proper records of earthquakes. They began to develop all manner of instruments to enable them accurately to observe movements in the earth's crust and its effect on buildings. In 1956, this resulted in the foundation of the Strong Motion Earthquake Observation Committee. This was later incorporated within the Earthquake Research Institute at the University of Tokyo, which has since achieved worldwide fame as an authority on the subject of earthquakes.

Concentration of nuclear power stations

As mentioned before, Fukui succeeded in rising above the setbacks of the 1940s. Nowadays, the city is largely known for the manufacture of glasses and textiles. The polyester originating from Fukui is apparently so good that top designers, such as Issey Miyake, swear by it. In addition, however, a significant source of revenue comes from the generation of nuclear energy. The region is home to the largest concentration of nuclear power stations in Japan: 15 in total.

Naturally, it does not bear thinking about that an earthquake such as the one in 1948 might hit these nuclear plants; alas, in Japan, this is not wholly out of the question. Japan has few natural resources of its own for fuel; in consequence, the government has formed a strong attachment to nuclear power.

According to the Japanese government, the industry is completely safe because the power stations are built to be "quakeproof." Theoretically, these plants should be able to withstand an earthquake measuring 6.5 on the Richter scale, where the epicenter is directly below the power station. Some scientists do, however, have their doubts about the Japanese government's risk assessments. According to them, these assessments have been based on outdated seismic research. These scientist-critics point to the fact that seismic activity in the Fukui area could soon increase, with all the disastrous consequences this potentially entails.

Landslide in Tajikistan

This was one of the most gruesome disasters of the twentieth century, yet very little is known about it. The tragedy that hit Tajikistan in 1949 was kept hidden from the outside world by Stalin's soviet regime.

Khait, Tajikistan

July 10, 1949

24,000 dead

Traces of the landslip can still be seen to the left and rear of the former town of Khait

For centuries, the Pamir Mountains in the east of Tajikistan, on its border with China and Afghanistan, has been a region visited by few foreigners. In the nineteenth century, it lay at the center of an area fought over constantly by tsarist Russia and colonial Great Britain, and visitors were seldom welcome after 1917 once it was incorporated within the communist Soviet Union. Occasionally, the soviet regime would admit mountain climbers, and for a time there was even a Russo-American joint venture in connection with seismology. The Pamir Mountains were, and still are, notable as a unique region subject to a great deal of subterranean activity, often proving the point to spectacular effect. For example, as the result of an earthquake in 1911, a completely new lake was formed—the Sarez Lake—which is over 38 miles (60 km) in length and, in places, around 1,640 ft (500 m) deep.

Foreign visitors were certainly not present, however, when at the beginning of July 1949 the inhabitants of

the Dharakhavz valley were assailed by several minor earthquakes. Although these earthquakes were relatively minor, they did result in rocks detaching themselves in various locations and creating avalanches. Some villages were rendered uninhabitable due to the avalanches and landslides, with their populations having to live out in the open from July 7 onward for fear of repeat quakes. On July 10, another earthquake did indeed occur—a major one, measuring 7.4 on the Richter scale.

The consequences of this were catastrophic. An immense slab of rock broke from the summit of Mount Chokurak, estimated at nearly 100 square miles (250 million square meters). During its descent, this gigantic slab split into two, creating a river of rubble and mud. This wave of annihilation traversed the valley at great speed and soon reached the town of Khait, 7.5 miles (12 km) further down. At that time, the population of Khait was around 24,000; the entire poplation was buried alive

within a few minutes under a deluge of stones and boulders. The entire town disappeared under this blanket of rubble, which in some places created hillocks nearly 200 ft (60 m) high. In addition to the town of Khait, a total of some 150 villages and settlements in the valley disappeared, all of them overwhelmed by the landslide.

Excavations

Some time after the disaster, the authorities decided that a number of valuable items needed to be unearthed to prevent others from carrying them off in the future, such as weapons, money, and identity papers. With extreme difficulty and effort, several bank vaults were hauled to the surface, but it turned out that the stacks of paper money they had contained had been completely pulverized by the force exerted from the deluge of rubble. There was certainly no need to fear that any looters whatsoever would ever be able to resurrect anything of value from the ruins.

In the meantime, the outside world remained uninformed about this gruesome episode. Naturally, among scientists and seismologists in the wider community it was realized that something or other had happened, but the authorities kept quiet about the consequences of the event. It was only long after the passing of Stalin and at the beginning of reforms to the communist system toward the end of the 1980s that more details began to emerge. It was only then that seismologists registered the fact that a disaster had occurred in Khait comparable to that which occurred 20 centuries earlier at Pompeii, in Italy.

A similarly devastating landslide of the type experienced in Khait later took place in Peru, in 1970. An earthquake caused an avalanche of ice to fall from the summit of Huascarán (at 22,204 ft/6,768 m, the highest mountain in the country), which was followed in turn by a landslide. This river of earth and rock raced downhill at a speed of 250 mph (400 km/h) and wiped out the town of Yungay, 7.5 miles (12 km) distant from the mountain. It is estimated that the death toll reached 20,000.

New threats

Little is yet known about the precise series of events in Khait, partly because there were no surviving witnesses who experienced it at close quarters. A monument near the place of the tragedy has now been erected to the victims, with researchers remaining active at the site in order to study the disaster and its consequences. At the same time, thorough research is also being conducted into possible new threats and preventive measures against them. The area continues to suffer from tremors and earthquakes. In 1989, an earthquake registering a magnitude of 5.3 on the Richter scale caused a major landslide that claimed 274 lives and rendered 30,000 people homeless. In 2003, landslides yet again occurred, creating a great deal of destruction although fortunately not causing any fatalities.

The greatest fear at present is an earthquake that might cause the Sarez Lake to overflow. This natural dam, which was created following the earthquake of 1911, is showing signs of fissures and a minor tremor in the wrong place could be all it takes for the dam to succumb and for water to cascade below in a gigantic wave. A report by the United Nations states that such a flood could reach as much as 625 miles (1,000 km) downstream, probably causing the greatest disaster in the history of mankind in the process.

For that reason, a variety of projects have been undertaken since 1999 around the Sarez Lake under the leadership of the United Nations, paid for, in part, with money from the World Bank. Scientists are considering the possibilities for supporting the dam using technical resources and thus reducing the risk of a rupture. Another option is to allow the water to flow out gradually. In the interim, warning systems are being put in place to enable the timely prediction of any ruptures and thus to enable the nearest population centers to be alerted and, if necessary, evacuated.

The uppermost part of the landslide, from Mount Chokurak

This photograph, taken from above, shows the hummocky remains of the landslip on the valley floor.

Flooding of Zeeland, the Netherlands

A rarely occurring combination of spring tides and a northwesterly storm was the cause of disastrous floods in the Dutch province of Zeeland. Following this disaster, massive investment was made in the Delta Works: a project to protect the Netherlands against severe flooding.

Zeeland,
the Netherlands

January 31–February 1, 1953

1,836 dead

In some places, the water rose to ceiling level

Aerial photograph of part of the disaster area, showing one of the many breached dikes

Apart from the province of Zeeland, disaster also affected parts of North Brabant and South Holland. This photograph was taken in Dordrecht.

Several times over the centuries, great floods have assailed the southern islands in the Dutch provinces of Zeeland and South Holland. The most destructive of these were the St. Elizabeth's Flood in 1421, in which an estimated 2,000 lost their lives, and the All Saints' Flood of 1570, which claimed approximately 20,000 victims. There were further, smaller floods, too, in 1916. Thus there was an awareness of the danger and, consequently, dike monitoring with warning systems. Coincidentally, two days before the flood of 1953, the Public Works and Water Management Department had released a report containing proposals for closing off a number of inlets in connection with the potential flood risk.

As early as the Saturday afternoon of January 31, the KNMI—Royal Dutch Meteorological Institute—had identified that a storm of exceptional force was approaching from the northwest. The storm had already sped across Scotland and was curving straight toward the Dutch coast. In consequence, the meteorologists on duty issued the usual warnings, which were broadcast on the radio and also sent by telex to the dike monitoring authorities in the city of Rotterdam and the towns of Willemstad, Bergen op Zoom, and Gorinchem. KNMI staff knew that dangerous developments could occur overnight and made frantic attempts to have their radio bulletins broadcast through until morning. For many people in Zee-

land, the radio was their only means of communication with the outside world, but broadcasts were never made during the night—the broadcasting station ceased all programming at midnight, every night, with a rendering of the national anthem. At the station's headquarters in Hilversum, it was decided that, even on this particular night, they either could not or would not make an exception.

Extreme high tides

And so the storm charged onward, while most people on the islands went to bed. People had experience with storms often enough in the past, of course, so there was not too much concern about this one. It was during the night, however, that the storm reached its height. The wind force measured in excess of 11 on the Beaufort scale, and gusts of up to 90 mph (144 km/hour) were recorded. Since this also coincided with the spring tides—the period when the sea reaches its maximum height on the flood tide—sea levels were extremely high. Half way through the night, instruments recorded a height of 15 ft (455 cm) above mean sea level. The dikes were unable to withstand this, and one by one the waters broke through. In the middle of the night, the population was awakened from its sleep either by the noise of the storm, by inundations of water, or by warnings from neighbors. Many people tried to save themselves by making for higher ground, often heading to a church or farm in the vicinity. Others lacked such good fortune and had to climb into the loft or onto the roof of the house. It was there that thousands spent the rest of the night and following morning, while the sea churned all about them.

The situation further deteriorated that afternoon, the spring tide bringing with it yet another tidal surge with even higher water

levels. Many people were washed from their roofs and subsequently drowned. Others managed to save themselves and floated for hours on driftwood or other floating material. Events took a tragic course for many people: whole families were torn apart. More often than not, children and the elderly lacked the strength to survive the waters, in the cold, without anything to eat or drink and without any prospect of rescue.

Organized rescue operations only really swung properly into action toward the end of Sunday afternoon, by which time it was already too late for many of those affected. At that time, many of the rescue facilities we have today were not yet available, such as helicopters, and most people had to be rescued using simple, small fishing boats. In the end, over 70,000 people were evacuated, and for most of them it was to take more than 18 months before they could return to their neighborhoods. In total, over 650 acres (170,000 hectares) of land had disappeared beneath the waves, while some 10,000 homes had been completely destroyed and a further 35,000 had sustained serious damage. Approximately 40,000 head of cattle and 165,000 fowl drowned, with the total financial loss running into millions of guilders, the Dutch currency of the day.

The provinces of South Holland (particularly the island of Goeree-Overflakkee) and parts of North Brabant that bordered Zeeland were also affected. In addition, the storm also caused flooding on the northern Dutch island of Texel (1 dead), in Belgium (14 dead), and in England (216 dead). A ferryboat also sank on the Irish Sea, with 134 drowned.

Open your purses and close the dikes

In the Netherlands, a major fundraising effort was soon underway to help the victims. A great

deal of clothing and furniture was collected, but also a lot of money, thanks to the campaign entitled "Open your purses and close the dikes," which was conducted primarily by means of radio broadcasts. Relief supplies were also sent from abroad and many volunteers came forward, including servicemen, doctors, and nurses. Help arrived from Scandinavia in the form of prefabricated housing: throughout Zeeland, wooden homes appeared that could be erected in a surprisingly short time. Nevertheless, their quality was high, demonstrated by the fact that some of these houses can still be seen today.

For the Dutch government, the disaster was the impetus for expanding on the plan conceived previously by the Public Works and Water Management Department and accelerating its implementation. The plan was known as the Delta Works and provided for closure of the large marine inlets between the islands, raising the level of the dikes, and tidal surge barriers that could be raised and lowered as necessary. Work was started in 1958, with the final dam being built in 1989. Initially, the cost was budgeted at a cost today of 1.5 billion euros, but the final bill exceeded 5 billion. The most striking of these constructions is the Oosterschelde Dam. Original-

ly, the intention was for the Oosterschelde estuary, just like those of the Haringvliet and Zeeuwse Meer, to be completely closed to the sea. For ecological reasons, however, and to protect fish stocks, it was decided in 1976 to fit the dam with sluice gates. The Oosterschelde Dam now has 62 openings, each of them 130 ft (40 m) wide, which can be closed in the event of extreme high water.

Although the Delta Works

have now been completed in full, the question remains whether they will be enough to keep the sea at bay forever. Given climate change and the global rise in sea level, it is likely that further measures will have to be taken at some point in the future.

Earthquake in Chile

Of all the many earthquakes recorded to date, this was the most violent and intense, measuring 9.5 on the Richter scale.

CHILE
Santiago de Chile
The Valdives   ATLANTIC
PACIFIC

Arauco Peninsula
(Chile)

May 22, 1960

3,000 dead

The houses in the city of Valdivia withstood the earthquake without collapsing, but did not remain undamaged. The unstable ground on which they were built was to blame.

Because of its geographical location, Chile is one of the countries of South America most vulnerable to earthquakes. Its territory stands on a tectonic plate – the Nazca plate – that is subject to movements during certain periods. These movements will continue until the subduction (the movement of one plate over another) of the Pacific Ocean ceases. For this reason, Chile has many volcanoes. Earthquakes have been the worst natural disasters that the country has suffered, however, particularly the one of May 22, 1960.

A warning

On May 21, a tremor measuring 7.7 on the Richter scale shook the Arauco peninsula. It damaged many houses and destroyed historic buildings in cities such as Concepción, Coronel, Lota, and Arauco. Several hundred people were killed in their sleep, crushed by the rubble of their own homes. The government feared the worst. The number of victims was not as high as it could have been, however, as people ran out of their houses when they felt the first movements. The earthquake was a warning of the one that was to devastate the Valdivia area the following day.

At 2:55 p.m. on May 22, a tremendous quake struck the region. The seismologists could not believe what their detection equipment was telling them: 9.5 on the Richter scale. Of all the earthquakes known, this was the most intense, the one that released the most energy, although luckily not the most fatal as regards human lives.

The epicenter was nearly 200 ft (60 m) below the bed of the Pacific Ocean and more than 62 miles (100 km) off the country's coast. The tremor lasted ten minutes. Thanks to its duration, the people of the region had time to run into the streets and squares, trying to escape the treacherous shelter of their homes as had happened the day before. Otherwise, the number of deaths would have been much greater.

It is calculated that nearly 3,000 people died, although some put that figure at 10,000. Living conditions in the area were very hard and people were not prepared for a disaster of this magnitude. Houses were built of stone and materials that could not well withstand such an event. Many villages lacked a reliable census, and in some areas the earthquake swallowed everything in its path because of the avalanches of rocks and the holes in the ground it created, so that the number of vic-

tims will never be known for certain. The material damage was assessed at more than 550 million dollars. More than 60,000 houses were destroyed and millions of Chileans were left homeless.

The cause of most of the deaths was not the earthquake itself, but a tsunami that arrived minutes after the tremor. The destructive power of the wave was enormous. It was so intense that it reached Hawaii, the Philippines, and even Japan, claiming many victims all over the Pacific.

Countless cities suffered the effect of both phenomena, with Valdivia and Puerto Montt the worst affected, being closest to the epicenter. Most of Valdivia's houses were destroyed. In some places the city sank nearly 7 ft (2 m). The landslides buried many buildings and the tsunami waves overwhelmed much of the coastline in the area, engulfing the whole of its seafront.

At Puerto Montt the destruction of buildings was worse. More than 85 percent of them disappeared.

A changed landscape

The landslides and rain changed the course of the region's rivers and even created lakes where none had

been before, such as the one formed in the San Pedro river in the Andes. Other lakes disappeared or simply joined together. Small islands that had accommodated the fishing trips of the Valdivians were swallowed by the sea, although new islets also appeared. In total, 13 of Chile's 25 provinces were affected by the earthquake—a large proportion of the country's infrastructure was destroyed, with the consequent economic loss.

One last illustration of the terrifying nature of the episode of May 22, 1960: the zone worst affected by the tremor was approximately 19 miles (30 km) long by 310 miles (500 km) wide, an enormous area that suddenly sank by nearly 7 ft (2m), at the very moment – 2.55 p.m. – when seismographers from half the world were setting out.

Unfortunately, geologists' forecasts for this region are not optimistic. Taking into account factors such as geological structure and geographical situation, the prediction is that earthquakes like the one in 1960 will be repeated every 25–100 years.

Two days after the earthquake, the Cordon Calle volcano started erupting. Although lying 125 miles (200 km) from the epicenter, panic spread across the region.

A ruined house in Castro on the island of Chiloé, severely damaged by the tsunami.

Tsunami in Chile

What followed the earthquake of greatest magnitude were waves as high as 82 feet.

CHILE
Santiago de Chile
ATLANTIC
The Valdives
PACIFIC

Valdivia region
(Chile)

May 22, 1960

2,300 dead

Hilo after the tsunami had passed.
Thirty-two-foot (ten-meter) waves hit the town, which had suffered similar events on other occasions.

Hilo, Hawaii.
The town's seafront and much of its interior were severely battered by the giant wave. Sixty-one people died on Hawaii.

This disaster was the result of the most powerful earthquake ever recorded in the history of seismology. Disease, hunger, and psychological problems are among the – sometimes insoluble – difficulties the survivors of a natural disaster have to confront. These phenomena cause a new catastrophe for those who survived the first one. Unfortunately, this has happened in many cases, as with the tsunami that followed the tremendous earthquake in Chile on May 22, 1960.

Double punishment

The region of Valdivia in Chile was the scene of the biggest earthquake ever recorded – 9.5 on the Richter scale. The earthquake destroyed thousands of houses and caused profound changes in the landscape of the whole region, even creating lakes in the Andean region and new islands off the Chilean coast. Dozens of towns were affected. In many, and in Valdivia, Coronel, and Concepción in particular, the inhabitants fled in terror to avoid being buried by their own homes, running toward open spaces, in some cases to the town square and in others to the ports.

A few minutes later, a tsunami caused by the tremor reached the cost of the Valdivia region. In the places nearest to the epicenter of the tremor, the wave rose as high as 82 ft (25 m). The people who

had taken refuge in the harbors paid dearly for their attempt to escape. The wave – or waves, for two more arrived, the second and strongest at 5:30 p.m. and the third at 8:00 p.m. – killed an estimated 2,000 people.

On the island of Chiloé, as in other villages, many residents flung themselves into their boats before the arrival of the giant wave. They thought that, if they were in the open sea, they would escape from a new earthquake. Tragically, this was not the case. None of the 500 who sailed away from the island returned. The sea swallowed them. The same thing happened in Quetalmahue, from which 200 boats packed with people had set off: all sank without trace.

In Valdivia, the port area was devastated. The sea surged over half a mile (1 km) inland. Those quick enough to flee from the earthquake saved themselves by taking refuge in high places, such as hills and even trees. The material damage caused by the giant wave was great. Its trail of destruction did not end in Chile, however, but continued into the Pacific.

Unstoppable advance

Hours after it had raked the coast of Chile, the effects of the tsunami reached the west coast of the United States. California was worst affected. The highest wave to reach

its coast was nearly 7 ft (2 m) high and traveling in excess of 62 miles (100 km) an hour. In Los Angeles and Long Beach, 300 boats were set adrift and more than 30 sank. Some of the yachts with the deepest drafts broke free from their moorings, hit the wharves, and sank. Because of the collisions between such vessels, hundreds of gallons of gasoline and synthetic oils entered the sea. The danger of fire was great, but fortunately the coastguards were able to take action and this threat did not materialize. In San Diego, the ferries could not put to sea and the wharves were seriously damaged. Southern Alaska and the Aleutian Islands were also hit by the tsunami, although it had weakened by then.

On Easter Island, several moais – the island's famous statues – fell due to the impact of the wave. Fourteen hours after the first tsunami had struck the Chilean coast, Hawaii was unable to withstand the wave. The east of the island, especially the Hilo area, suffered the most. In 1837, 1877, and more recently in 1946, several tsunamis had caused nearly 100 deaths among the population. On those three occasions, the waves had come from the Aleutians, but the experts had not realized that the phenomenon could approach from Chile too. The sirens sounded when the wave was sighted, but the first one was litte more than 3 feet (1 m) high. The residents of Hilo, unworried by what they assumed was a false alarm, came out of their houses. Minutes later, the succeeding waves crashed in, some of them nearly 20 ft (6 m) high. The town's fragile buildings could not withstand them. Whole houses collapsed before this heavy attack by the sea. Roads, bridges, wharves, everything was flattened. The few structures that remained standing were modern buildings made of resistant materials. Sixty-one people died, with material damage assessed at 26 million dollars. The tsunami did not stop in Hawaii, but pursued its murderous course to the coasts of Japan. The town of Onagawa on Honshu – Japan's biggest island – bore the brunt. Twenty-two hours after devastating the Valdivia region, the

tsunami reached that modest Honshu settlement. Again, the waves struck the coastal regions several times. The first was some 16 ft (5 m) high. Curiously, although Onagawa was the worst damaged town, the 122 victims of the tsunami were recorded in neighboring places. In Onagawa, the alarm service operated perfectly and its inhabitants took refuge in the highest parts of the town. As in Chile, anything high would do: roofs, trees, and especially the hillsides surrounding the town. The material dragged along by the waves, such as pieces of wood, created further destruction, demolishing many houses on the coast.

Samoa and New Zealand were also affected by the Chilean tsunami, though no one died because of it. The tsunami spawned by the earthquake that had raked the Valdivia region had a devastating effect on many towns around the Pacific.

The number of dead was estimated at 2,300 – in Chile it could never be ascertained which fatalities were caused by the tremor and which by the wave – and the material damage assessed at more than half a billion dollars. Due to events such as the one just described, the Pacific coasts now have a network for detecting and warning of tsunamis. Unfortunately, they are a highly unpredictable phenomena, but with adequate infrastructures their effects can be lessened, as demonstrated by the case of Onagawa.

Aerial view of Chiloé, which was totally devastated by the tsunami. Many of the dead were inhabitants of this island.

Eruption of Mount Agung

The intensity of this eruption caused the collapse of the volcano's summit. When it eventually fell, the mountain lost 328 ft (100 m) in height.

The Island of Bali

March 1963

1,148 dead

Fertile land for crops after the eruption of Agung in 1963.

The temple of Besakih, saved from the fearful activity of the mountain in 1963. Many Balinese believe it was a miracle that it remained intact.

Agung in the background of this heavenly picture of the island of Bali. Its powerful image dominates the territory.

When least expected, a heaven can become a hell. That is what the Balinese and hundreds of tourists must have thought in March 1963 during the eruption of Agung, one of the most ferocious of the 20th century. Although the number of victims did not reach the figure of similar cataclysms, its effect on the life of the island and especially the climate of the planet rendered it a significant catastrophe.

A relentless eruption

The mention of Bali has long evoked images of beaches, crystalline waters, and exotic dancing-girls in one of the most idyllic places on Earth. In March 1963 however, the volcano Agung awakened. Situated on the eastern side of the island, this mountain was virtually unknown until the early nineteenth century. Then, in 1808, 1821, and 1843, it erupted. Little information is available about the events of 1821, but the other two eruptions are known to have been almost identical. An earthquake preceded each one, with the volcano later expelling columns of ash and pumice, but from 1843 it had remained calm, causing no trouble to the islanders.

On February 16 and 18, 1963, a series of earthquakes shook several villages near the volcano. No one paid them much attention. As on previous occasions, however, the tremors heralded an eruption. On February 19, the first explosions occurred. Small fragments of rock were thrown out of the crater and landed nearly 4 miles (6 km) to the south. Days later, the first showers of ash fell on Rendang and Selat, near the volcano, to be followed by small pyroclastic masses traveling in the same direction. The rain that fell on the island affected the slopes of Mount Agung, forming mudslides due to the water and deposits of pyroclastic materials. These lahars destroyed one of the island's main roads. At the end of the month, lava was seen surging out of the crater and flowing for a distance of more than 4 miles (7 km). The two more destructive or paroxystic phases of the eruption followed, the first on March 17. The previous night, there had been constant explosions in the crater. As the explosions grew bigger, the columns of gas emitted by Agung climbed higher. Activity was at its maximum for ten hours.

The volcano threw out all kinds of debris: igneous rocks, lapilli, ash, and pyroclastic material that covered a radius of over 6 miles (10 km). The ash layer was some 16 in (40 cm) thick, which gives an idea of how harmful it could be if it fell on a human being. More than 13 rivers were inundated by the material expelled from the volcano. At one, the river Luah, pyroclastic clouds were burning at temperatures of over 750 °F (400 °C) and rising into the air at 50 miles (80 km) an hour. The destruction caused by these flying, flaming masses was tremendous.

The following day, it rained, the rainwater combining with the material ejected by the volcano to form new mudslides. One of these reached the town of Amplapura, completely destroying it. The second phase of the eruption occurred on May 16. It started at 5.00 p.m. and lasted four hours. Ash and debris were expelled with enormous fury, reaching six valleys and two rivers to the north of the volcano. These rivers of pyroclastic material were some 7½ miles (12 km) long and carried every-thing along in their path. Then the crater starting throwing out igneous rocks, up to 6 in (15 cm) in diameter. The result was catastrophic for the huts and homes of the Balinese, built as they were of flammable materials, particularly wood. The rocks were accompanied by columns of ash.

After the eruption, geologists who visited the area reported deposits of ash around Agung more than 3 ft (1 m) thick. After May 16, the activity of the volcano started to decline. Though it continued to expel pyroclastic material, this was in in smaller

amounts, much to the relief of the people. The period of intense activity was followed by the collapse of the summit, which reduced Agung's height from 10,301 ft (3,140 m) to 9,973 ft (3,040 m). By the end of that year, the volcano's activity had decreased to a few fumaroles.

Agung and the Balinese

The death and devasatation wrought by the eruption was terrible: 1,148 people died; 296 suffered serious injury; and more than 100,000 lost their homes. At global level, the gases expelled by the eruption caused a severe temperature drop in the northern hemisphere. The island's harvests were ruined, causing a major subsistence crisis.

In spite of the idealized image of Bali, its people are humble and their means of living meager.

Many of those affected by the volcano relocated from the eastern to the western side of the island, where they felt safer.

It is curious that, in spite of the damage it caused to the island, the Balinese consider Mount Agung sacred. In March 1963, the materials ejected by the volcano left the temple of Besakih unscathed. To the island's inhabitants, this was a miracle: proof that, while the gods wanted to demonstrate their power, they did not wish to destroy what men had built in their honor. Thus Agung is feared and revered in equal measure.

Good Friday Earthquake

Seismologists believe that this earthquake and the tsunami that followed, some of whose waves reached a height of 220 ft (67 m), affected the whole planet.

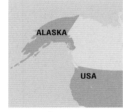

Alaska
(United States)

March 27, 1964

119 dead

Fourth Avenue in the center of Anchorage, Alaska. Several buildings were left almost 10 ft (3 m) below the road surface, presenting this peculiar appearance.

Many natural disasters are like the famous Russian dolls. Once one has been released, others follow. Sometimes, the origin of a terrible disaster is to be found in an earlier event. This is what happened in the Good Friday earthquake that struck the west coast of Alaska, Canada, and the United States. The earthquake was big, but the greatest number of deaths was caused by the tsunami generated by the tremor.

On dangerous ground

Alaska is a wild land that even today shows clear and certain signs of resisting subjugation. Its extreme climate and nature carry both advantages and disadvantages for its inhabitants. The advantages are manifest. Nature-lovers can enjoy a territory such as that described by Jack London. Unfortunately, however, this environment, although a delight to the eye, can be treacherous.

Alaska is a highly seismic region. Its territory is threatened by the Pacific plate, which is in a constant state of subduction (when one tectonic plate rubs against another) with the North American plate. The vertical movements of the seabed caused by this subduction are the principal causes of earthquakes and tsunamis. The tsunamis generated in the Alaskan peninsula, its gulf, and the Aleutian islands can cause serious damage anywhere in the vast Pacific Ocean. When a giant wave is produced in the neighborhood of Alaska, however, it does not necessarily mean it was preceded by a tremor. According to experts, large submarine landslips can be the cause of the tsunamis that strike these coasts.

At 3:36 a.m. on March 27, 1964, a tremor was recorded with its epicenter in the depths of the Collage fjord in Prince William Sound. It measured 9.2 on the Richter scale. This was the most powerful earthquake yet recorded in the United States and the second most powerful since the Chilean earthquake of 1960. It lasted four interminable minutes.

The tremor caused enormous changes in the geology of the area. It was fortunate that only nine people lost their lives. An area of over 50,193 sq. miles (130,000 km²) suffered damage as a result of the earthquake. Kodiak Island and many other territories experienced vertical displacements of some 50 ft (15 m). It caused an extraordinary event – moving an entire island (Latouche) 60 ft (18 m) south of its former position. Human settlements also suffered damage. The worst hit city was Anchorage, 75 miles (120 km) from the epicenter. More than 30 buildings in the city center collapsed, including apartments, warehouses, and office blocks. All the city's schools were destroyed. In another district near the center, Turnagain Heights, the damage was still greater. Landslides tore down 75 houses. Electricity, gas, telephone, and drinking water supplies were out of action for days. Other towns, such as Portage, were completely annihilated by the surface movements. It sank to nearly 10 ft (3 m) below sea level. In despair, its inhabitants abandoned it – forever.

Tsunamis – a fatal trap

Most of the destruction was not caused by the earthquake, however, but by the tsunamis it generated. A few minutes after the tremors began, the first wave reached the coast. In all, five waves arrived at various intervals, some more than an hour apart. The first of the gigantic waves was not the strongest, giving the residents of Alaska and British Columbia – the worst affected part of Canada – time to get organized and evacuate the areas that might be struck again. The waves caused 129 deaths. In Shoup Bay, they reached their maximum height of 220 ft (67 m). In Alaska, although the wave did not reach Anchorage, it did affect other places. Seward and Kodiak were the worst hit, as they suffered the tremor and the subsequent tsunamis, landslips, and fires. The small, native villages of the region, such as Chenega, were totally destroyed, as was Valdez, which was later rebuilt on firmer ground. Material damage was assessed at 80 million dollars. In Canada, the waves arrived three hours after the occurrence of the earthquake. The worst affected place was Port Alberni, where more than 400 houses were destroyed by the action of the waves. At Hot Springs Cove, 16 of the village's 18 houses disappeared beneath the waves. Luckily, no one was killed in Canada, although the material damage was great, being estimated at over 50 million dollars. The tsunami reached the west coast of the United States as well. Washington State escaped virtually unscathed, but in Oregon and California the damage was more serious. Four people lost their lives in Oregon, where much of the damage was caused by the overflowing of the rivers, into which the waves had surged.

In California, the tsunami killed 13 people along the coast and sank several boats. The damage was assessed at more than 10 million dollars.

The earthquake and subsequent tsunamis had global repercussions. Seismologists believe that Earth as a whole was affected by the tremor. Following the tremor, various movements in the Earth's crust lasted more than a year. Phenomena linked to the earthquake succeeded one another in the most varied places. In South Africa, the water levels of wells rose and fell for no apparent reason. And in Louisiana, several pleasure boats sank without explanation.

The earthquake and tsunamis of Good Friday 1964 have passed into history as the most powerful in the history of North America. The preparedness of its communities, the sparse population of the affected areas, and the coincidence with public holidays were determining factors in the saving of lives. If it had not been for these factors, the death toll would have been even higher.

Ruined buildings in the residential district of Turnagain Heights. Seventy-five houses collapsed due to the instability of the ground in that area.

Denali school, showing severe structural damage. As it was Good Friday, the classrooms were empty, their pupils enjoying a public holiday.

Good Friday Tsunami

Its waves reached heights of 230 ft (70 m) in areas near Valdez, Alaska, and speeds of over 340 miles (550 km) per hour on the coast of Seward.

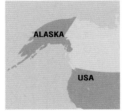

Alaska
(United States)

March 28, 1964

122 dead

Aerial view of Valdez, Alaska. Note the town's seafront, totally flooded by the gigantic wave.

The earthquake had been the most intense ever recorded in the United States and the second most intense in seismological history. It was accompanied by the most powerful tsunami ever to have struck the coasts of the United States and Canada. Like the tremor, this phenomenon was the second most intense in history. Both followed the brutal earthquake and tsunami that occurred in Chile in 1960.

The coup de gràce

The earthquake, which occurred on March 27 in Alaska, started at 3:36 a.m. in the depths of Collage fjord, some 75 miles (120 km) east of the state capital, Anchorage. It lasted around four minutes. Considering that most seismic vibrations last only a few seconds, the destructive capacity of this one becomes obvious, especially in view of its magnitude on the Richter scale: 9.2.

The measurement taken on the Mercalli scale produced amazing figures. The Mercalli scale is divided into sections, numbered I through XII. The tremor of March 1964 revealed an intensity of XI. Alaska is an area of high seismic risk, as it is in the subduction zone of the Pacific and North American plates. The tremor set off the tsunami that surged into the areas already devastated by the earthquake, with several waves arriving at different intervals. After a few minutes, the first and least intense waves reached British Columbia. About three and a half hours later, however, the really gigantic waves made their appearance. Four or five of them crashed in, depending on the zone, at intervals of between 15 and 30 minutes. The first and smallest constituted a warning to the inhabitants of the areas that would be severely damaged: Kodiak, Seward, and Valdez, all in Alaska, and Alberni and Port Alberni on Vancouver Island. The waves reached heights of 220 ft (67 m) in Shoup Bay and 230 ft (70 m) in areas near Valdez.

As well as the principal tsunami, most of the affected places had to withstand small local tsunamis caused by coastal landslides, though these did not arrive at speeds anything near 340 miles (550 km) per hour as was the case with some of the waves that hit the coast of Seward.

Worldwide nightmare

The tsunami affected Alaska in particular. It spared the state capital, Anchorage, but the tremor did not and, due to the liquefaction of the avalanches of rocks, caused heavy damage in the city. In Valdez, some 112 miles (180 km) from Anchorage, the giant waves caused huge destruction. When it arrived, a container ship, the S.S. Chema, was being unloaded. The giant wave lifted the ship up, depositing it on the wharf, and then returned it to the sea, where it stayed adrift for hours, endangering everything that came near it. The sudden lifting of the ship caused 28 deaths.

Most of the buildings and houses on the seafront were destroyed. At 30-minute intervals, 4 more waves arrived, forcing the residents of Valdez to flee to the hills surrounding the town. There they spent the night in freezing temperatures. The case of Seward was not much better. The waves struck the seafront in such a way as to reach the Standard Oil refinery located there. The vehicles dragged along by the sea hit the gas and oil pipes, causing them to explode. The fire soon reached the huge fuel tanks, which burned for days. Twelve people died, including firefighters who rushed to the refinery and attempted to contain the flames. As a result of the explosions at the refinery, the railroad station and its tracks were destroyed.

Kodiak Island experienced the most incredible episodes of the tsunami. It is one of Alaska's leading fishing centers. The giant wave appeared when the fishing fleet was anchored in the harbor of St. Paul. The 160 boats were forced to the edge. Some even crashed into warehouses and harbor installations. The port buildings were torn from their foundations and driven into the town, to the amazement of the residents. The two small fish, crab, and salmon-canning factories were swept away by the waves.

In Canada, the town of Hot Springs Cove was totally destroyed and the villages of Alberni and Port Alberni also suffered considerable damage. On the west coast of the United States, the waves caused the deaths of 17 people, most of them in California, thousands of miles from the epicenter of the tremor. In Crescent City, ten people died. The average height of the waves that struck the Californian shore was 13 ft (4 m). Material damage was assessed at 10 million dollars in California alone, and in total was estimated at 120 million dollars. The state of Oregon also suffered in the tragedy. Four people were killed there. The waves even reached Hawaii although, due to a series of geological circumstances and the Pacific alert system, no serious damage was caused. In Hilo, the tsunami reached a height of nearly 10 ft (3 m), but its speed was much weakened. Hours later, Japan recorded the tsunami's death throes on its eastern coast. The waves that had caused terror in Alaska were now only a few inches high.

The Good Friday tragedy prompted the United States authorities to set up the West Coast and Alaska Tsunami Warning System (WC&ATWC), a tsunami alert and observation service like the one set up in 1949 for the Pacific Ocean and which researches the tsunamis and earthquakes that can occur in Alaska, Oregon, Washington, California, and British Columbia. Its operation is identical to its sister entity in Hawaii, which has brought a degree of tranquility to the residents of those latitudes.

The railroads at Seward Port, Alaska, were damaged, first by the earthquake and then by the waves launched by the powerful tsunami.

A fishing boat and truck belonging to an oil company at Resurrection Bay. The tsunami helped start a series of fires in the refineries of the affected area.

Niigata earthquake

The theory that the weight of fallen snow encourages earthquakes in this area is gaining credibility every day.

Niigata
(Japan)

June 16, 1964

28 dead

Japan is one of the countries that suffers most from earthquakes. Its people have learned to live with them, although it is never easy. Thanks to this experience, the population's preventive measures and preparedness for earthquakes are excellent, but this, of course, does not free Japan's cities from destruction, such is the intensity of the tremors of this Asian giant.

A phenomenon not to be forgotten

Niigata is one of the administrative districts of the biggest island of the Japanese archipelago, Honshu. Its most important city bears the name of that district, Niigata, an economically active region famous as the source of the Shinkanshen, or bullet train.

Both Niigata and its neighboring districts lie in a zone of great geological activity. The faults there are subject to various east-west compression movements that are felt in distant places such as Chubu. At the time of the Samurai, the Japanese blamed the gods for the earthquakes they had to endure. The underground battles between Kashima, the protector of Earth, and Namazu, a bellicose giant catfish, had direct consequences on the Earth's surface. In many cases, tremors were seen as a divine punishment inflicted on mortal beings.

Beyond that charming and mystic interpretation, Japanese geologists know what they are confronting. The Niigata earthquake confirmed a seismological fact: the significance of the liquefaction of a very large tremor. Its devastating effects in the Niigata and Alaska earthquakes of that same year – a curious coincidence – prompted Japan's experts to undertake further studies. Liquefaction occurs when unconsolidated sediments saturated in water lose their capacity to support weight when strongly shaken by a seismic wave. When this happens under buildings and structures, it can severely damage them and even cause them to collapse.

Another risk with this phenomenon is that it renders affected buildings unsafe. A building's foundations can be damaged, but it is difficult to ascertain the extent of this. In Niigata, to avoid greater loss, the houses, offices, shops, etc. affected by the liquefaction were evacuated until they could be declared safe again.

The Niigata tremor occurred on June 16, 1964. Seismographers recorded a magnitude of 7.5 on the Richter scale. The earthquake also affected the towns of Aikawa, Sakata, and Sendai. Damage extended through nine administrative districts. The eastern part of the island of Awashima was raised by nearly 5 ft (1.5 m) while the western part sank by over 3 ft (1 m) as a consequence of the tremor.

A few minutes after the tremor – between ten and fifteen minutes, according to reports – panic returned to the streets of Niigata. A gigantic wave was approaching the important port of the area at high speed. The tsunami generated waves of 10–16 ft (3–5 m) in height. Their impact was tremendous. The town's harbor installations were destroyed by their violence.

The economic effect was considerable. Fishing and cargo vessels were based in the town, some of which sank. Others were unable to work for weeks because of the wretched state of the port. The damage was huge: the tsunami was not confined to that area, but reached Ryotsu Bay on the island of Sadogashima. There, the wave was 10 ft (3 m) high.

From there, it pursued its course to the Noto peninsula, although by then it was smaller, around 3–6 ft (1–2 m) in height. On the island of Oki in the remote district of Shimane, the fertile rice fields were destroyed by the tsuna-mi. Unfortunately, the local people depended on the rice for their food.

The disaster did not end there. While the town's residents were recovering from the terror caused by the wave, an aftershock finally demolished those buildings that had sustained severe structural damage. Three hours later, a second, less intense aftershock constituted the final act of the disaster. Between the two aftershocks, a series of fires spread through Niigata. Short circuits within houses and the explosion of several fuel tanks in the harbor were to blame. While the town did not experience events such as those in Tokyo in 1923 or Kobe in 1995 and the fires were controlled, many buildings were still destroyed.

A new explanation?

The earthquake claimed 28 victims, which is not many considering the destruction caused by the conjunction of what could be called cataclysmic factors: the tremor, the fire, and the tsunami. More than 2,000 buildings were destroyed, 290 of them by fire. Most of the buildings succumbed due to liquefaction. In one case, the Kawagishi-cho apartment buildings, looked quite bizarre, ending up almost horizontal, like dominoes on the point of falling over. Their internal structure, however, remained intact. All the damage was due to the instability of the ground. The same effect was seen in many buildings. Fortu-nately, they had been designed to withstand earthquakes. In spite of this, however, the loss of buildings was considerable. The same thing happened to the Showa bridge, which had only recently been inaugurated, but collapsed because it was sited on unstable ground. Some parts of it could not withstand the tremor and the soft, malleable ground, while others remained standing, though with minor damage.

Years after this tragedy, Japanese and North American experts ascertained what may have triggered earthquakes such as the one at Niigata: snow. The enormous amount of snow that falls on Japan's mountains in winter produces great pressure on the surface – up to 1,845 lb/yd^3 (1,000 kg/m^3). When spring comes, the snow melts and the accumulated pressure is released, causing earthquakes. The theory is only in its infancy and there are no models for applying it. What is certain is that more and more attention is being paid to it. Could it help prevent future disasters? We do not know, but researchers are optimistic.

Unfortunately, the hypothesis formulated here could not help warn of a new tremor in the Niigata district. On October 23, 2004, an earthquake in Chuetsu caused nearly 50 deaths and, for the first time, the derailing of a bullet train.

Several apartment blocks collapsed because of their precarious foundations. The instability of the ground, which encouraged liquefaction, also played a significant role in this earthquake.

The Showa Bridge had been open only a few weeks. It suffered severe damage, as can be seen from this photograph.

Droughts and famine in India

Extended periods of drought in India in the mid–1960s resulted in major famines. For decades, they painted a picture of a country wracked by poverty and misery, despite many positive developments in the years afterward.

A man leads his livestock through the dusty desert area of Thar, Rajastan

Hundreds of people working on an irrigation system close to the town of Vaini

India has regularly had to contend with major periods of drought. Agriculture in India is dependent to a significant degree on rainfall during the southwesterly monsoon in the months from June through September. Seventy-four percent of all annual rain falls in that period. Problems are quick to arise if the rains in that period should be less than this, or if no rain falls at all, with the situation exacerbated since the British coloni-

zation of India: since that time, much forest has been cleared to make way for plantations. In the past, the forests were responsible for capturing rainwater, creating underground reservoirs that could be reached by sinking wells. Over the centuries, however, the majority of these forests disappeared, with wells having to be dug ever deeper.

The droughts in the mid-1960s mainly affected the Indian states of Maharashtra (of which Mumbai is the capital) and Bihar (in the northeast of the country, with Patna as its capital). As a result of the monsoon rains not appearing, the harvests failed (especially in Maharashtra in 1965 and 1967, and in Bihar in 1966) on which 70 percent of the population was dependent. The droughts also resulted in major shortages of drinking water, so that livestock perished. For many country people, a humble pair of goats or sheep and a few chickens were an important source of income and food; thus famine came knocking at the doors of many when these, too, were lost.

1965 and 1966 were also disastrous years for food production on a wider, global scale. Drought also occurred at this time in Argentina, Australia, the Soviet Union, and in parts of Europe and Africa. In 1966, the FAO—the United Nations Food and Agriculture Organization—released a disturbing report that showed how the world had been on the brink of a gigantic famine. It was mainly thanks to extremely good grain harvests in North America that it had been possible to keep world food stocks generally stable. In consequence, the United States registered a record in its grain exports in those years and a minimum level of stock in storage.

Shocking images

Images of the famine in India shocked the whole world. It was the first time in history that images of starving people had been broadcast on television. Famines in India and in Biafra, Nigeria in 1967 made many in the rich West aware of the poverty in developing countries. In the Netherlands, a major fundraising operation was organized in 1966 entitled "Food for India."

Meanwhile, in India itself, the consequences of the droughts were not restricted solely to people in the states directly affected. Wheat, rice, and sugar were placed on ration throughout the nation. The government tried to reach starving groups of people with grain imported from the United States and food supplies donated by China and the Soviet Union. Nevertheless, an estimated 1.5 million people died of hunger in those three years. The entire Indian economy groaned under the strain of the food shortages, and the Gross National Product fell for three years in succession.

It was not, however, the first time that the country had had to deal with famine. When India had been under British rule, major

famines had arisen several times and claimed the lives of millions of people, such as the Bengal Famine of the 1940s. Often these famines were not solely due to drought, but also to British measures affecting traditional land usage, agriculture, and food distribution. At that time, of course, there was no television coverage, and the British authorities did their best to keep these disasters concealed from the outside world.

Green Revolution

Following the famines of the mid-sixties, the Indian government decided on drastic measures. The intention was to develop agriculture so that food shortages could never happen again. New, stronger varieties of rice were developed that produced more rice grains per plant. The use of artificial fertilizers was encouraged, and storage reservoirs and irrigation channels were built. This program, announced as the "Green Revolution," proved to be extremely successful. From 1951 until 1976, India was a net importer of food; since then, it has enjoyed surplus production, with year-on-year increases in the amount of food exported.

The country has still had to contend with dry periods in the interim, particularly in 1972, 1987, and 2002. Portions of the population experienced food and drinking water problems during these periods of drought, but their effects were no longer as catastrophic as they had been previously. But the Green Revolution also brought with it a number of disadvantages, the consequences of which are only now beginning to be felt. For example, the use of artificial fertilizers and intensive irrigation has led to soil exhaustion, resulting in increasingly poor harvests. In the state of Punjab, one of the leading regions in India during the Green Revolution, much of what was formerly farmland has dried out completely. The water table has fallen dramatically in large parts of the country, resulting in water shortages presenting earlier in times of low rainfall.

El Niño

In recent years, a great deal of research has also been conducted into the causes of the planet's extreme periods of drought, heat, and rainfall. The meteorological phenomenon of El Niño has been proven a major influence in this. El Niño is a warm ocean current in the

eastern half of the Pacific Ocean and makes an irregular appearance every few years. Peruvian fishermen have long been familiar with this phenomenon, referring to it as "El Niño," meaning "The Child," because it usually commences at around the time of Christmas and thus celebrations of the birth of the Christ child. Not all droughts in India coincide with the El Niño phenomenon, but it has been demonstrated that droughts during this event are more extreme than they would be otherwise.

Meteorologists are coming to understand more and more about these phenomena and their impact, so that India is now in a generally good position to predict periods of drought in good time. Partly because of this, Dr. Swaminathan,

one of the architects of the Green Revolution, believes that India should be doing even more to prevent problems during droughts. According to him, it should be taken into account that a period of drought can occur twice in any five-year period, and measures should be taken in light of this fact. More reservoirs should be built, and more rainwater needs to be captured during the monsoons. In addition, a timely switch should also be made to growing types of crop that require less water in those areas prone to drought.

Girl in Bilhar, 1966

USA
Washington D.C.
ATLANTIC
Gulf of Mexico
PACIFIC

Hurricane Camille

Hurricane Camille was one of the most ferocious ever to have struck the territory of the United States.

August 14–22, 1969

256 dead

Camille was the most powerful hurricane of 1969. The storm took many inhabitants of the southern United States, and even the meteorologists, by surprise. Curiously, it affected the areas that have again been hit by the passage of Hurricane Katrina, which were likewise visited by another giant storm, Hurricane Andrew.

Direct to the United States

Hurricane Camille represented the height of the hurricane season of 1969. Unlike those of similar storms, its Caribbean tour, devastating many islands in the area, was very brief, its action focusing on the United States. Camille began as a tropical wave on the west coast of Africa on August 5,

1969. Until August 14, when it reached the island of Grand Cayman, the wave did not increase in size. On that day, the storm's internal winds reached 56 miles (90 km) an hour. The meteorologists classified it as a tropical storm and christened it Camille. On August 14 and 15, the storm's circulation widened and the wind speed rose to 112 miles (180 km) an hour. The following day it became a hurricane and struck the west coast of Cuba, though without causing serious material damage.

Having crossed Cuba, the storm weakened, its winds falling to 100 miles (160 km) an hour. The meteorologists thought it would continue thus until it reached the southern United States, maybe weakening further on its way. They were wrong. As Camille crossed the Gulf of Mexico, it picked up strength again. Hours before reaching the United States, it returned to category 5 on the Saffir-Simpson scale. On August 17, before touching down in the state of Mississippi, an aircraft of the Meteorological Service tried to measure the hurricane's speed, but could not. It is estimated that it must have been close to 212 miles (340 km) an hour. On the night of August 17, Camille reached the city of Bay St Louis in Mississippi. The eye of the storm had a diameter of about 12 miles (19 km). Once over dry land, the storm lost much of its strength. By August 19 it had become a tropical depression. It veered to the east, precipitating torrential rain in Virginia at some 31 inches (790 mm) an hour and causing the worst floods in the history of that state. It continued to the east until it dissipated, but not before its winds had increased to nearly 72 miles (115 km) an hour and it had become a tropical storm again for a few hours. It finally dissipated in the Atlantic Ocean.

The true intensity of this hurricane remains a mystery. No meteorological instrument survived the storm's passage across the states of Alabama and Mississippi. What is more, it is possible that when it reached Mississippi its winds were stronger than 212 miles (340 km)

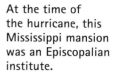

At the time of the hurricane, this Mississippi mansion was an Episcopalian institute.

The institute after Camille had passed through. No trace of the magnificent building remains.

Biloxi, Mississippi. A fishing boat "parked" in the driveway of a house in the town, such was the strength of Camille.

an hour. Together with Hurricane Katrina, and apart from the Labor Day Hurricane of 1935, Camille was the fiercest storm ever to have struck the United States. It caused severe damage and a large number of deaths and injuries. In total, 256 residents of Alabama, Mississippi, Louisiana, and Virginia disappeared – of whom 113 in Virginia perished in the floods. A further 8,931 people were injured. Many casualties occurred because hundreds of residents in potentially vulnerable coastal and inland areas rejected the request to leave their homes, preferring to stock up on provisions because they thought they would be able to withstand the storm in their houses or basements. Neither they nor a large number of meteorologists believed the forecast. Camille's winds, however, proved highly destructive, although the storm had slowed on reaching American soil.

One of the places worst hit by the storm was Harrison County, Mississippi. Something seldom seen in a hurricane occurred there. It became an area of total devastation. Over an area of nearly 68 sq. miles (176 km²), everything was flattened. Absolutely nothing remained standing. In some places on the coast, the winds and strong waves dragged fishing boats and yachts into built-up areas or deposited them in the middle of freeways. The floods in the state of Virginia were the worst disaster caused by Camille. The intense rain caused landslides of mud, roads were cut off by fallen trees and by the water itself, which turned them into canals and destroyed more than 120 bridges in the area, and destroyed thousands of houses, as well as claiming the victims already mentioned. When the floods subsided, only one state freeway remained intact.

The material damage caused by Camille was assessed at 6 billion dollars.

Slow recovery

The emergency services hastened to the states afflicted by the hurricane. The government set up a financial aid program to try to mitigate the losses. These were difficult times for the American economy. It should be remembered that, at that time, the country was involved in the Vietnam War. Once Camille had disappeared, more than 5,000 prefabricated houses were erected in various parts of Alabama, Virginia, and Mississippi. The army helped clear the debris and established field hospitals and reception centers. Months after the tragedy, 85,000 people were still living in aid centers.

Thirty-six years have passed, but Camille remains in the memories of many. During the recent Katrina disaster, people of a certain age who were caught up in this tragedy were making comparisons with the actions of Camille, so enduring were the latter's effects on their lives. Places such as Biloxi, which suffered severely in the 1969 hurricane, were on global television at the beginning of September, due to Katrina's apocalyptic visit. Witness statements constantly cite Katrina as an even worse phenomenon than Camille.

All that remained standing in this Florida town was the handrail of a swimming pool – nothing else.

Earthquake in Peru

This earthquake marked a "before" and "after" in the daily lives of millions of Peruvians – and of government institutions too.

Callejón de las
Huaylas
(Peru)

May 31, 1970

66,700 dead

The poorly constructed buildings in the town of Huaraz collapsed under the quake, as this photograph shows.

The worst natural disaster in Peru's history occurred on May 31, 1970 and was caused by the earthquake of Callejón de las Huaylas, so called because of the region where it happened. Several factors combined to make the disaster so enormous.

A devastated region

Peru is a country of wild orography and is subject to frequent earthquakes, like its neighbor, Chile. In spite of that, the country has not always been prepared for them. It took a tragedy like the one in May 1970 for the authorities to react to the danger posed to the population who were exposed to the threat of violent earthquakes.

At 3:23 p.m. on May 31, a strong tremor lasting 45 seconds sowed terror in Callejón de las Huaylas. The epicenter of the earthquake, which measured 7.5 on the Richter scale and VIII on the Mercalli scale, was under the sea, opposite the coastal towns of Casma and Chimbote. The small and picturesque town of Casma, famous for its adobe houses, was totally destroyed, while Chimbote suffered huge damage to its industrial installations and hundreds of homes.

The area affected by the tremor was a region of varied topography between the coast and the Marañón river and between parallels 8° and 10.5° south, covering practically the whole of the administrative district of Ancash and the southern part of the administrative district of La Libertad. In the coastal regions struck by the tremor, the ground cracked, emitting jets of mud and water, some of them over 3 ft (1 m) high. Surprisingly, the reinforced concrete and brick buildings withstood the shaking very well, but that was not the case with the shanties and rural buildings, which collapsed in minutes.

Moments after the tremor ceased – witnesses calculated it at one or two minutes – the worst happened. Due to the intensity of the quake, the top of Mount Huascarán wobbled and finally collapsed. The rock fall from the mountain's summit caused a gigantic landslide of stones, ice, and mud: over half a mile wide, nearly a mile long, and, in some places, 525 ft (160 m) high. In its descent, this mass reached speeds of over 75 miles (120 km) an hour. More than 2.8 billion cubic ft (80 million m³) of various materials were deposited at the foot of Huascarán, totally burying the towns of Yungay, Caraz, and Ranrahirca and causing severe damage to dozens of small villages. Twenty thousand people died in Yungay alone.

It is worth recounting here the terrifying tale of the engineer Mateo Casaverde, who was traveling round the area for work and was picked up by the Humboldt rescue organization: "We were driving from Yungay to Caraz and, when we got to about the Yungay cemetery, the earthquake started. Our vehicle, a Chevrolet half-ton van, 1969 model, jumped vertically with so much force it was difficult to control. From the hillside, we could see how the adobe houses were collapsing and a bridge nearby on the road. At the same time we saw small landslides with a lot of dust falling on the Cordillera Negra. We abandoned our vehicle when the earthquake had practically finished. We heard a low-frequency noise, distinct, but not very different from the noise made by an earthquake. The noise was coming from the direction of Huascarán and, between Yungay and El Nevado, we saw a gigantic cloud of dust, almost clay-colored. A torrent of alluvium had formed, starting from the north side of Huascarán and coming down. It was about 3:24 p.m. In the area where we were, the last place that offered us any kind of shelter from the landslide was the cemetery, built on an artificial hill, an Inca tomb. We ran about a hundred yards along the road until we got to the cemetery, which had also suffered the effects of the earthquake. Once in there, I looked towards Yungay. At that moment, I could clearly see a gigantic wave of light gray mud, about 200 ft (60 m) high, with a crest starting to break, at a slight angle, about to hit the left side of the town. There was no dust from that wave. In our dash to the steps, we managed to reach the second terrace and found the way to the third terrace, which was more obstructed, with a man, a woman, and three children trying to reach it. We were moving to the right, on the same second terrace when, like a dry whiplash, part of the landslide reached the front of the cemetery, practically at the same level as the second terrace. The mud passed a few hundred yards below our feet. The sky grew dark because of the amount of dust, possibly originating from the houses that had been destroyed in Yungay. We turned our gaze: Yungay and its 20,000 people had disappeared."

Administrative chaos

The earthquake and subsequent landslide from Huascarán caused 66,794 deaths, about a million people lost their homes, and 100 villages were destroyed or severely damaged. It is calculated that three million Peruvians were affected by the earthquake. Power stations such as the one at Cañón del Pato, hundreds of schools, and thousands of acres of cultivated land were destroyed. The material damage was assessed at 500 million dollars.

The government was completely overwhelmed by the disaster. It

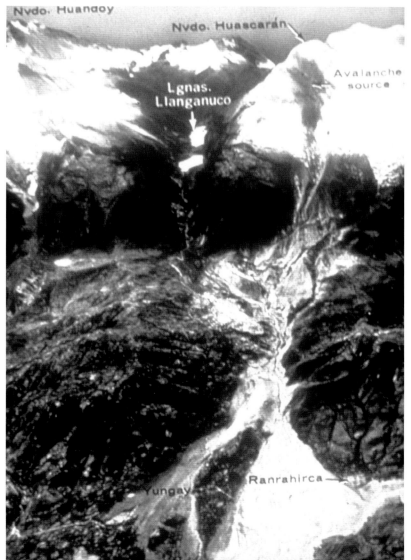

Nvdo. Huandoy

Nvdo. Huascarán

Lgnas. Llanganuco

Avalanche source

Ranrahirca

Yungay

was unable to coordinate the rescue services or to administer the aid received from more than 60 countries, which included generous assistance from the United States Agency for International Development (USAID). Dozens of villages were cut off after the quake. Unusable roads and tracks, when added to the incompetence of the government, compounded the chaos in the region. Criticism grew ever more severe. Finally, two years later, the government set up the National Civil Defense Institute as a means of prevention and help in future disasters. Meanwhile, the reconstruction of the area struck by the quake should have improved the living conditions of its inhabitants. In some cases it did; in others, regrettably, it did not.

Peru was – and still is – a country with huge social problems. The terrible disaster of 1970 only exacerbated the situation of the most needy.

The earthquake caused a series of landslides on Mount Huascarán, which buried the towns of Yungay and Ranrahirca. As a result of the quake and its subsequent landslides, 66,700 people lost their lives

Photograph of the place where the avalanches and landslips occurred. Rocks descended the slopes of Huascarán at speeds approaching 170 miles (270 km) an hour.

Cyclone and tidal surge in Bangladesh

In 1970, a cyclone and subsequent deluge caused one of the most severe natural disasters in centuries. The floods claimed an estimated 500,000 lives.

Bangladesh

November 12–13, 1970

500,000 dead

Residents of Manpura, about 110 miles (175 km) to the south of the capital city, Dhaka, in the ruins of their homes

Bangladesh contends with all manner of natural disasters: floods, cyclones, earthquakes, and extended periods of drought. Bangladesh lies on the deltas of three major rivers: the Ganges, the Brahmaputra, and the Meghna. These rivers regularly burst their banks during the rainy season and, as a result, a fifth of the whole country regularly lies under water. Every ten years or so, more than a third of the nation's land can become inundated. It is partly because of these floods that the region is so very fertile and particularly suited to the cultivation of rice. This explains why, over the centuries, people have left less productive areas and flocked to the Bangladesh delta region. In consequence, Bangladesh is among one of the most densely populated countries in the world, with a population currently around 145 million.

Cyclones

Cyclones are a recurrent phenomenon in Bangladesh. The Bay of Bengal to the south of the country is an area where cyclones develop, usually in the neighborhood of the Andaman Islands to the southeast of Bangladesh. From there they then travel across the sea toward the coast, increasing in strength as they go. The cyclone that tore across the land during the night of November 12 through 13, 1970 had a wind speed of 140 mph (224 km/hour). This cyclone, named the Bhola cyclone after the island and district where so many lost their lives, brought about a tidal surge with waves up to 20 ft (6 m) in height. Since the surge struck at the same time as a high tide, the flooding was especially severe. Furthermore, as large portions of the Bangladeshi coastal region lie below sea level, the floods were able to penetrate far inland.

Although Bangladesh, then still officially called East Pakistan, had suffered tidal surges frequently before, little or nothing had been done in the way of defensive measures against the seawater. A proper system of dike and levee management typical of low-lying areas surrounding river deltas, such as in the Netherlands or in Louisiana, did not exist. The worst affected areas were the islands at the mouth of the Ganges, home to towns such as Charfasson and Tazumuddin. The city of Chittagong, populated by millions, was also hit and here, too, many victims were mourned.

It is estimated that 100,000 fishermen were killed while at work: a third at sea and the rest at the river mouths. There were many victims too among the families of agricultural laborers, who lived in or near to the rice fields in the lowest lying areas. Since they were generally the poorer families, living in simple cottages or huts, they had no form of protection whatsoever against the floods. Afterward, the total death toll was estimated at 500,000. It was reckoned that a further million head of livestock had perished (buffalo, goats, and sheep), and twenty thousand fishing boats and four hundred thousand homes destroyed.

Movement for independence

A significant, if indirect, consequence of the Bhola cyclone was the upsurge of anti-Pakistani sentiment among the Bengali population. On gaining independence in 1947, British India had been divided into two parts: predominantly Hindu India and Muslim Pakistan. The Bengalis in the delta region were also overwhelmingly Muslim, which is why this part of British India came under the administration of Pakistan as East Pakistan. In the decades that

followed, however, it transpired that, despite the quite considerable contribution made by Bengalis to the Pakistani economy, they were given little voice in successive government administrations. This gave rise to an independent movement, which gained increasing support following the floods of 1970 due to discontent over the perceived lack of assistance from the Pakistani government. In 1971, this led to a civil war in which India ultimately lent its support to the Bengalis. Following international intervention, the war was brought to an end in December 1971, and Bangladesh achieved its independence.

As a result of the natural disaster there was the first appearance of major benefit concerts. In the 1960s, former Beatle George Harrison had become friendly with the Indian musician Ravi Shankar. Shankar had played sitar on some of the Beatles' numbers and was himself of Bengali extraction. Since the disaster, millions of Bengalis had been living in refugee camps, and the civil war had only aggravated their plight. Ravi Shanker and George Harrison decided to hold two benefit concerts, which took place in the afternoon and evening of August 1, 1971 at Madison Square Garden in New York. A large group of performers took part in the concerts, including Bob Dylan, Eric Clapton, Leon Russell, Billy Preston, and Ringo Starr. The concert was filmed for cinema release, and an LP of the event was also made. All the proceeds were given to Unicef, the United Nations Children's Fund, which put the money into aid projects in Bangladesh. Thus the Concert for Bangladesh, as the project was named, became the forerunner of subsequent large-scale benefit concerts, such as Live Aid.

Still more disasters

Since 1970, Bangladesh has frequently endured cyclones and flooding. The years 1985, 1988, and 1991 saw particularly powerful tidal surges, which claimed thousands of lives. The floods of

1991 were especially disastrous because, although there were many fewer fatalities than in 1970, the damage caused was much greater. An estimated 1.7 million homes were destroyed, with a much larger area being inundated with water. Efforts to prevent disasters have increased significantly since that last great flood. With the help of experts from various countries (including Japan, Denmark, and the Netherlands), work has been done on establishing an extensive system of levees and canals to better contain the waters.

In addition, much time and money has been devoted to the development of an early warning system that utilizes satellite monitoring. These systems are not yet so far advanced that they can be fully relied upon at present, but what is perhaps of even greater importance is the improvement in local communications. Evidence shows that, at the time of natural disasters, national government agencies have often been aware well in advance of approaching storms and tidal surges, but that an infrastructure to warn the local population in time was lacking. Since the great flood, warning systems have been implemented in many places that involve the appointment of one person charged with spreading a warning quickly throughout his or her particular village or district. This enables the great majority of those who have no access to the telephone or Internet to be alerted to danger. At times of threat, they can flee to the safety of refuge centers, many of which have been built in recent years.

Aerial photograph of the affected coastal area of Patuakhali, littered with dead livestock

Bridge over the River Karnaphuli, in the vicinity of Chittagong, severely damaged by the cyclone and tidal wave

Tornados in thirteen states

In 1974, 148 tornados occurred within 18 hours in a massive outbreak that affected 13 American states. Statistically, it is estimated that such a phenomenon should take place just once every 500 years.

Thirteen US states

April 3–4, 1974

330 dead

Approaching doom: one of the dozens of tornados to hit many American states in April 1974

Tornados are a regular occurrence in the central and eastern United States, particularly in the months from May through June. The so-called "Tornado Alley," which runs roughly from Texas in the south to Nebraska in the north, sustains several of these violent windstorms each year. Nevertheless, the largest such outbreak ever to take place in one day was not in this region, but further to the east. The states most badly affected were Alabama, Georgia, Tennessee, Kentucky, and Ohio.

In the weeks leading up to the catastrophe, weather stations and tornado hunters had been gathering as much information as possible and pooling their resources. People were kept up-to-date with developments and an early-warning system was in place.

Clashing air currents

Tornados are born when cold and warm currents of air come together. In the American tornado season, warm, moist air blows in from the Gulf of Mexico toward the north, meeting overland with warm, dry air from the Mexican mainland and cold, dry air from Canada. Ground air can be sucked upward so strongly in some places that it forms a localized low-pressure area, toward which surrounding air flows in a spiral or helical formation, in the same way as water in an emptying bathtub. At the beginning of April, air currents in the mid-eastern United States precisely mirrored these conditions, which were further exacerbated by a strong jet stream from Canada. On top of this, the weather was sunny, causing the lowest layer of air to heat up even more.

On April 2, 1974, several weather stations were already predicting that a large number of tornados would develop during the following day. Warnings were issued that night and again the following morning, which most authorities and residents took very seriously as the

April 1 tornados had already caused a great deal of destruction. This probably saved the lives of many, above all in the states of Alabama and Tennessee, because people there had time to find secure places of refuge.

On April 3, around 2:00 p.m., the first tornados started appearing in a phenomenon that would endure until the following morning. Ultimately, a total of 148 tornados traveled across the mid-eastern United States. The path taken by these storms averaged a distance of some 20 miles (30 km), whereas that of the tornados in 1973 had been less than 5 miles (7.5 km). Of the 148 tornados, 6 were recorded as force F5, and 24 as force F4: the two highest measurements on the Fujita scale. Some tornados tore a path nearly 100 miles (150 km) long and some exceeded 5 miles (8 km) in width. One tornado even passed over the Great Lakes via Michigan into Canada, before turning back again.

The severity and number of tornados was unprecedented and, despite all the warnings issued, many inhabitants of the affected areas were still taken by surprise. Several places were hit by two tornados in quick succession. In Alabama, relief crews were unable to reach the town of Newburg, which had been hit by Tornado 90 at 6:30, because Tornado 91 came racing after it at 7:30. In the Tennessee counties of Franklin and Lincoln, a number of towns were also hit by Tornado 90, which dragged Tornado 92 in its wake for a long time.

Destructive force

The destructive force of the tornados was colossal. Many of the fatalities included people living in trailer parks, who were sucked into the air together with their homes and possessions. Thirty-one were killed in the community of Brandenburg in Kentucky, including a large number of children who were playing in their schoolyard at the time.

The worst affected of all was the small town of Xenia in Ohio, through which one of the F5 tornados tore its path. The tornado spent nine minutes there, twice as long as a tornado normally stays in any one place, destroying nine churches, four schools, and more than 1,300 homes in the process.

In total, there were 330 fatalities on April 3 and 4, 9 of whom were in Ontario, Canada. More than 5,400 were injured, with the damage being estimated at $3.5 billion.

Remains of a school and school bus in Xenia, Ohio, April 5, 1974

Amid the devastation: searching for possible survivors in Brandenburg, Kentucky

Earthquake in Guatemala

This earthquake left about a sixth of Guatemala's total population homeless.

Gulf of Mexico
GUATEMALA
PACIFIC
Guatemala City

Guatemala

February 4, 1976

23,000 dead

The Agua Caliente bridge, totally destroyed. Access to nearby places was thus prevented for days.

The saying "troubles never come singly" is certainly true and can be applied to many of the catastrophes described in this book. A further and grievous example would be the earthquake that struck Guatemala in 1976. The country was embroiled in a violent guerilla war that cost many lives and finally ended in 1996, after a struggle that had lasted more than thirty years. The Central American country was just another pawn on the global chessboard of the Cold War.

Guatemala shaken

Much of Guatemala's problematical situation was due to interference in its politics by the United States. Nevertheless, it was also America that helped Guatemala the most when the time came for its reconstruction. The United States had a firm operations base in Guatemala in its war against Fidel Castro's Cuba and a perfect place from which to control the Panama Canal. Although Guatemala's political classes benefited from that situation, the majority of its population did not. When the tremor of 1976 occurred, things were made even worse.

At 3:03 a.m., the earth shook for 49 long seconds. Seismographers assessed the earthquake at an intensity of 7.5 on the Richter scale. The Motagua fault crosses 80 percent of Guatemalan territory, and a movement deep beneath the ground caused the disastrous quake. The epicenter was some 94 miles (150 km) northwest of the capital, Guatemala City, near Gualán, and the hypocenter about 3 miles (5 km) deep. The intensity of the quake was felt in Mexico City and even Honduras, which suffered floods, the failure of electricity supplies, and the destruction of three towns on its border with Guatemala. Fortunately, there were no deaths on this occasion; a few weeks beforehand Hurricane Fifi had swept through Honduras, claiming about 10,000 victims.

For a few minutes, those who survived the tremor in Guatemala either tried to take refuge in a safe place or began to search for friends and relations. A replica of the earthquake at 3:30 a.m. claimed an even greater number of victims. It is calculated that, of the 23,000 who died in the earthquake, most were the result of the second telluric movement. Thousands were seized with terror. They were in the street, in the dark, and freezing cold.

A few hours later, ambulances and firefighters began to arrive. Those who were able to do so formed squads to help the rescue services look for survivors and clear away debris. Specialist rescue and hospital emergency teams worked tirelessly.

About a million people lost their homes, representing a sixth of Guatemala's total population. The capital saw many of its buildings reduced to rubble, especially the countless adobe dwellings that are a feature of that country. The situation in the interior was not much better. The earthquake devastated dozens of villages with their humble adobe houses, as had happened in the capital. Communications were severely damaged by the landslides that blocked the roads and cracked the asphalt, preventing travel. In spite of that,

however, the country's economy was not seriously affected. In general, brick and reinforced concrete buildings withstood the jolts, and the textile and chemical factories and subsidiaries of North American and European companies resumed activity after a week or so of cleaning up. The electricity supply was restored very quickly. The same cannot be said of the drinking-water supply, however, which became unreliable in many parts of the country. Agriculture felt the effects of the earthquake, although fortunately the quake happened before harvesting had begun and the Guatemalan peasants were able to gather their crops without further incident. Irrigation channels were broken and there was damage to machinery and grain stores, but these were not major problems in the long term.

Before the arrival of international aid, thousands of Guatemalan volunteers came to the affected areas, as did the army. At the time, foreign observers noted the highly efficient and professional part played by the Guatemalan armed forces.

Reconstruction and missionaries

Most of the humanitarian assistance Guatemala received came

Canada was the other main source of aid to Guatemala. Like its neighbor, it supplied food, medicines, clothes and building materials, mainly timber.

Also vital to the reconstruction of the rural areas were the missionaries. For decades, missionaries had been one of the backbones of the rural communities, together with the parish priests. Their role was particularly relevant in the native communities, creating a link between the indigenous people and the authorities.

In spite of the missionaries' goodwill, however, they were not well received in some villages. It was claimed in some quarters that the distribution of aid was partisan. Unfortunately, this case is not unique, like the government's total failure to understand matters of humanitarian aid. Nevertheless, the work of those people who came from the United States, Canada, Spain, England, and Germany — the countries that provided most of the missionaries or volunteers during the catastrophe — is worthy of praise.

Landslide at San Cristóbal. Curiously, events such as this enthused many geologists, as they revealed tephra deposits dating from the Pleistocene era.

An irrigation channel destroyed by the tremor.

from the United States. In just six days, the sum of 19 million dollars had been collected to help the victims of the catastrophe. America mobilized army units to help reconstruct the country and sent tons of food, medicines, warm clothing, and building materials. Experts stressed that the maximum number of houses should be built in the shortest possible time. It was February, and the rainy season was about to begin. The rain-

fall and the cold threatened those who had had the misfortune to lose their homes and were living in the street, and they feared the worst. They no longer trusted adobe as a building material, however. Thus, prefabricated houses and timber were sent to the places where housing was needed. In time, faith was restored in adobe, although with slight variations, such as metal roofs or a metal beam or two as support.

Earthquake in Tangshan

The rebuilt city constitutes a shining example of the new zeal in China.

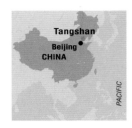

Tangshan, China

July 28, 1976

At least 250,000 dead

Panorama of part of the disaster area; nowadays, Tangshan is once again a prosperous city of 7 million people

Of all the countries in the world, China is probably at greatest risk from earthquakes. The country is vulnerable to this type of natural disaster because of the movement, in opposite directions, of two tectonic plates: the Indian plate, responsible for the creation of the Himalayas, is moving northeast, while the Pacific plate is moving in a westerly direction and, in the process, slipping under the Eurasian plate.

Thus China also has a long history of seismology. Though a highly developed warning system was in existence in the 1970s, the earthquake in Tangshan, some 90 miles (140 km) to the southeast of Beijing, still took many by surprise. This was firstly because Tangshan, given the state of scientific knowledge at the time, was not considered to be in a high-risk area and, secondly, because the warning system was not operating properly at the time.

Mine workings

The earthquake, registering a magnitude of 7.8 on the Richter scale, occurred during the night of July 28, 1976, at 3:40 a.m. In the city of Tangshan, whose population was then 1.6 million, almost everyone was in bed asleep. Many were killed instantly as rubble fell onto them from collapsing buildings. Tangshan was an important mining center and the workings below ground both in and surrounding the city further exacerbated the disaster.

There was no question of any efficient relief attempts during the first few hours; these could only be mounted once day had broken. A major problem was that only one access route to the city remained passable. To add to the misfortune further, an extremely strong aftershock of 7.1 occurred 15 hours after the first quake, burying under yet more debris relief workers and many of the original victims who, though still alive, had remained trapped.

Piles of bodies

The dead were heaped into great piles in the open air and buried quickly. In the years that followed, this caused a recurring problem, because in times of heavy rain decayed body parts would rise to the surface and have to be re-interred elsewhere. The Chinese authorities later set the official death toll at 250,000, but many estimates are higher, at nearer 500,000 victims. A total of 100,000 relief workers were recruited, including members of the military and volunteers from across the country. Appeals for aid in the form of goods or money were broadcast throughout China.

The consequences of the earthquake were not confined to Tangshan. The province of Hebei sustained damage in several places and the port of Tianjin, over 60 miles (100 km) to the southwest of Tangshan, also had to count the cost of destruction. The earthquake was felt in Beijing as well

Survivors stare in dis-
belief at the vast
heaps of rubble left
by the earthquake

Huge-scale havoc:
buildings not leveled
were seriously dama-
ged

and, for a long time afterward, many people camped out on the streets for fear of their buildings collapsing.

In hindsight, the large number of casualties in Tangshan would appear to have resulted from the way in which the warning system of the time operated. The system had four warning categories, ranging from long-term alerts to those for acute threats. Only in the latter case was the population routinely advised. In the summer of 1976, the national seismological survey was aware of the possible occurrence of an earthquake, but it was not felt that the threat was imminent and the warning was issued only among regional and local authorities. Subsequent research has shown that half the population of Tangshan was nevertheless aware of the warning, which had been spread by word of mouth. People had not taken the warning all that seriously, however, because it had not come directly from the authorities.

Power struggle

For a long time, little was known outside China about the earthquake and its consequences. It had become clear through diplomats and correspondents in Beijing that a major disaster had taken place, but the authorities did not allow any foreigners into the area and refused any form of help offered from abroad. Furthermore, at that time, a major power struggle was underway in the uppermost echelons of the government in China. Party chairman Mao Zedong was seriously ill and actual leadership was in the hands of four important figures in the Communist Party, including the then wife of Chairman Mao.

Among senior party members, however, there was serious dislike of this quartet, which was later referred to as the "Gang of Four." Mao died on September 9, 1976. His official successor, Hua Guofeng, had paid a visit to Tangshan on behalf of the government on August 4. Hua Guofeng was a protégé of strong man Deng Xiaoping, who had the Gang of Four arrested and sentenced shortly after Mao's death.

Reconstruction was begun in Tangshan soon after the earthquake and completed at high speed. To give an example, while it took 30 years to complete repairs following the San Francisco earthquake of 1906, work was finished in Tangshan within 10 years. Nowadays, Tangshan is one of China's most prosperous cities, with a population of seven million people. It has also been awarded the title "Brave City of China." A

monument has been erected to the victims of the earthquake in a square in the downtown area of the city, where a memorial ceremony is held every year.

Earthquake in Romania

Romania is one of the European countries most threatened by various natural disasters, and Vrancea suffers two or three large earthquakes every century.

Vrancea region
(Romania)

March 4, 1977

1,600 dead

It is not usual for a European capital to suffer a great natural catastrophe. Although flooding or a volcanic eruption such as that of Etna in 2002 may well occur somewhere on the Old Continent, large tremors and their casualties are more often associated with geographical areas such as America or Asia. Certain parts of Europe, however, are active seismic zones where earth movements are part of the way of life. One such country is Romania, which has suffered the most earthquakes on the continent.

The Carpathians, a seismic region

Romania is the European country most affected by various natural dangers. Floods, landslips, soil erosion, avalanches, and, occasionally, severe drought have had considerable economic and social repercussions. Due to the multiple natural risks to which the area is exposed, many scientific experts on the subject come from Romanian universities, which is of great benefit to the wider scientific community.

Two thirds of Romania's territory is occupied by hills, plateaus, and imposing mountains, particularly the Carpathian range, so meaningful to lovers of horror novels and movies. Not all of the country's geological formations are the same, however; on the contrary, variety is the norm. The same applies to its climate, which undergoes considerable variations depending on the region concerned, a factor that is particularly significant in disasters such as floods or avalanches.

The most important seismic zone of Romania is the Vrancea region, situated southeast of the Carpathians. In that respect, it is also one of the most important in Europe and possibly the most active and best researched, both by the country's own experts and foreign scientists. This region is typified by high seismic activity,

with two or three earthquakes of great magnitude – around 7 on the Richter scale – each century. The biggest to have occurred to date took place on March 4, 1977. As well as being the center of the dreaded earthquakes, Vrancea also suffers great floods and landslides. The combination of those risks and the special geology of the place have made it especially difficult to administer. Governments have had numerous problems with the area's infrastructure, as have its inhabitants, who are exposed to serious risks. Nevertheless, the Carpathians are one of the country's most popular tourist attractions and the area has fertile agricultural land. Therefore, abandoning the area, which is also rich in ancestral cultural traditions, is not really considered an option.

The situation is very similar in the Sub-Carpathians. Here, the frequency of the tremors is exacerbated by the severe instability of the ground, which together are conducive to slides or avalanches of mud and stones over half a mile long. The area to the east of the mountains poses the greatest danger, as it is the most densely populated. Although tremors are not as frequent as in other places in the range, the falls of various materials onto roads and villages cause serious problems.

The region is formed of various valleys, which have sometimes been cut off by great rock falls. Another significant factor is the high rainfall in the mountain chain, which favors phenomena such as mudslides and causes rivers to breach their banks, with serious flooding.

In spite of this problematic heritage, the harshness of the 1977 earthquake surprised both local people and foreigners alike. Like other similar phenomena, it took place during the night, at 9:20 p.m. The tremor lasted just a few seconds and measured 7.4 on the Richter scale. Various experts recorded its epicenter at a depth of 59 miles (94 km), in the Vrancea region – of course.

Bucharest affected

In the Carpathian region, cracks in the ground, avalanches, and fissures developed, which were particularly severe in the village of Colti. The most spectacu-lar aspect of the earthquake, however, was the effect it had on the country's capital, Bucharest. The losses suffered were very great. The official count gave a figure of 1,570 dead and 11,000 injuries of various kinds. Thirty thousand homes were destroyed or severely damaged. Over 30 large buildings were totally ruined. The economic effect was critical for Romania and its domestic policy. Although at the time experts estimated the losses at some 2 billion dollars, that figure is now considered too low. The earthquake drew attention to the extreme vulnerability of buildings constructed without any kind of earthquake resistance measures, as was clearly demonstrated by the behavior of buildings constructed using the latest standards of safety regarding telluric movements. While about 10 percent of the buildings erected before World War II collapsed, only one in every 10,000 of those constructed using earthquake resistance measures was destroyed. The figures could not be more eloquent, and are even better than those for other parts of the globe affected by tremors, such as Japan, where reinforced buildings have received special attention.

After the earthquake, the government increased the safety measures in many buildings and devised new building standards so that vulnerabilities in the construction of any kind of building would not be repeated, especially in the apartment blocks in vogue at the time. Nevertheless, the management of the tragedy by the government, presided over by the dictator Nicolai Ceaucescu, was lamentable. In one of the megalomaniac impulses so typical of that gentleman, he decided to rebuild Bucharest. Using cranes and gigantic mobile platforms, he moved whole districts from one part of the city to another and demolished churches and buildings of great architectural value. The impoverished economy of Romania could not cope with the Pharaonic plans of the Carpathian genius – as he liked to call himself – and the remodeling of Bucharest was halted.

Even today, traces of Ceaucescu's wild urban development experiments remain, testifying to the incredible pictures in newspaper reports and documents of the time. One can hardly believe one's eyes.

Rock fall and cracks in the village of Colti in the Buzau mountains. In spite of this appearance, it was the country's capital, Bucharest, which suffered the worst of the earthquake.

A new crack at Colti. The country's modest resources made this earthquake an unprecedented disaster in the history of Romania.

Eruption of Mount St. Helens

The biggest landslide in history occurred in seconds: nearly 2 cubic miles (3 km³) of material came down at speeds in excess of 155 miles (250 km) an hour.

Southeastern
Washington State
(United States)

May 18, 1980

57 dead

The column of ash
and gas emitted by
the volcano during
its eruption in 1980
reached a height of
over 15 miles (25 km).

Volcanic eruptions continue to be astonishing events. Whatever progress volcanologists and geologists make in their research, the moment of the eruption is always a surprise. Predictions are always exceeded. The case of Mount St. Helens is a good example of how disconcerting an eruption can be. Although it was under constant surveillance, it defied all established forecasts.

An historic avalanche

Mount St. Helens is in the southeastern part of the state of Washington in America, about 96 miles (154 km) south of the city of Seattle. It is a strato-volcano that has been active throughout its history. The indigenous people of the area, the Klicki-tats, call it Louwala-Clough, meaning Mountain of Fire, or Smoking Mountain. The volcano forms part of the Cascade mountain range, which

contains other volcanoes. St. Helens is the best-known peak.

Before its eruption, the area surrounding the volcano was frequented by day-trippers eager to walk through the beauty spots of the region. Volcanologists were also frequent visitors. On March 20, 1980 an earthquake measuring 4.1 on the Richter scale was recorded, with its epicenter in the depths of the volcano. The media paid no attention to the phenomenon. Five days later, access to the mountain was closed to climbers. On March 27, Mount St. Helens became active again after 123 years of lethargy. A small explosion formed a crater that emitted a column of ash nearly 2 miles (3 km) high. The curious could not observe the phenomenon because of the clouds covering the mountain's summit. For days, several tremors were recorded.

On April 3, following expert observation, a state of emergency was declared in the area around the volcano. Ash, stones, and ice were being continuously expelled from the summit and represented a danger. For safety reasons, tourists were evacuated, and two exclusion zones were demarcated close to the volcano. No one was allowed to remain inside these zones at the time of the eruption. The work of the forest rangers and watchmen was difficult, as there was a network of roads that anyone could enter to satisfy their curiosity. To the surprise of the experts who had gathered in the area, the volcano stopped erupting between the middle of April and the first week of May. Internal gases and magma continued to grow inside it, however, forming a lava dome on its north face that was growing at a rate of nearly 7 ft (2 m) each day. On May

106

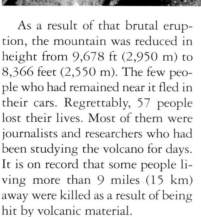

17, in view of the risk of avalanches and landslides, the area's residents were moved out of one of the exclusion zones. The other zone was evacuated the following day, amid scenes of chaos. May 18 dawned sunny and calm. The scientists, who were not at all sure what the volcano was going to do next, did not have to wait long. At 8:32 a.m., an earthquake measuring 5.1 was detected. What happened later surprised everyone. After experiencing hundreds of earthquakes for weeks, the volcano could not withstand this last jolt. In seconds, the biggest landslide in history occurred. Nearly 2 cubic miles (3 km³) of the mountain descended at a speed of over 155 miles (250 km) per hour. The avalanche released the pressure within the volcano, causing an explosion that threw out rocks and igneous material in a radius of tens of miles. The ice on its summit melted and, mixed with ash, lava, and rocks, followed the avalanche. The Plinian explosion produced a column of ash over 15 miles (25 km) high in barely 15 minutes. In three hours, the ash had reached the East coast. Air traffic was canceled throughout the United States.

As a result of that brutal eruption, the mountain was reduced in height from 9,678 ft (2,950 m) to 8,366 feet (2,550 m). The few people who had remained near it fled in their cars. Regrettably, 57 people lost their lives. Most of them were journalists and researchers who had been studying the volcano for days. It is on record that some people living more than 9 miles (15 km) away were killed as a result of being hit by volcanic material.

Ecological disaster

The flora and fauna of the area were completely annihilated. It is believed that more than 5,000 deer, 1,500 moose, 200 bears, and thousands of birds, fish, and rodents disappeared. The territory was devastated. The pyroclastic masses that escaped from the north side at over 2,190 °F (1,200 °C) were deposited on the ground together with the ash and pumice, forming layers 65 ft (20 m) thick, whose temperature, two weeks after the eruption, was still some 1,200 °F (650 °C). Eighteen million trees were felled instantaneously by the force of the avalanche and the material thrown out by the volcano. Spirit Lake, at the foot of Mount St. Helens, received the impact of the landslide, the temperature of its water increasing to more than 212 °F (100 °C). All its fauna died. The lake is now twice its former size, due to the eruption. Vegetation and animals have returned to its shores, but life is not possible in its waters.

The material damage was also very great. The volcano destroyed 200 homes, 47 bridges, 19 miles (30 km) of railroad track, and around 190 miles (300 km) of road.

It is calculated to have cost a billion dollars to rebuild the area affected by the eruption.

Mount St. Helens is still dangerous. The movements of the Juan de Fuca tectonic plate under the Pacific Ocean and those of the continental plate where the volcano stands contain the threat of another explosion soon. In the last decade, the volcano has been active, showing fumaroles and some magmatic and seismic activity. The nature reserve that was created around it is one of the most closely watched in the country and an example of how, after an eruption, life can blossom in a devastated environment. Nevertheless, it is thought that an explosion as devastating as that of 1980 will not be repeated for centuries.

The sticky streams hardened on one side of St. Helens. Note the gigantic size of the formation.

In March 2005, the volcano emitted a column of ash and steam, alerting the people of the area. The mountain has been exhibiting significant signs of activity since September 2004.

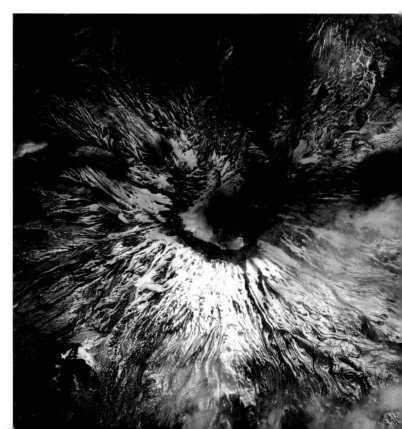

El Asnam earthquake

In just a few hours the town became a mountain of rubble, as if no dwelling could withstand the action of the earthquake.

El Asnam
(Algeria)

October 10, 1980

5,000 dead

A ruined school
in El Asnam.
Luckily, the earth-
quake occurred
after classes had
ended for the day,
so the lives
of thousands
of children were
saved.

Algeria is the African country most often struck by earthquakes. The former French colony has suffered earthquakes since the eighteenth century, as far as we know. Although the tremor that destroyed the town of El Asnam was not the worst of all, it did highlight some lessons for future disasters, but without much advantage, as we shall see.

Tremors to the south of the Mediterranean

Algeria is in northern Africa, between Morocco to the west and Libya to the east. The Mediterranean Sea bathes its northern coast. The country has two zones clearly delimited by the Atlas range. Most of Algeria's population is concentrated to the north of the Atlas Mountains, where the emerging industry is centered, especially tourism, which is becoming increasingly important to its inhabitants. Luxury hotel complexes line the beaches of

northern Algeria, Europeans being their principal clientele. The area south of the Atlas Mountains is predominantly agricultural, with many of its people relocating to the cities of the north in search of a better standard of living.

Most of the earthquakes that have struck Algeria have occurred in the north, between the Mediterranean and the Atlas range. There are several faults in the zone whose movements are fatal to the places concerned. The first earthquake in Algeria that we know of took place in 1716 and totally destroyed the town of Blida. According to the reports of the time, 20,000 people died in the disaster. Centuries later, these phenomena have continued until they reached El Asnam – after the brutal tremor of its neighbor, Agadir, in Morocco, in which 15,000 of the city's people died.

At 1:30 p.m. on October 10, 1980, a strong convulsion sur-

prised the people of the town. Seismographers from various parts of the country were not lying: the tremor measured 7.3 on the Richter scale. Destruction in the city was on a massive scale. Three hours later, with rescue services in the area and people among the rubble trying to help, a replica tremor measuring 6.3 again terrorized the citizens. For many of them, however, it was not their first experience of a tremor. In 1954, during Algeria's French domination, when the place was called Orléansville, a tremor destroyed the city for the first time, claiming 1,700 victims. Its people rebuilt the place and called it El Asnam. Since then, its population has trebled.

In 1980, 150,000 people lived in the city and a further 50,000 in its suburbs. The growth of the place was uncontrolled. Its buildings did not fulfill even the mini-

108

mum safety standards, and in the suburbs wretched-looking shacks and huts were crammed together in chaotic succession. Few of them survived the quake. In the center of El Asnam, hundreds of buildings collapsed, causing the deaths of 2,000 or more people. The initial calculations that reported 20,000 deaths were certainly exaggerated. In the towns around El Asnam there were about 1,000 casualties. The town's main hospital collapsed, presenting enormous difficulties for the health services after the disaster. On the one hand there was nowhere to treat the thousands of people injured and, on the other, there was no one to care for them, as many of the health center's staff had been killed in the tragedy.

All that the authorities and emergency services that had come to the town could do was evacuate the injured to the capital, Algiers, or to the port of Oran. Both cities were at least 93 miles (150 km) from the suffering town. Many patients died on their way to hospitals in those cities.

Other places where many lives were lost were a mosque, some large stores, and a college, as well as a luxury hotel. The four stories of the latter were reduced to rubble, most of the occupants of its rooms being killed. The city's buildings, badly designed and worse built, could barely withstand the vibrations caused by the seismic waves. The tremor turned their brick and plaster walls to butter. In just a few hours the city was reduced to a heap of rubble. According to several witnesses, in some districts, when the replica of the main tremor occurred, little remained to be destroyed. Most of the buildings were already a jumble of bricks and corpses. In most of the buildings that disappeared, the walls gave way, but the roofs did not, crushing the people living in them. The tragedy left some 145,000 people, that is to say most of the town's inhabitants, homeless. The tremor was also felt in the area around El Asnam, 180,000 people being left with nowhere to live.

A new reconstruction

Hours after the tremor, the first excavators arrived at the scene of the tragedy. Rescue experts and unknown people helped to disinter those who had been buried. The assistance given by France and Switzerland was crucial. Dogs

specially trained to do this type of work were a great help. Unfortunately, few people could be rescued. Those who had been buried died almost instantaneously. The type of construction used in the buildings did not help create pockets of air between the rubble. Once beneath it, the chances of surviving were minimal.

Seeing the situation, the authorities decided to embark on an intensive inoculation campaign. Typhus was a latent danger. The state of the city made rapid and effective health action advisable. For once, luck was on the side of the people of El Asnam and no deaths were caused by outbreaks of typhus or dysentery.

Months after the earthquake, the Algerian government, with

the help of the United Nations, announced an aid program to rebuild the town. This was done. El Asnam rose again, this time with a new name, Chleff. But the rebirth did not last long. In 2003, a new tremor struck the wretched city, killing 2,250 people and injuring more than 10,000.

A vertical crack nearly 10 ft (3 m) long. Fractures like this were common during the earthquake.

The eruption of Chichón

The various emanations the volcano produced on this occasion caused an enormous economic and ecological disaster throughout the zone.

Chiapas
(Mexico)

March 28 through
April 4, 1982

1,200 dead

Volcanic eruptions cannot be avoided, but the damage they do can be minimized with adequate vigilance, preventive measures, and education of those exposed to the risks of an eruption, among many other factors. Although it seems incredible, just 20 years ago this action was not being taken, thus contributing to disasters in many parts of the world. An example is the volcano El Chichón, which was thought to be inactive – until it erupted.

Catastrophe in Chiapas

El Chichón is in the Chiapas region of Mexico and is the country's southernmost volcano. Although the violence of the 1982 eruption makes the following description sound unlikely, it is a small mountain compared with its neighbors. It is, however, much more powerful. Before 1982, the countryside surrounding El Chichón looked very different. A dense,

rich forest clothed its slopes. The nearby land was fertile, though this did not help the impoverished inhabitants, most of whom belong to indigenous peoples such as the Zoques, Tzotzitles, Tzeltales, and Choles, who grew coffee, maize, and oranges and also raised livestock.

The youngest of the region's volcanoes was inactive and peaceful. It had entered into activity in the years 700, 1350, and 1850, its eruptive cycles, at intervals of 500–600 years, allowing the local people to live a peaceful life, unaware of El Chichón's internal mysteries. From the paleogeological data experts have studied, it is known that the mountain's earlier eruptions had certainly been powerful and released large amounts of pyroclastic materials. In 1982, the volcano was believed to be inactive. It was not viewed as presenting any danger, so activity in its crater was not monitored. Months before March 28, several tremors were recorded in the area, which some people linked to El Chichón, but the mountain continued to appear impassive. The passage of time has ratified the opinion of those who thought the mountain was the source of the tremors. At 11:30 p.m. on March 28, a tremendous roar emanated from the summit of El Chichón and a towering column of tephra burst from its volcano bowels. The seismic activity and violent eruption killed some 100 people. Hundreds of inhabitants of neighboring places fled, abandoning all their possessions. The fields of crops were drowned in the tephra surging from the volcano. By 5:30 a.m. the following day, the column had spread to the Yucatán peninsula and Haiti. Ash was pouring down on many villages, covering them in soot, and was recorded at a depth of 16 inches (40 cm) some 43 miles (70 km) from the volcano. The weight of the ash caused roofs to cave in and created a multitude of respiratory problems.

The inhabitants of Nicapa, to the northeast of the volcano, took refuge in the local church, but a small tremor caused its final collapse and claimed the lives of 10 people. To the north of the mountain, most of the fatalities and damage were caused by the incandescent tephra that fell on the houses. Thousands of people sought refuge in other villages and small towns, but had to be evacuated because the radius of El Chichón's eruption was increasing with every passing hour. The cocoa, banana, and maize plantations were destroyed. From March 30 to April 3, a series of explosions succeeded one another, increasing the size of the column of ash and gases. In Mexico City, some 406 miles (650 km) from the volcano, visibility was reduced to a few yards. On March 31, a new explosion raised the column to the troposphere until it rapidly vanished. Ash covered more than 92,000 sq. miles (240,000 km²). At the beginning of April, the emissions of pumice and igneous rocks constantly increased in volume. Several fires started, making access to the area around the volcano impossible. The temperature of the deposits of pumice stone, some 10 ft (3 m) thick, was over 660 °F (350 °C). In the village of Francisco León, 3 miles (5 km) from the volcano, the atmosphere was unbreathable. On April 4, during the last of the violent eruptions, the pyroclastic flows attacked the village, killing around 140 of its inhabitants. The parishes of the area estimated the number of people dead or lost during the eruptions at somewhere between 200 and 1,200, although other sources set the figure at barely 200 dead.

Economic and environmental catastrophe

The various eruptions of March and April 1982 represented an enormous economic and ecological disaster for the affected area. Thousands of birds died during that time, thus allowing a proliferation of insects that finished off what little remained of the maize harvests. When harvesting was resumed, the phenomenon was repeated, as the insects were at their ease, free from the presence of the birds that usually preyed on them. The weak economy of the Chiapas region received a severe blow due to the eruption. It had destroyed not only the homes of thousands of people, but also their source of income. At the end of July

1982, more than 60,000 inhabitants of the region were still living in refuges and assistance centers, with nowhere else to go. El Chichón's eruptive episode also severely affected the environment. The gases and ash expelled darkened a large part of Mexican territory, while other places enjoyed beautiful reddish dawns and sunsets, as happened before in the eruptions of Tambora in 1815 and Pinatubo in 1991. The amount of carbon dioxide produced and stored in the stratosphere caused temperatures to fall throughout the northern hemisphere. It was not known that this had occurred until 1985. The eruption of El Chichón was the first in which emissions of that type were studied in relation to temperature variations and other phenomena.

El Chichón is still active and, because of the 1982 eruption, is closely watched.

A terrible picture showing tragic victims of the 1982 eruption.

In spite of the beauty of this small lake, its interior, full of acids, is not inviting to bathers. Such lakes frequently form in volcanoes.

A small village destroyed by the action of El Chichón. Its eruptions have always represented a serious danger for the people of the region.

Java
(Indonesia)

April 1982 through
January 1983

68 dead

Eruption of Galunggung

This eruption produced a column of ash and igneous material more than 3 miles (5 km) high.

The problems caused by Indonesian volcanoes are many. Firstly, these giants represent a threat to the people whose livelihood depends on them. The crop fields fertilized by their ash are very productive, and therefore represent a great opportunity to earn a living without too much difficulty. The extraordinary population increase of the country and the areas close to the volcanoes, however, means that eruptions are increasingly dangerous, even in the case of closely observed mountains. Galunggung and its activity clearly demonstrate how hazardous life can be next to one of these mountains.

West of Java

Situated in western Java, Galunggung is one of the island's most active strato-volcanoes. It forms a volcanic chain with other mountains, including two giants whose names make the people of the region tremble: Papadayan and Mount Merapi (see pp 42–43). The position of Galunggung, some 62 miles (100 km) southeast of the city of Bandung, makes it one of the archipelago's most dangerous peaks. As if that were not enough, about 11 miles (17 km) from its slopes lies the city of Taskilmalaya, capital of the district that bears its name. The metropolitan area of the two cities combined has a population of more than a million, so a large-scale eruption could have disastrous consequences.

The slopes of Galunggung include some geological formations that have been the subject of debate among geologists for decades. At the beginning of the twentieth century, European expeditions to the volcano discovered on its southeastern slope a place the local people called the 10,000 Hills of Tasik Malaya. Soon, several theories were posited as to what those hills were, how they had been formed, and what the local people used them for. At first, it was believed that the mounds were made by man, using materials from a series of rock falls in the crater. Another explanation was that the small hills were created by the accumulation of earth and other materials originating from the nearby rice fields – again, by human action. It was thought that the small hummocks were used as a refuge from enemy peoples during bloody tribal battles or as a barrier against mosquitoes and rats from the rice fields. Over time and with the improvement in earth exploration and sounding equipment, geologists realized that the 3,684 hills were formed during an explosion that had occurred 4,000 years ago. The eruption had caused great destruction in the nearby forests. As noted, their curious configuration had puzzled scientists for decades.

The history of Galunggung's eruptions is not very extensive, although the volcano has remained active since records of the island of Java have been kept. The first eruption for which records exist occurred in 1822. Since then, four other episodes of activity have taken place. Although it has not become active very often, the eruptions of this volcano have been extremely destructive. In the first recorded episode, in 1822, the activity took the local inhabitants by surprise. Unfortunately, there is little information about the phenomenon. It seems that, during the paroxystic phase of the eruption, the volcano emitted a column of ash and smoke over 9 miles (15 km) high. If that is true, it would have been one of the biggest eruptions of the nineteenth century and also the one with the most widespread effects in history. The pyroclastic material thrown out by the crater and the lahars that flowed from it caused the death of 4,000 people. It also destroyed 114 villages.

The last eruption

The last eruption of Galunggung occurred in 1982, with disastrous consequences for the economy of the area. Activity started in 1982 and did not end until January of the following year. During those months, the eruption produced a new dome in the crater and modified its morphology. The crater grew to a width of 2,000 ft (600 m) and a depth of 1,000 ft (300 m). The explosion destroyed much of the crater that had

formed in the 1918 eruption. It was classified as VEI 4 – bearing in mind that VEI is the Volcanic Explosiveness Index, ranging from 1 to 8, so that destruction it caused was considerable: 68 people lost their lives and 22 communities were destroyed beyond hope of reconstruction.

The eruption produced a column of ash and igneous material that climbed over 3 miles (5 km) high. The materials released from that formation destroyed many crop fields and caused material damage assessed at over 15 million dollars. Famine and disease were rife in the area because of the event.

The authorities were able to lessen these problems thanks to outside help. Nevertheless, as on many occasions, the skirts of Galunggung were not abandoned,

owing to the fertility of its soil. The 1982 eruption highlighted another problem. The eruptive column could have caused another disaster. A British Airways Boeing 747 flying over the volcano on its way from Perth to Kuala Lumpur narrowly avoided an accident. The ash blocked three of its four reactors, causing it to drop 10,000 ft (3,000 m). Fortunately, the experience of the aircraft's pilot saved the plane and its hundreds of passengers from catastrophe. Days later, the same thing happened to a small DC-9 and another 747. Because of the eruptions of these giants, flight paths over southeast Asia have had to be changed, with inevitable financial implications. It is preferable to mourn a momentary financial loss, however, rather than an aeronautical disaster.

An eruptive column rises from the crater of Galunggung.

One of the cinder cones formed in the crater. The fumaroles surrounding it reveal its activity.

The ash expelled by the giant onto a village in Java.

Droughts in Sudan and Ethiopia

The great drought in Ethiopia in 1984 led to a femine so major it was described as being of biblical proportions.

Eastern Ethiopia

1984–1985

1,000,000 dead

A girl pulls a container filled with waste

In March 1984, the government of Ethiopia issued a plea for help, as five million of its people were in danger of starving to death that year. The normal spring rains had not arrived and crop disease had caused the harvest to fail in the province of Sidamo, traditionally referred to as the breadbasket of Ethiopia.

As the harvest from the previous year had largely failed as well, Ethiopia had at its disposal only six million tons of grain, one million tons less than was necessary to feed its people. By that summer, ten thousand were already suffering from starvation and related illnesses. Relief organizations warned that, in total, six million people were at risk of starving to death. That October, the estimate was increased to eight million. By then, the famine had already claimed two hundred thousand lives. People were dying every day, particularly the elderly and young children. In the settlement of Gode in eastern Ethiopia, small quantities of food were being distributed to the starving masses at just three points in the town.

In December 1984, severe storms suddenly arose from nowhere, and the tender young plants that had just been planted were destroyed. This fresh blow only served to multiply the already massive stream of refugees. Ten thousand Ethiopians journeyed to the food camps established by foreign aid organizations. Every day, some two thousand people fled from the famine, the civil war, and the war with neighboring Somalia, crossing over the northern border into the Sudan, where problems soon began to arise as well.

Apart from the drought and storms, political factors were also to blame for the disastrous proportions of this famine. The Ethiopian government was accused of continuing to fund the civil war when it could have diverted these resources to emergency aid. According to relief organizations, the government should have sounded the alarm as early as 1981, when persistent droughts had caused harvests to fail. Criticism was also directed toward western countries for not responding swiftly enough to the appeal for assistance.

International aid

Since the overthrow of Emperor Haile Selassie and his regime in September 1974, Ethiopia had become a Marxist state. The government of Mengistu Haile Mariam spent a great deal of its revenue on establishing a new state based on communist principles. In addition, the protracted civil wars with anti-communist rebels and the Eritrean independence movement swallowed up a great deal of money. Partly because of this, western governments were hesitant about furnishing Ethiopia with funds; it was therefore some time before a program of aid was properly established.

The various wars, combined with two years of drought, placed millions of people in peril. The refugees from war and those who had ended up in war zones suffered particularly badly. There were also accusations that the Ethiopian government was ignoring the true extent of the famine. President Mengistu did not appear to have the political strength to cope with the crisis. The limited

The sparsely vegetated Sudanese desert offers neither food nor shelter.

Anonymous grave in the desert

amount of food aid reached the afflicted regions only with difficulty, as these were largely warring or rebel-held areas.

Relief organizations continued to blame western governments for not doing enough to help. In September 1984, the British emergency aid charity Oxfam applied pressure by making a huge donation of its own, attempting to shame the West into action. The charity gave £500,000 (nearly $1,000,000 at current exchange rates)—the largest donation it has ever made. At the same time, relief organizations and diplomats continued to blame the Ethiopian government for giving insufficient priority to the famine: food parcels from Europe were being used to feed the country's troops. September came and went and yet, despite assurances from the government, not a single military vehicle had been deployed to assist with the famine.

In the meantime, Europe had mountains of surplus grain at its disposal following record harvests. Relief organizations repeatedly asked whether they could be given 60,000 tons a month until the end of 1985, but, according to the authorities, Europe had already met its annual aid quota: relief organizations were forced to buy their grain from the free market. In the end, Europe yielded, and food aid began to get properly underway from October onward, continuing throughout the whole of 1985.

Public donations

Coverage of the disaster increased considerably in the second half of the year, resulting in mounting public donations. In the United Kingdom that October, £5 million ($9.5 million) was raised in just three days. In December, public donations from a variety of countries amassed still more millions. In the meantime, the Ethiopian government intensified its war against the movement struggling for the independence of Eritrea and continued to supply its troops with goods intended as aid.

At the end of 1984, "Band Aid," a large group of British pop musicians under the leadership of singer Bob Geldof, recorded the benefit single Do They Know It's Christmas? and raised millions in the process. Soon afterward, American stars followed suit under the name "USA For Africa" with their single We Are The World. On July 13, 1985, Geldof organized two huge benefit concerts in London and Philadelphia, realizing an estimated $100 million.

Improvement

In an initial campaign to combat the famine, the Ethiopian government attempted to force large numbers of peasant families in the afflicted areas to abandon their homes and villages and relocate to the south of the country. This, however, met with stiff resistance. Another government proposal was to move peasant farmers to specially built villages with facilities such as schools, medical care, and water: the villages were indeed built, but their facilities fell short of expectations.

Very gradually, the situation in Ethiopia improved, though famines have recurred since then.

Earthquake in Mexico

The brunt of the earthquake was borne by Mexico City, particularly its business center and the residential areas that had mushroomed over the previous 40 years.

Mexico

September 19, 1985

5,000 dead

Juárez hospital in ruins. More than 400 people died under its rubble. Patients and medical staff were still being rescued ten days after the tragedy.

The large windows on the bottom floor of this store could not resist its collapse. Four of seven stories ended up in this small space.

If experts from various fields were to be asked which megalopolis on the planet was at greatest risk of suffering a major natural catastrophe, most would undoubtedly opt for Mexico City. Apart from its severe environmental problems – the air pollution levels soar above all recommended limits – earthquakes are a constant threat, as they are in Los Angeles.

An uncalculated risk?

During the last few decades, Mexico City has grown into one of the world's most highly populated urban sprawls, with almost 18 million inhabitants. It goes without saying, therefore, that any disaster is likely to take on immense proportions in human terms.

The city's great vulnerability to earthquakes can be explained by its subsoil, for underneath its huge mass lies Lake Texcoco, which was drained by the Spanish Conquistadores on their arrival in Mexico. This lake leads to liquefaction and a subsequent instability in the buildings, so the effects of even the slightest tremor are greatly intensified.

The earthquake that hit the city on September 19, 1985, reached 8.1 on the Richter scale; it was not only very intense, however, it was also prolonged, lasting almost 3 minutes. The earthquake surprised many of the city's inhabitants, striking at 7:17 a.m. as they prepared for work or school. If it had occurred a couple of hours later, the effects would have been far worse, as the offices, banks, stores, schools, and universities would have been full of people. The following night, a sequel of 6.5 on the Richter scale rocked the city and its populace a second time. The epicenter of the earthquake was situated in the coastal mountains of the province of Michoacán and its expansive wave extended for more than 160 miles (260 km). It is thought that the tremor affected, to some degree, an area of around 320,000 sq. miles (825,000 km²), seriously damaging buildings in Ciudad Guzmán, Colima, Guerrero, Michoacán, Morelos, and Veracruz. Major landslides and avalanches of rocks occurred in areas close to Jalisco and Colima, causing severe damage to roads.

The earthquake also caused a tsunami that caused damage in Lázaro Cárdenas, Zihuatanejo, and Manzanillo as a result of waves 6–10 ft (2–3 m) in height. As far away as Texas, New Mexico, and Idaho, variations in the water levels in wells and cisterns were observed.

A few hours after the earthquake, criticism started to fall on the federal government. The brunt of the disaster had been borne by Mexico City, especially its business center and most of the areas that had mushroomed unchecked over the previous 40 years. The city's inhabitants blamed their political representatives for failing to control this chaotic expansion. The city had grown upward, as a result of high blocks that often looked impressive, but were usually built with shoddy materials.

The earthquake revealed the city's lack of planning and defective construction methods. Statistics do not lie: during the 20th

century, Mexico City endured no less than 42 earthquakes registering over 7 on the Richter scale. How was it possible that the lives of millions of people had been toyed with so irresponsibly? Of almost 3,600 buildings damaged by the earthquake, 412 collapsed completely – most of them having between 8 and 18 stories.

The authorities have been evasive about the death toll. The official count was close to 5,000, but foreign observers and the general public have always maintained that the figure was nearer to 30,000. The city center was turned into a nightmarish landscape of rubble and twisted metal. More than 50,000 people required medical treatment of some kind, and medical services were overwhelmed.

International aid was swift to arrive. Latin American countries were the first to answer the call, along with Spain and the United States. In the following days, more than 40 nations provided assistance to Mexico City and its beleaguered inhabitants. From Septem-

ber 1985 through February 1986, no less than 296 airplanes landed in the city's airports with humanitarian aid of all types; thousands of anonymous financial donations poured in over the next few months. Several eminent international figures also visited the disaster site, including Felipe González, the President of the Spanish government, Nancy Reagan, the American first lady, and Alan García, the President of Peru.

Lessons learned?

The humanitarian assistance mainly comprised medical supplies, clothes, and rescue equipment. Heavy machinery was sent to clear the debris, along with field hospitals to provide first aid close to wrecked buildings and devastated neighborhoods. The heroes of the rescue operation included ordinary citizens who pulled dozens of people out of the ruins, as well as the highly trained sniffer dogs sent by various countries which detected hundreds of people who would undoubtedly otherwise have died.

One person deeply affected by the catastrophe was the famous Spanish tenor, Plácido Domingo, who lost his uncles and cousins in the earthquake. He worked alongside the rescue teams to try and save them, but to no avail. He subsequently gave a series of benefit concerts, with all the box-office takings going to victims of the disaster.

Twenty years have passed since the earthquake, during which Mexico City has continued its rampant expansion. Yet poor planning practices still lead to the inevitable question: what will happen if an earthquake like that of 1985 occurs again?

A large parking lot in the center of Mexico City, unable to bear the strain. Hundreds of scenes like this were seen throughout the city.

Bogota ATLANTIC
Nevado
COLUMBIA

PACIFIC

Líbano
(Colombia)

November 13, 1985

23,000 dead

Eruption of El Nevado del Ruiz

In just a few minutes, the material thrown out by the volcano took the lives of 21,000 of the 28,700 inhabitants of the town of Armero.

The story of El Nevado del Ruiz is a tragic example of how prevention is of the essence in volcanology. If attention had been paid to the signals emanating from the volcano in the previous weeks, thousands of lives would very possibly have been saved. The eruption of the Columbian volcano and its aftermath were seen on television by millions of people, and many still have these images indelibly etched in their memory.

Precedents to the tragedy

El Nevado del Ruiz is situated in the district of Líbano, Colombia. Part of the volcanic chain of the Andes, it is 17, 716 ft (5,400 m) high and the most active volcano in the northern region of South America. The term "nevado" refers to its snow-covered summit, although the warming of the Pacific Ocean has meant that it now bears less and less snow.

El Nevado is a stratovolcano. The eruption in November 1985 was not the first to have tragic consequences for the inhabitants of Tolimá and Caldas, the departments in which the mountain stands. El Nevado had already unleashed its fury in 1595 and 1845. Both eruptions, like the one in 1985, were distinguished by the destructive power of the lahars formed in the explosion. Lahars are channels that occur when ash and

other volcanic matter become saturated with water and run downhill, normally along a pre-established watercourse. Some lahars are formed by saturation resulting from rain, while others – as in this case – take shape when snow and ice melt during an eruption. A lahar formed in the latter manner swept down the valleys of the Rivers Gualí and Lagunillas after the 1595 eruption, killing 636 people, while in 1845 an enormous lahar destroyed the Lagunillas valley for a second time, with over 1,000 casualties. Strangely enough, the town of Armero was founded on the ground deposited by this lahar, although it would become lamentably famous in its own right in 1985.

El Nevado roars again

On November 13 of that year, at 3:06 p.m., a violent explosion sparked off the eruption of the volcano. It had presented signs of activity since November of the previous year, through mild earthquakes, explosions, and columns of smoke from various fumaroles. The Columbian government did not have at its disposal any equipment or qualified scientists capable of predicting the disaster. In February and July 1985, however, several groups of journalists and geologists visited the area with sophisticated seismographic equipment and var-

ious reports were delivered to the government in October. These stated categorically that El Nevado del Ruiz would erupt, in a matter of weeks, and that the local towns were therefore in danger. The authorities dismissed these warnings as alarmist and would only consider evacuating Armero, Ambalema, and other towns in the event of a disaster.

At 5:00 p.m., the volcano started to expel pyroclastic material and ash over Armero. The mayor and local priest appealed for calm. Two hours later, the Red Cross started to evacuate the town, but it suspended the operation when the rain of ash came to a halt. At 9:08 p.m., when everything seemed quiet again, lava surged from the volcano with enormous energy, melting the snow on the peak. It is believed that the volcano emitted more than 350 million cubic ft (10 million m³) of pyroclastic material over a radius of more than 60 miles (100 km). Unfortunately, a storm descended on Armero, hindering the observation of this phenomenon. The pyroclastic material fused with the melted snow and started its fateful

Aerial view of Armero, with the town totally destroyed after the passage of the lahars thrust down by El Nevado.

descent, forming lahars that traveled at more than 30 miles (50 km) per hour. One of them reached the River Cauca and inundated the town of Chinchiná, killing 1,927 people. Other lahars ran along the gullies formed in 1595 and 1845; one of these, which went through the valley of the River Gualí, was 30 ft (50 m) thick, but luckily it did not encounter any populated zones. The lahars gathered speed before reaching the River Lagunillas and the neighboring town of Armero two hours after the eruption.

The scene in Armero was truly apocalyptic. In just a few minutes, the flow of mud, snow, and pyroclastic material wiped the town off the face of the earth, along with over 21,000 of its 28,700 inhabitants. Armero had to endure four more avalanches before the situation calmed down; one lahar, which hit at 11:35 p.m., was over 16 ft (5 m) thick.

When the rescue teams reached the site, the spectacle was nightmarish: masses of deformed trees; cars, trucks, and buses smashed to smithereens; mutilated bodies and crushed animals — all mixed in a thick layer of grayish mud. Despite the efforts of the emergency teams, many of Armero's residents were swallowed by the mud. Nearly 23,000 people and 15,000 animals died; 4,500 townspeople were injured; and more than 8,000 were left without a home. The disaster produced material losses of around 1 billion dollars, or 20 percent of Columbia's GDP.

Sadly, this tragedy could have been averted. Months before the eruption, however, a different team of scientists had visited the crater on account of the tremors and explosions. They found nothing abnormal — so, should all the blame be laid at the door of the government? The eruption of El Nevado del Ruiz and the tragedy of Armero did serve some purpose, however: the media coverage made the general public aware of natural disasters, while the eruption provided valuable findings on the geology of volcanoes.

The peak of El Nevado del Ruiz. Part of the crater wall has disappeared — it crashed on to the nearby valleys, causing thousands of deaths.

The lahars around Armero are clearly visible in this photo; their descent left 23,000 dead.

Spitak earthquake

Seventeen years later, the heartrending effects of this disaster are still clearly visible.

Black Sea ARMENIA Spitak Jerevan

Mediterranean Sea

Spitak (Armenia)

December 7, 1988

25,000 dead

The earthquake in Spitak, Armenia, demonstrated the importance of having suitable infrastructure on hand in cases of extreme urgency. At the time of this cataclysm, Armenia was one the poorest republics in the former Soviet Union. Nowadays, more than a decade after gaining its independence, the country continues to have the same problems, especially with respect to seismic activity.

An area fraught with dangers

Armenia has one of the most precarious economies in the world and its citizens have to endure constant hardship as a result. Financial difficulties go hand in hand with a distinctive geological configuration, as it forms part of an extensive region – running from Turkey to the Arabian Sea and right up to the Indian border – that is at great risk from earthquakes. Armenia's economic deficiencies were exposed in the face of this earthquake, as effective monitoring stations, geological teams, and, above all, qualified health and emergency workers all proved to be beyond its means.

The former Soviet republic had experienced several major earthquakes prior to 1988, and the latter even shared almost the same epicenter as two that occurred in 1899 and 1940. Furthermore, in 1920 and 1926 hundreds of people died as a result of two earthquakes in the Spitak area. The town of Spitak and its surrounding region in northern Armenia is rich in history. Its archeological sites have revealed some of the oldest known human settlements – although many of these treasures were unfortunately destroyed by the 1988 earthquake.

On December 1, six of the seismic stations in northern Armenia detected a tremor of 3.5 on the Richter scale, but this was not considered out of the ordinary in such an active area. Five days later, however, after a series of further tremors of a similar intensity, the underground water level in Noyemberyan rose by over 6 ft (2 m). This was a sign that a major earthquake was imminent.

As so often, the response from the authorities proved sadly wanting. They acknowledged the activity, but were unsure as to where exactly the earthquake could hit and, moreover, whether it would be of any importance. The answer was not long in coming. At 11:41 a.m. on December 7, an earthquake registering 6.9 on the Richter scale and lasting a few seconds devastated the town of Spitak.

Although the tremor was not exceptionally powerful, the destruction left in its wake was immense. Some of the weakest buildings in Spitak and other devastated towns like Gyumri and Vanadzor were schools, and when they collapsed thousands of children were crushed under the rubble. In Gyumri and Spitak, over 95 percent of the buildings were flattened. The quality of the construction was appalling, and the worst affected structures were obviously those of several stories – including hospitals. With the region's hospitals in ruins, no first aid was available, because hundreds of doctors had died and medical equipment was buried in the debris. The area was plunged into chaos.

The squalid conditions in which the survivors found themselves were coupled with the effects of an exceptionally harsh winter – the temperature in Armenia can drop as low as -31 °F (-35 °C). The local government was powerless to react and so left the rescue operation in the hands of foreign NGOs and the Soviet government.

The president of the Soviet Union, Mikhail Gorbachov, broke off a visit to America to coordinate the emergency program with the help of overseas aid. None of the destroyed towns had taken any preventive measures and they even lacked procedures for a possible evacuation, which was finally undertaken with the help of foreign military forces. The local police and fire service were overwhelmed by a situation for which they were totally unprepared. Both electricity and water supplies had been cut off by the earthquake. Ten days later, with hospitals out of operation and no other buildings fitted out to take their place, the corpses piled up in the street posed a threat of epidemics that could spread like wildfire in such hazardous circumstances.

International assistance arrived on December 12. Countries such as Bulgaria, the United States, France, Sweden, Syria, and the former Czechoslovakia contributed

The poor quality of the buildings pushed up the death toll from the earthquake. This photo shows a telecommunications building.

An old church in the town of Leninakan, with little of its former splendor in evidence. The supports for its high roof were flimsy, so it collapsed immediately.

The ruins of an enormous windmill on the outskirts of Spitak. Survivors were found trapped inside it two weeks after the disaster.

food, medicines, medical teams, clothes, and other support. The remaining inhabitants of the devastated towns were gradually evacuated – in all, more than 100,000 were taken to safety. The earthquake left a tragic toll: 25,000 dead, 100,000 wounded – 4,000 of whom were crippled for life – and more than 500,000 homeless.

An uncertain future

The country had still not recovered by the early 1990s, so the Armenian president issued several requests for international assistance. In 2005, 17 years after the disaster, over 9,000 families are still living in prefabricated buildings that barely deserve to be called houses – they are more like metal containers and lack even the most basic facilities.

Apart from housing, the Spitak area has another serious problem: unemployment. The dire poverty that already existed was exacerbated by the earthquake, and no sign of recovery is in sight. Armenians are emigrating to Europe in search of a better life. The 1988 disaster showed up the inadequacy of Soviet seismological policies, leading Western experts to conclude that the sums allegedly assigned to the prevention and investigation of earthquakes were pure invention. In addition, the official death counts from earthquakes occurring in the Soviet Union were inaccurate, although unsurprisingly they always erred on the low side.

Armenia's fragile economy has unfortunately prevented it from investing in a better future. One positive aspect of the tragedy, however, was the spontaneous and wholehearted solidarity that it generated, especially from other Soviet republics whose standard of living was barely higher.

Loma Prieta earthquake

This disaster was the most significant of all those that have hit this region since 1906.

Loma Prieta
California
(United States)

October 17, 1989

62 dead

Chance plays a role in the outcome of a natural disaster. The inhabitants of California know this only too well. Were it not for a baseball game, we would perhaps be talking of a much higher death count as a result of the Loma Prieta earthquake in 1989.

San Francisco, yet again

The San Francisco earthquake in 1906 made clear to the world that California is the American state most vulnerable to this kind of disaster. It stands on the San Andreas Fault, one of the world's major seismic hotspots, and has been the subject of exhaustive research. The earthquake that occurred on October 17, 1989 was the most significant one to hit the region since 1906. It was 5:00 p.m. when a tremor of 7.1 on the Richter scale surprised the inhabitants of California. Its epicenter lay some 6 miles (10 km) from Loma Prieta, one of the most popular mountains in the San Francisco area. In contrast to the San

Francisco earthquake, this tremor did not produce any large cracks – although some were detected in the subsoil of the Santa Cruz Mountains, these did not exceed 3 miles (5 km) in length – and the lateral movements that affected the surface barely measured 1 inch (2 cm), especially in the Monte Madonna area. Nevertheless, some of the distinguishing features of the San Francisco earthquake did recur.

Almost 18,000 houses were destroyed, mostly in Santa Cruz, close to San Francisco. This small city was famous for its late-19th- and early-20th-century architecture. Its pretty brick houses with wooden roofs attracted hordes of tourists and photographers. Many of these buildings had been damaged by the 1906 earthquake, but no efforts had been made to reinforce their wooden structures as a precautionary measure and they were poorly equipped to resist an earthquake of this magnitude. Bricks cannot maintain the struc-

ture of a building in such circumstances, particularly if they are combined with woodwork. To make matters worse, these houses were built on unstable terrain with a propensity to liquefaction.

The ten-second tremor was sufficient to topple hundreds of houses, but nevertheless luck proved to be on the Californians' side. The first stroke of good fortune concerned the landslides that occurred in the Santa Cruz Mountains. Their width varied from a few dozen yards to over a mile, and they swept with them loose rocks, soil, and small trees. They coincided with one of the region's driest periods for several years, however, and this worked in favor of the local residents. If moist earth had combined forces with rain or water from rivers, more than 300 houses would have been at serious risk.

Despite the absence of surface cracks and heavy landslides, material damage was considerable, especially with respect to roads and bridges. Interstate Highway 280 was mangled out of all recognition and remained out of use for weeks. In San Francisco, some shopping streets, such as Fifth Street and Market Street, became impassable on account of their shattered asphalt and rolling terrain. The police made every effort to protect stores by cracking down on looters and even shooting at them when necessary. In another part of town, Marina District, 27 fires broke out. Many fire hydrants were put out of action by the earthquake and, as in 1906, the fire department was overwhelmed: volunteers were recruited to help control the flames by forming human chains passing buckets of water from hand to hand. This area also saw hundreds of its houses topple like cards, as they had been built on soft soil that proved unable to support their structures.

Most of the earthquake's 62 casualties died in Santa Cruz as a result of the collapse of houses in the historic center or on the Cypress flyover on the Nimitz road. This was built on two levels, rather like an aqueduct, and the

A street in a housing project close to San Francisco shows the effects of the earthquake. Similar cracks, and even bigger ones, could be seen far and wide in the area surrounding the city.

General view of the streets of the Marina District. Hundreds of buildings like the one in this photo were affected by fires.

tremor caused the top section to plummet on to the part below, crushing cars underneath huge pieces of concrete and killing 42 people outright.

Despite this heavy toll, the tragedy could have been far worse, especially as it occurred in the rush hour. The inhabitants of the San Francisco area were fortunate because that particular day coincided with the first game in the World Series baseball confrontation between two Californian teams – the Oakland Athletics and the San Francisco Giants. Many people were watching the game in their houses, in bars, or in Candlestick Park stadium itself. If the freeways had been experiencing their normal traffic flow, the scale of the disaster in human terms does not bear thinking about. Because of the exceptional circumstances, the ball game was brought to a halt.

History repeating itself?

The final toll of the earthquake was 62 dead, 3,757 wounded, 18,000 houses destroyed, and material losses in the region of 6 billion dollars. The worst hit were the historic buildings of Santa Cruz, the bridges – 80 out of a total of 1,500 were affected – and the roads, which in some cases were only reopened two months later.

The earthquake demonstrated that, in many respects, the lessons of the past had been learnt, as the modern buildings fitted with anti-seismic structures were barely damaged. In other cases, however, the geologists' warnings about the dangers of building on sedimentary soil went unheeded.

The fate of Marina District and the historic center of Santa Cruz graphically illustrated the consequences of ignoring such advice.

Apartment block in the Marina District. The earthquake severely damaged the ground floor, which is on the point of collapsing. The ruins all around bear witness to the magnitude of the earthquake.

Earthquake in Iran

This area, which is particularly susceptible to earthquakes, lacks the means to mitigate the immense damage they can bring in their wake.

Province of Gilan
Northern Iran

June 21, 1990

40,000 dead

The adobe roof of this building, like so many others, was unable to withstand the earthquake and caved in. Only four narrow steel girders remain in place.

This photo shows how buildings reinforced with girders and sturdily rooted walls resisted the earthquake more effectively.

Water tank in the town of Rasht. As incredible as it may seem, it was originally 150 ft (46 m) high; only these remnants of the structure were left standing.

The comforts of modern life lead us to think that, if a major catastrophe were to hit the heart of a city, disaster relief would arrive as soon as it was needed, as well-communicated streets would enable ambulances, fire trucks, and other services to arrive on the spot in no time. Unfortunately, however, the reality has proved to be very different – and, if this is the case in big cities, what can happen in rural communities or towns with insufficient means to come to the assistance of their population? The earthquake in the province of Gilan, in Iran, highlighted this problem with stark clarity.

A century of devastation

Iran is situated in one of the parts of the world most susceptible to earthquakes. The meeting of Africa and the Arabian Peninsula gives rise to a continental drift toward Eurasia, at a rate of just over half an inch (16 mm) per year.

Earthquakes in this region have been known to kill hundreds of thousands of people since 700 A.D. In the twentieth century alone, a total of 126,000 deaths have resulted from 14 earthquakes scoring over 7 on the Richter scale, while a further 51 earthquakes measuring 6–7 have occurred as well. In all, nine cities were totally devastated in that period.

On June 21, 1990, a tremor of 7.7 emerged as the biggest earthquake ever to hit the Caspian Sea region. This minute-long tremor began at 12:30 a.m., when people were in bed, meaning that the death count was far higher than it would have been if the disaster had struck during the day.

The epicenter of this earthquake was situated on the exact meeting point of the Arabian plate and the Eurasian plate, i.e., in the province of Gilan, between the towns of Rudbar and Manjil, in northern Iran.

This initial tremor was followed, in a short space of time, by two more, which proved even more destructive because the two tectonic plates collided a very short distance from the Earth's surface. The impact was so powerful that it shook the city of Rasht,

330 miles (100 km) from the epicenter and only 660 miles (200 km) northeast of Tehran, and even some parts of neighboring Azerbazhan, where some buildings were damaged.

The areas affected included not only the towns of Rudbar, Manjil, and Lushan but also some further

700 villages, of which 300 were completely flattened. The statistics are chilling: 40,000 dead, 6,000 wounded, and thousands homeless.

Causes of the disaster

The fact that this earthquake occurred during the night aggravated its consequences, but it was

124

not the only factor that turned this event into a veritable catastrophe. Like so many times in the past, several features coincided to make its effects more devastating.

Firstly, local construction materials played a key role. If houses had been prepared for earthquakes, much of the damage could have been avoided or at least reduced, but instead they were built with fragile materials like brick, wood, and adobe.

Secondly, the construction techniques used were also unsuitable. The buildings lacked any reinforcements and so the walls toppled at the first tremor, bringing down the whole structure. Furthermore, the few houses that had been built in a modern style had rejected the traditional layout designed to obviate the effects of earthquakes. These attempts to keep up with the times had made the fatal error of spurning time-honored customs.

Finally, the quality of the soil on which these Iranian towns were built was of crucial significance, as liquefaction is common in this area, particularly on the banks of the Caspian Sea. This causes the land temporarily to lose its solidity and start to behave like a viscous liquid. Anything built on such an uncertain support has an unpredictable future.

History repeating itself

Taking into account all these factors and the large number of earthquakes that have previously hit not only this region, but also the whole of Iran, it is baffling to see its inhabitants suffer time after time from the same afflictions.

The circumstances of Iran, however, do go some way toward justifying this vicious circle. On the one hand, its urban population is growing rapidly, and so houses have to be built to keep up with this

expansion – which undoubtedly means that speed takes preference over quality. On the other, the country's fragile economy affords few resources for the reconstruction of devastated areas. These factors are further exacerbated by Iran's lack of any program for refurbishing affected buildings, or even building regulations that take into account the possibility of earthquakes. Moreover, Iranians are in such a parlous financial state that all their efforts are focused on covering their basic needs rather than taking precautions against a hypothetical earthquake.

In view of all this, it is hard to envisage a better future for Iran. There is always room for hope, however, and the death toll for a subsequent earthquake of 6.6 on the Richter scale, in November of the same year, was a mere 21. Was this luck – or lessons learned?

A group of totally wrecked adobe houses in Mandil, Iran. Adobe proved completely inadequate in the face of tremors on the scale of the 1990 earthquake.

Cyclone and flooding in Bangladesh

The hurricane that hit the coastline of Bangladesh in 1991 took approximately 138,000 lives and caused damage amounting to over a billion euros.

Bangladesh

April 29, 1991

138,000 dead

Part of the city of Chittagong hit by floding as a result of the cyclone

Homeless: this man shelters under a temporary roof of coconut palm leaves and bamboo in Banshkali

The devastating cyclone Marian that visited Bangladesh in 1991 was one in a long series of natural disasters to befall the country, but one of the severest of its kind and among the most catastrophic.

On the night of April 29, 1991, the cyclone reached the neighborhood of Chittagong in the southeast of Bangladesh. Spurred on by gusting winds of some 145 miles (235 km) per hour, waves measuring 20–26 ft (6–8 m) in height washed over the coast and its islands. Some 138,000 people were killed, most of them by drowning. Among those who drowned, the majority were the elderly and children. Approximately one million homes were razed to the ground, rendering roughly ten million people homeless.

Catastrophic

The effects of the cyclone were also catastrophic for agriculture. The harvest was lost over a large area and much livestock was drowned. The drowning was a tragedy in more senses than one: cows are particularly important in Bangladesh for plowing the fields and transporting goods. A far larger area of agricultural land was ruined due to its flooding by seawater. This left the soil brackish and unsuitable for cultivation for a long time afterward. Drinking water was also contaminated.

The port of Chittagong was particularly hard hit by Marian. The cyclone had lifted up a 100-ton crane and smashed it against a bridge over the Karnaphuli River, breaking it in two. Other bridges were also damaged and made impassable due to the storm, which afterward hampered relief efforts. Many ships, several among them from the Bangladesh naval fleet, capsized and blocked the port. Sea dikes were badly damaged elsewhere on the coast, and many jetties and landing stages were swallowed up by the surge. The estimated material losses caused by the disaster amounted to over a billion dollars.

Cyclone nursery

The Bay of Bengal is a veritable nursery for tropical storms, particularly during the monsoon season. It was there meteorologists first observed cyclone Marian, by satellite on April 23, initially recording it as a major depression. On April 27, the storm reached hurricane force and set course for Bangladesh. On the night of April 29, Marian reached the coast at Chittagong. Thus it was already known for several days that the tropical storm was making for Bangladesh. Nevertheless, many Bangladeshis were given only a few hours' advance warning.

Although several places of shelter had been built following the destructive cyclone of 1970, many people failed to reach them because of the late warnings. Furthermore, not everyone knew where the brick shelters were located. Investigations showed that 22 percent of the people who had been unable to reach shelter failed to survive the disaster. The shelters withstood the calamity well, and everyone who did succeed in finding a place in one of these refuges survived.

The timing of the disaster was unfortunate for the government of Bangladesh. Barely two months before, an end had been brought to years of military dictatorship on the election of the country's first woman prime minister, Khaleda Zia. The new government had not yet had the time to plan for such an emergency.

The problems did not concern the availability of relief supplies as such. Sufficient emergency stocks were present in the government warehouses known as "Go Downs." Relief organizations, such as the Red Cross, also had supplies to hand. Collaboration between the government and relief organizations did, however, leave something to be desired.

The greatest problem was distribution of the relief aid. The infrastructure was already substandard, and the cyclone had only worsened the situation. As a result, the government barely succeeded in reaching the afflicted islands. The cyclone had knocked most

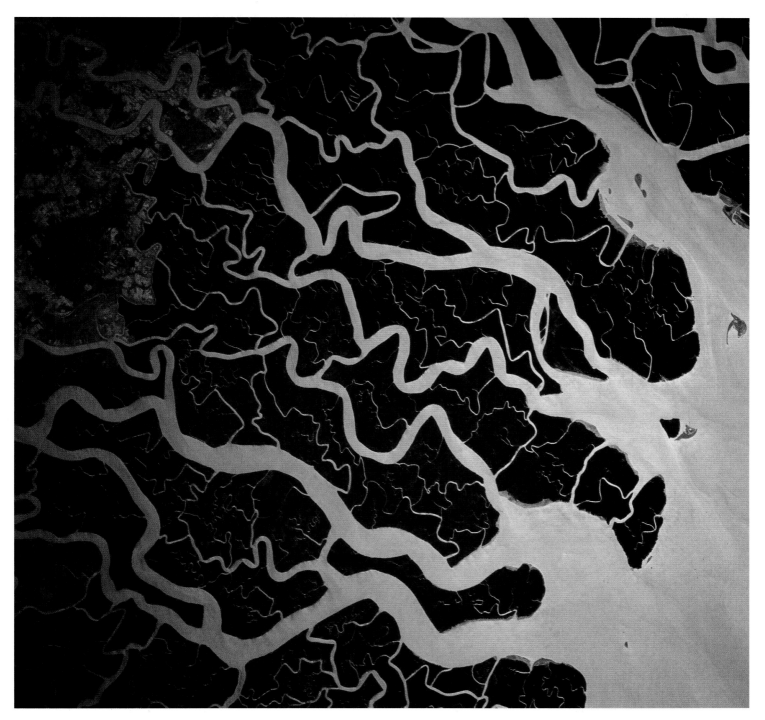

naval ships and military aircraft out of action. To assist the government with its emergency aid, military help was sent by countries such as the United States, Japan, the United Kingdom, and neighboring India, Pakistan, and China.

Water management

In a country that is dependent on water for its rice harvest, freshwater flooding is essential for the crop. These floods occur each year, and the numbers of victims they take are comparatively small. These "normal" floods are called borshas. An exceptionally large flood is referred to as a bonna. In 1999, 1,000 people were killed by just such a bonna.

The Dutch government and Dutch development aid organizations have been supporting Bangladesh for years in the development and implementation of proper water management plans. Plans such as these are no luxury for the most densely populated country in the world. Bangladesh is located on the meteorologically highly turbulent Bay of Bengal and, partly because of deforestation in the Himalayas, is having to deal with increasing quantities of rainwater channeled by the many rivers that empty along its coast into the Bay of Bengal. Climate change is a great danger to Bangladesh. If sea levels were to rise by just 40 inches (1 m), ten to fifteen million Bangladeshis would have to find another place to live.

Apart from flooding, Bangladesh also has to contend regularly with tornados and cyclones, with the coastal areas being most severely affected by these. Over the past few years, the government of Bangladesh has taken steps to reduce the number of victims claimed by cyclones. One example is the establishment of a radio warning system in collaboration with relief organizations. Its headquarters is based in the capital, Dhaka, and is connected to 143 local radio stations. These, in turn, are in contact with thousands of volunteers, who can issue alerts to people by megaphone and help with their evacuation.

Since the sea dikes give inadequate protection, approximately 1,600 concrete shelters have been constructed in coastal areas. They stand on concrete feet and are one or two stories high. Each shelter has room for approximately 1,500 people. Under normal circumstances, they are used as schools or community centers.

Satellite image of part of the delta area that makes up most of Bangladesh

127

Nicaraguan tsunami

The subsoil area affected by the break in the ground was huge: some 135 miles (220 km) long by 22 miles (35 km) wide.

Nicaragua

September 1, 1992

170 dead

In 1992, the coast of Nicaragua was struck by a tsunami that destroyed several villages. The country's unpreparedness and the unexpectedness of the phenomenon caused a great many deaths. The event provided valuable information on the earthquakes that generate giant waves, however, and also helped create a warning center for the country.

The silent tsunami

Although at first the news of the Nicaraguan tsunami surprised even the country itself, it should be pointed out that it was not the first time something like this had occurred. Previously, two earthquakes with their epicenter in the Pacific Ocean had generated tsunamis that claimed many victims. The first happened in 1854, due to an earthquake measuring 7.3 that ravaged Costa Rica. It is known that the giant wave reached Nicaragua, but there is little information beyond this. The second occurred in 1902, when an earthquake caused the formation of a wave that resulted in about 200 deaths, most of them in El Salvador. As experts on the subject have affirmed, tsunamis in Nicaragua are caused by large earthquakes in the contact zone of the Cocos and Caribbean tectonic plates, which abruptly change the seabed. The waves generated increase in height enormously when they reach the shore. Large earth-

quakes in other parts of the ocean, submarine avalanches, volcanic eruptions, and landslides on the shores of great lakes are other phenomena that can cause giant waves, both on the oceanic coasts and in Nicaragua's great lakes.

The tsunami of 1992 was also caused by a strong tremor. It was 6:16 p.m. on September 1 when a tremor measuring 7.6 shook the depths of the Pacific Ocean some 75 miles (120 km) west of the country's coast. Subsequent studies have confirmed that the rupture in the seabed was huge – it is believed that the affected area measured some 135 miles (220 km) long by 22 miles (35 km) wide – and it happened slowly, which is why the earthquake had various characteristics on the surface. Firstly, the external vibration, where it was felt, lasted one minute and forty seconds. Remembering its magnitude, this was a lengthy tremor. Secondly, the earthquake was barely felt by the people of the areas reached by the tsunami. This is known as a silent earthquake or silent tsunami. Subsequent research has confirmed this phenomenon in other Pacific tsunamis. Although the tremor is considerable, it is seldom perceived with the noises typical of such events.

The earthquake generated a powerful tsunami that reached the Nicaraguan coast about twen-

ty minutes after the telluric movement ended. Both the size and the huge speed of the waves were unusual. The tsunami came as a complete surprise to the people of the Nicaraguan coast. The country was not prepared for such an attack. There was no effective seismic network, reports of the disaster were not circulated adequately, the level of preparedness and organization of the Department of Seismology of INETER (Nicaraguan Institute of Territorial Studies) was insufficient, and communication with the local emergency services was poor. Finally, and most seriously, communication with neighboring countries and the Pacific Tsunami Warning Center (PTWC) was non-existent.

The lessons of the tsunami

In total, three giant waves reached the coasts of Nicaragua. The area surrounding the villages of San Juan del Sur and Masachapa was the worst affected. Some 27 villages, with a total of 70,000 inhabitants, were affected by the seaquake. The worst damaged were El Tránsito, Masachapa, and El Popoyo. In the first of those, the waves reached a height of some 33 feet (10 m). The coastal area of that small village had no kind of sea defenses, so the sea surged in. It destroyed most of the houses, some 200, and killed 16 people.

El Tránsito, Nicaragua. This small village almost disappeared beneath the wave that raked the Nicaraguan coast in 1992. Fifteen people lost their lives.

A wall is all that remains of this house on the beach at El Popoyo. Other buildings withstood the assault of the waters much better.

The beach at Marsella. Waves 26 feet (8 m) high destroyed the old beach. Note the devastated ground and the severely damaged building in the background.

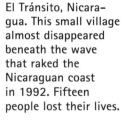

Luckily, the first wave was not very big, which gave the unfortunate residents of El Tránsito time to flee. In Masachapa, the waves surged more than a mile inland. Nine people died. In El Popoyo, the tsunami reached a height of 19 feet (6 m), killing 15 people and destroying most of its buildings.

Other severely damaged villages were La Boquita, Casares, San Martín, Pochomil, San Juan del Sur, and Corinto. In the latter, food stores and fuel tanks were destroyed. The village's drinking-water wells were unusable as they were contaminated by seawater. The waves even reached Costa Rica, but did not cause any deaths. In Nicaragua, 170 people died, 500 were seriously injured, and some 13,000 lost their homes. The material damage caused by the disaster was assessed at some 25 million dollars. To the misfortune of many local families, the Pacific fishing fleet was partly destroyed. It is true that the authorities acted too late and not very effectively, but also that the time between the end of the tremor and the arrival of the first wave was short. There were no good studies of the possibility of

tsunamis in the area and it was not expected that an earthquake like the one on September 1 would cause a seaquake of such magnitude.

Since then, the seismologists of much of the American continent have been studying the possibility of similar events in the future. The catastrophe enabled INETER to develop a tsunami warning system, based on identifying tsuna-

mi-generating earthquakes. In 2002, a series of observation and warning posts was organized which, theoretically, will raise the alarm when necessary. It operates similarly to the well-known Pacific Tsunami Warning Center, but on a more modest scale.

Tsunami in Flores Island

A grove of palm trees along the shoreline lessened the huge impact of the tsunami, thus preventing much greater damage.

Flores Island
(Indonesia)

December 12, 1992

1,690 dead

Indonesia, a high-risk zone

The islands that form the Indonesian archipelago lie at a point where three tectonic plates converge. The Asian plate, the Pacific plate, and the Indo-Australian plate rub against one another and frequently collide, causing earth movements that often in turn produce the greatly feared tsunamis. This was precisely what happened to Flores Island, temporarily interrupting its tranquility.

This chain reaction began on December 12, 1992, when an earthquake measuring 7.5 on the Richter scale shook the waters north of the island's eastern coast. At 1:29 p.m., local time, the magnitude of this earthquake was so devastating that it was even felt in Bali, some 430 miles (750 km)

from its epicenter. Only two minutes later, the tsunami's waves reached the coasts of Flores Island, and three minutes afterward had totally inundated much of its north coast. The epicenter of this whole catastrophe was some 20 miles (35 km) northeast of Maumere, the biggest town on the island. The fault caused by this seismic movement covered the distance between Cape Batumanuk and Cape Bunga – in precise terms, it was 68 miles (110 km) long by 21 miles (35 km) wide. So powerful was it that a group of Japanese scientists calculated that between December 30 and January 5, according to the Richter scale as many as 1,000 aftershocks were felt in each of the archipelago's small islands.

The land rose in several places on the various coasts. Cape Batumanuk rose between 18 inches (0.5 m) and 43 inches (1.11 m), and the same thing happened in the village of Kolisia, 16 miles (25 km) northeast of Maumere. There, the land increased in height by up to 5 ½ ft (1.6 m). The special feature of this tsunami was that its waves came in two bands, with waves of different sizes striking the coast of Indonesia. Of the two, the second wave – which struck the south coast – was much more destructive than its companion, because of all the sediment it had dredged up and the configuration of the land it encountered when it arrived. In any case, the devastation caused by this tsunami both in Flores and in other

nearby islands was a landmark as regards both the number of human lives lost and the amount of material damage.

The town of Wuring, nearly 2 miles (3 km) northwest of Maumere, was totally inundated due to its situation only a few feet above sea level and the great height of the wave. It arrived at a speed of 8.8–10.8 ft (2.7–3.6 m) per second. Most of the houses were torn down and 87 of the 1,400 people who lived there lost their lives. Some 25 miles (40 km) from Maumere lies the small island of Babi, only 1½ miles (2.5 km) in diameter. There was only one flat piece of land there, along the coast. This housed two villages, one Muslim and the other Christian; 263 of the 1,093 people of the two villages fell victim to the great wave. The village of Riang-Kroko (on Cape Watupajung) was one of the worst hit. Thus, while the previous waves had been barely 23 ft (7 m) high, at Cape Watupajung they rose as high as 86 ft (26.2 m) above sea level. The population of the village was 406, distributed among 200 houses. When the wave withdrew, no sign of life remained.

Compared with Babi and Flores itself, the village of Nebe was differently affected. Most of its houses were brick built, so not even this wave could destroy them. In addition, the sea encountered a crucial rival that mitigated its devastating effects: there was a grove of palms running along the shoreline. It was these trees that reduced the impact, which could otherwise have been much worse. As a result, only two of the one hundred and fifty people in Nebe died. In total, the Flores Island tsunami killed 1,690 people and destroyed 18,000 homes.

The phenomenon was characterized particularly by its advance in two bands, the great height of its waves, and the speed at which the waves hit the coasts.

The waters return to their bed

Nevertheless, two facts became clear regarding the damage these indomitable waters usually cause in that area. Firstly — as had happened with previous tsunamis — the number of women who died was double the number of men. This demonstrates a singular social behavior that prevails recurrently in those islands: when danger arises, the men run to save themselves, seeking refuge, leaving their women behind, as it is the women's job to take care of the children and old people.

Secondly, and focusing more on prevention than survival, it is fundamental to point out another fact that could save many lives in future, the best example of which is the village of Nebe. Because of the few losses the tsunami caused there, it was accepted that the place had benefited from an effective, natural protection: dense vegetation in the form of a green belt around the coast had demonstrated that it was the best protec-

tion against the waves. Great trees and woods are capable of dissipating the rolling power of this wildly turbulent sea, as are the coral reefs that lie off the coasts. Perhaps if that fact had been known beforehand it would have helped reduce the damage that 20 tsunamis have caused in the area over the last 300 years.

This picture shows how the tsunami sank large sections of ground. Shortly afterward, the small cliff in this photograph disappeared, the victim of yet another wave.

The village of Wuhring on Flores Island, Indonesia, destroyed by the tsunami. Many buildings such as those in this photograph could not withstand the strength of the waves.

This photograph of Lewobele shows how the land sank in several parts of the island.

USA
Washington D.C. ●
Mississippi River

PACIFIC

ATLANTIC

Caribbean sea

United States

June through
September 1993

50 dead

The Great Flood of 1993

Both because of its duration – 200 days – and because of the geographical area it affected – tens of thousands of square miles – this disaster was absolutely unparalleled.

These two satellite photographs illustrate the growth of the Mississippi and Missouri. The 1993 floods were the worst to have affected the United States in decades.

Forced landing owing to rain at St. Louis. The water almost submerged this private jet.

The agriculture and livestock of the United States suffered great losses. The picture shows some cows that managed to escape the flood.

The Great Flood of 1993 was one of the worst phenomena of its kind to have occurred in the United States. Only the Great Mississippi Flood of 1927 exceeded it (see pp 58-9). Owing to some of its characteristics, however, the impact of the river was greater in 1993 than in 1927, especially as regards economic losses and the number of people displaced. What happened during those months remains engraved on the memories of many in the Mid-West of America.

Extraordinary conditions

The United States holds the Mississippi, one of the longest and mightiest rivers in the world. If the great variations in the country's climate and the meteorological phenomena that occur across its territory are also taken into consideration, it becomes clear that predicting the behavior of this, and other rivers, is not easy. This has been the case throughout history.

In 1889, 1916, and 1927, several floods occurred throughout the nation, with grim consequences. The one called the Great Flood of 1993 was the biggest in the last 70 years, along with the floods caused by hurricane Katrina in 2005. The 1993 disaster affected the states of Iowa, North Dakota, South Dakota, Kansas, Nebraska, Wisconsin, Illinois, Minnesota, and Missouri. A series of circumstances caused the floods between June and August 1993. For example, the precipitation that fell on North Dakota, Kansas, and Iowa was completely abnormal: 150 percent greater than the recorded average. The heavy rainfall could not be contained by the beds of the rivers in the area. At the same time, the soil had become saturated and chilled, and so absorbed less water than usual. The unabsorbed water ended up in the rivers, which began to grow disproportionately. Finally, there was the part played by human action. The desiccation of various areas adjacent to the rivers, the alterations to their natural courses, and the construction of dams were also crucial factors in that they interfered with the normal progress of Nature.

Unusual meteorological conditions were the cause of the persistent rain. Warm air currents originating from the Gulf of Mexico and dry air from Canada converged over the American Mid-West. Combined with other elements, they formed a ridge of high pressure that hung over the affected states for two months. During that time, it rained incessantly, to the extent that the ground and rivers could no longer absorb or channel the amount of water they were receiving.

In early August, the rivers began to overflow. At St. Louis, the Mississippi and Missouri were above flood level for nearly 150 days. Shortly afterward, all the big rivers of the Midwest followed suit, to the misfortune of the people of the area. The Missouri, Kansas, Illinois, Des Moines, and Wisconsin all breached their banks. Nearly 7,000 sq. miles (18,000 km²) were completely devastated. The level of damage was spectacular. Some 5,800 miles (9,300 km) of dams and locks were seriously damaged.

Tragic balance sheet

The floods took 50 human lives and more than 30,000 people were evacuated. Of the 56,000 buildings damaged, 10,000 were destroyed. The material damage was assessed at some 15 billion dollars. In the city of Des Moines, Iowa, for example, the flood destroyed the water-purification plant, leaving the population without drinking water for 20 days, in the height of summer. The water that flowed from the faucets and water-fountains in the city and in neighboring places was contaminated, with the attendant threat of epidemic. Millions of crop fields were destroyed by the

flooded rivers, bringing corresponding losses for their owners, whether of property – grain silos, barns, tractors, etc – or livestock. Harvests were also affected, causing a serious rise in the price of products such as maize, a significant component of people's diet.

The rise in the level of the Mississippi was very significant for the economy and industry of the states through which it flows. River transport using that important route was disrupted for weeks. The river's barges and ferryboats carry 20 percent of the country's coal, a third of its oil, and half its exported grain. Economists from prestigious universities calculated that the losses per day due to the interruption of riverboat traffic came to a million dollars, a considerable burden for any economy to sustain. Electric power stations also felt the lack of coal at the same time as cities and industries throughout the country. The highways and railroads in many parts of the states that were flooded remained impassible for months. The damage to the roads affected was assessed at over 500 million dollars.

What cannot be quantified is the suffering of the thousands who lost their homes. Many of them never returned and had to settle in other parts of the country, desperate and disheartened by their situation.

The Great Flood of 1993 was an abnormal phenomenon, even by American standards both because of its duration of over 200 days, and because of its extent, nine states and tens of thousands of square miles under water. On the other hand, in spite of the horrifying figures and the equally terrifying pictures, the number of victims was not as great as it might have been. The rescue services and preventive measures worked, although there were episodes of chaos and mass hysteria. Therein lies the difference compared with similar catastrophes, such as the Mozambique flood of 2000. One case concerned the world's richest country, and the other one of the poorest countries on the planet.

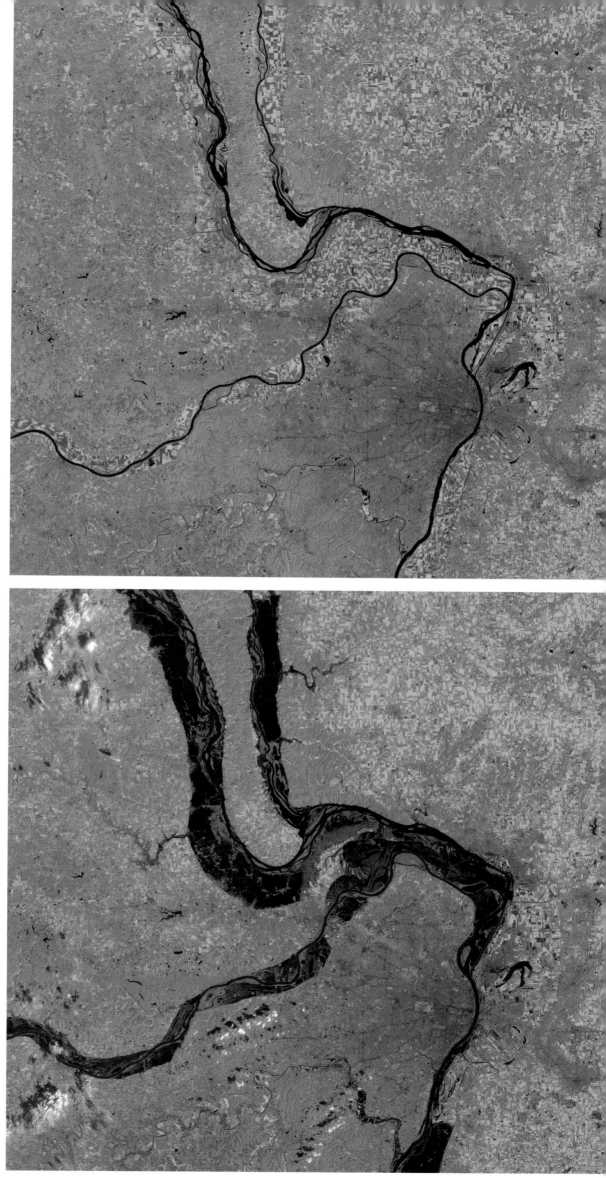

Tsunami in Hokkaido

The worst tsunami Japan suffered in its history.

Hokkaido and Okushiri (Japan)

July 12, 1993

202 dead

A fishingboat flung against one of the harbor's protection barriers. Next to it lies the rubble of houses near the harbor.

As is well known, the Pacific Ocean is the zone where most tsunamis are recorded, mainly due to the geological morphology of its seabed. The countries bathed by that ocean are exposed to the danger of earthquakes and the tsunamis they cause. In Hokkaido, northern Japan, the people are all too well aware of that fact.

Surprise in northern Japan

Hokkaido is Japan's second biggest island. It is situated north of Honshu, the country's biggest island, to which it is linked by the futuristic submarine train. The island's principal activities are agriculture and tourism. It is a favorite destination for millions of Japanese, in summer or winter.

Tranquility on the island was broken on the night of July 12, 1993. At 10:17 p.m., an earthquake measuring 7.8 on the Richter scale was detected on the west coast of Hokkaido and its neighboring island, Okushiri. In less than five minutes, a giant wave, or tsunami, struck the southwest coast of Hokkaido and Okushiri, the area that bore the brunt of the disaster. Hokkaido was damaged by the earthquake, which caused huge landslides. The giant wave it generated increased the devastating power of the earthquake, with 540 houses destroyed and 1,834 seriously damaged. Several fires were recorded in the southwest of the island, but fortunately they were brought under control. The bay of

Ota received waves up to 30 feet (9 m) high that completely destroyed 5 houses. In the neighboring towns of Suttsu and Setana the waves reached heights of 16–29 ft (5–9 m).

Having swept through those places, the height of the tsunami's front and its speed declined. Okushiri, a small island inhabited by fishermen south of Hokkaido, was savagely punished by the wave. The west coast received the tsunami's highest waves. The 12 houses in Monai, a small hamlet, were destroyed and 10 people died. The protection barriers with which the village and the valley that contained it were equipped may have controlled, or at least lessened, the strength of waves up to 65 ft (20 m) high. Tragically, the waves that struck Monai reached a height of 100 ft (31 m), and 50 ft (15m) just a few miles to the south. The vegetation on the surrounding hills was completely uprooted and destroyed.

After devastating western Okushiri, the wave changed direction and moved south. The worst affected village on that part of the island was Aonae, with 1,600 inhabitants. Five minutes after the earthquake, the first tsunami wave reached the village. The houses on the seafront were washed away and the surrounding districts suffered serious floods. Fires broke out on two boats at anchor in the harbor, which damaged nearby buildings. Bad luck pursued the two boats that had caught fire. Seven minutes

after the first wave, a second and stronger one flung the boats into the middle of the village.

The combination of the burning boats, strong northeast wind, and damage to some kerosene and propane storage tanks soon produced their effects: 300 houses were destroyed by fire, although there were only two victims. This second wave surged further in than the first, completely flooding Aonae to a depth of over 32 ft (10 m) in the lower part of the town and over 16 ft (5 m) in the highest. One hundred and fourteen people died, most of them by drowning. The roads and bridges of the area were left unusable. The only viable means of transport were boats that had lost their moorings and were drifting about the waters of the town, itself transformed into an infernal Venice.

The north and east of Okushiri suffered less damage, in spite of the 32-foot (10 m) waves that struck its coasts. In Inaho, in the north of the island, waves destroyed all its hous-

es and caused more than 600 million dollars' worth of material damage. Japan, the victim of natural disasters such as the Kobe earthquake of 1995 and the Tokyo earthquake of 1923, had suffered the worst tsunami in its history.

The destruction continues

The frenzied activity of the wave resulting from the earthquake on July 12 did not stop at Japan. Ninety minutes after the tremor, the waves reached South Korea. Waves nearly 7 ft (2 m) high were recorded at Aomori, where one fisherman died. The tsunami continued to the southeast coast of Russia, where it killed three people and caused severe damage to a factory at Kamenka in the Sakhalin Islands. In Russia, waves 13 ft (4 m) high were seen. Months after the tragedy, the fishing fleets of the affected countries – Japan, North Korea, South Korea, and Russia – were still feeling the results of the catastrophe. Nearly 700 vessels were lost or

seriously damaged – a considerable misfortune, considering that the people in areas struck by the tsunami live mainly by fishing. The gigantic wave of 1993, which mainly affected Hokkaido and Okushiri, is an example of how unpredictable this phenomenon can

be. In spite of Japan's early warning and protection measures, many areas found themselves defenseless before its might.

View of one of Aonae's landing stages, totally ruined. Only an obelisk remains standing. At this point, the wave was 32 ft (10 m) high.

The remains of the personal possessions of the people killed by the tsunami. Aonae, on Okushiri Island, was one of the worst affected areas.

Kobe earthquake

This earthquake has the sorry distinction of being the disaster with the highest economic cost in modern times.

Kobe (Japan)

January 17, 1995

6,433 dead

The end of prosperity

When this earthquake occurred, Kobe, in the south of Honshu Island, was a wealthy commercial city. Its port was the busiest in Asia and the second busiest in the world. Its intense commercial life had always given the city a cosmopolitan air. More than 100 different nationalities were represented among the 45,500 residents of its harbor district.

The city was the center of an economic nucleus with strong links to Osaka, Tokyo, Hakata, Nagoya, and Yokohama. It grew so fast after the Second World War that two artificial islands were constructed in its bay.

Its success received a sudden blow, however, in the early hours of January 17, 1995. It was 5:46 a.m. when an earthquake with its epicenter some 12½ miles (20 km) from the city, on the island of Awaji, brought everything down. Seismographers indicated a tremor of 6.9 on the Richter scale, lasting 20 seconds. The intensity of the tremor and the closeness of its epicenter to the city center were a fatal combination.

Kobe is in a seismic zone, so earthquakes are something its residents have to live with. That is why, since 1981, a series of state laws has required certain measures to be taken in the erection of buildings. Unfortunately, not all the city's buildings dated from that time. Destruction was particularly great in the city center and port area. The phenomenon known as liquefaction occurred on Kobe's main artery, due to the instability of the ground and the land reclaimed from the sea,

meaning that the unstable materials forming the ground moved as if they were liquid, felling hundreds of warehouses and cranes in the port. In the city, many gas pipes cracked during the tremor, letting their contents escape. Fires soon broke out. Unfortunately, many houses in Kobe were built of wood and plaster, enabling flames to spread at a terrifying rate.

It is calculated that a few minutes after the earthquake some 300 fires assailed the city. Extinguishing them was an arduous task. Most of the water pipes were unusable because, like the gas pipes, they had not withstood the earthquake. Firefighters could not gain access to certain parts of the city: the streets were impassible. The rubble of buildings and cracks in the road surfaces prevented access by any vehicle. About 7,000 buildings were burnt and some 700 people died in fires. The roads near the harbor could not withstand the shaking and even sank several inches. As if that were not enough, Kobe's oldest streets were narrow, which helped the fire to spread easily. Nevertheless, buildings such as gas stations, schools, office buildings, and electricity substations did withstand the tremor and the fires, becoming places of refuge, though there was no water or electricity.

Days after the disaster, many voices were raised among the people of the city, criticizing the lack of assistance during the first – and worst – hours after the earthquake, and the slowness with which it arrived once the situation was more

under control. Apparently, the lack of coordination between the government of the city and the central government and its administrative departments was at issue. The testimony of many of the firefighters refers to buildings saved by the action of citizens in the absence of any orders and resources from the emergency services.

The infrastructure was also severely damaged. Where highways and elevated railroads did not collapse, they became tortuous routes unable to support any kind of traffic, preventing ambulances and fire appliances from entering the city. At last, the fires were brought under control and help gradually arrived. As a result of the quake, 6,433 people died and more than 100,000 lost their homes. About 70,000 buildings collapsed. The material cost of the tragedy exceeded a billion dollars. The Kobe earthquake has the sorry distinction of being the most expensive natural disaster in modern times.

The reconstruction of Kobe

In spite of the magnitude of the tragedy, the people of the city and its government proposed the rebirth of the metropolis, as before. A plan was prepared for the city's reconstruction within 10 years. Reconstruction of the urban and social networks was vital. The city would help the people who had lost their jobs or relatives, or who had suffered psychological trauma caused by the cataclysm. The idea was to create a new sense of community. Three days after the earthquake, the first construction works on new homes began.

In 2003, the number of new homes was 200,000, more than originally envisaged. In two years, roads, bridges, and railroads were rebuilt, together with the key part of the city: the port. This highway reconstruction was not only important to the city itself; the whole country had suffered from its state in 1995, as demonstrated by the economic indices of those years. The new buildings complied strictly with the earthquake safety and prevention regulations: the disaster would not be repeated.

In 2005, the port of Kobe is already the third most important in

The main floor of this building had no anti-earthquake reinforcement – hence its position. Many buildings erected before 1975 looked like this.

Japan and among the first 30 in the world – a huge success after the appalling situation in which it was left ten years ago. The earthquake cost many lives, but was an exceptional test of the iron will of its people and institutions, who would never rest until they saw their city reborn.

A totally destroyed building blocks access to a street. Events such as the one pictured here delayed the arrival of emergency vehicles.

Picture showing the collapse of one of the bridges between two buildings; the lower one is still in place.

Avalanches near Mount Everest

The avalanches in the Himalayas in 1995 were the largest and most destructive ever recorded.

Sagarmatha/
Mount
Everest

NEPAL

Kathmandu

Bay of
Bengal

INDIAN OCEAN

Gokyo Valley, Nepal

November 11–12,
1995

49 dead

On the night of November 10, 1995, a huge avalanche took an encampment of Japanese mountain climbers by surprise near Mount Everest in Nepal. Eleven Japanese and thirteen Nepalese climbers, including eleven guides, were lying asleep when the snow overwhelmed them. The group had just returned from the Gokyo Valley, which is popular with mountaineers who do not seek to climb at extreme heights. The valley is a little over 12 miles (20 km) to the southwest of Mount Everest and over 175 miles (280 km) from the Nepalese capital, Katmandu.

A rescue team reached the village the next day by helicopter. The helicopter pilot later related how the whole village of Pangka lay buried under a thick blanket of snow and that they had only been able to see the rooftops of the mountain cabins. As well as the climbers, rescue teams were able to bring a further 85 people to safety from the Gokyo Valley. Twenty-five others met their deaths in other parts of the Everest region, either through smaller avalanches or because their houses had collapsed on them.

In the days following the great avalanche and landslides, a total of 517 people were rescued from the snow, including 238 foreigners. "This is the first time that such a major mountain-climbing area has been hit by an avalanche of this scale," said Prachanda Man Shrestha, then government spokesman for Nepal. November is the high season for mountain climbers in Nepal, and hundreds of foreigners had plotted out routes in the Himalayas just before the blizzards had begun..

Blizzards

Unusually severe storms for the time of year blew up on November 9 and 10. The fall is usually fairly dry in the Himalayas. The blizzards had been caused by a powerful cyclone from the Gulf of Bengal, which had moved uncommonly far inland compared to normal and thus had reached the Himalayas.

As bad luck would have it, the Nepalese meteorological service had not issued any warnings about the intensity of the storm or the path it was taking. The thick blankets of snow falling on the steep mountainsides had started to slip, giving rise to the huge avalanches and landslides.

Rescue missions were mobilized immediately. On November 11, the morning after the major avalanches, the police, army, Himalaya Rescue Organization, Ministry of Tourism, Nepalese Institute of Mountain Climbing, and travel agencies all pooled their resources to attempt the rescue of as many people as possible. Helicopters were deployed, evacuating people from the villages higher up and mountaineers' camps. Some of those involved were flown directly to the hospital in Katmandu. Rations and first-aid packs were dropped in places where the helicopters were unable to land due to deep snow, but where people had been spotted. For a long time, the higher villages remained cut off from the outside world and were completely dependent on relief maneuvers. The rescue mission was the largest of its kind ever to take place in Nepal.

A mountaineer's story

"It had been a dream for ages to go to Nepal," recalled American Deborah Plotkin. On November 1, she had begun the trek together with her husband, Ron, as well as six Nepalese guides, some porters, and two yaks. Concerned about an unexpectedly severe blizzard, one of their guides decided to wake them in the middle of the night, and they quickly gathered their things together. At around 2:30 a.m. they crept out of their tents and witnessed the avalanche: it made an infernal noise as it tore narrowly past their camp. Ron Plotkin recalled: "Just after I heard this immense rumbling, I looked around and saw that four of our Nepalese guides had disappeared, buried beneath the snow. In shock, we had to dig ourselves a path through the snow, many feet deep, sleeping at night in hollows that we made for ourselves in the snow."

Over the next few days, the Plotkins and their team tried to find a way back to civilization through thick drifts of snow, having to cross over icy streams to reach safety. At night, while in the self-made snow caves that afforded them some protection from the freezing cold, the Plotkins prayed that they might see their three children, aged 5, 9, and 14, once again in San Diego.

The hikers' paths in the Gokyo Valley had disappeared completely under the snow left behind by the avalanches. Under normal circumstances, the views of the mountain

Mountain climbers look out toward an avalanche, from their base camp on the flanks of Mount Everest

Spring expedition at height of approximately 21,300 ft (6,500 m)

An avalanche heads in the direction of three mountain climbers on Mount Everest

peaks and valleys are breathtaking from these paths. After two days and nights, the Plotkins finally crossed just such a mountain path, which they followed until they arrived in the hamlet of Chikoon. One of their guides, Ram Kumar, had died of hypothermia during their journey. The four guides who the Plotkins had watched disappear beneath the avalanche had, however, somehow managed to save themselves and were also brought to safety.

Worst affected area

Never before had avalanches affected such a large area or been responsible for so many fatalities during a mountaineering season in the Nepalese part of the Himalayas. The stunning valleys and high mountain peaks attract approximately 65,000 foreign climbers to the area each year.

The Himalayan avalanche disaster of 1995, is considered to have been the worst ever in Nepal. The tragedy was given a further twist when the huge quantities of snow began to melt a few months later. In March 1996, this resulted in a further series of avalanches; this time,

fortunately, they were smaller, and no lives were lost.

RUSSIA
Moscow
Sakhalin Island/
Neftegorsk

Neftegorsk, Russia

May 27, 1995

Over 2,000 dead

Earthquake in Neftegorsk, Russia

The earthquake that hit the Russian island of Sakhalin in May 1995 registered 7.6 on the Richter scale and claimed over 2,000 lives in the small town of Neftegorsk.

Many buildings in Neftegorsk and its surroundings were razed to the ground

A statue of Lenin remains standing in the wreckage of Neftegorsk

Two Neftegorsk residents sit dumbstruck amid the remains of their utterly devastated home

The island of Sakhalin is located in the easternmost part of Russia: its southern tip is separated from Japan by a mere 28 miles (45 km). It is an area where the Eurasian and North American tectonic plates meet and yet, up until the Neftegorsk tragedy, it was considered to be a seismically inactive zone. The epicenter of the 1995 earthquake lay close to the small town of Neftegorsk. In terms of the number of casualties, the larger town of Okha, some 38 miles (60 km) farther north and with a population of over 45,000, fared far better compared with Neftegorsk, which depended largely on the oil fields in the region. In Okha, there were no fatalities, and damage was limited. The experience in Neftegorsk was very different: almost two-thirds of its residents met their deaths during or shortly after the earthquake. Only 1,144 survived. The vast majority of its buildings were either completely destroyed or left in ruins.

The earthquake occurred on Saturday, May 27, 1995, a little after 11:00 p.m., local time. Almost immediately—within a minute of the quake, according to eyewitnesses—several

apartment blocks fell down. The town hall, a building owned by the local energy company, and several shops were also utterly demolished. A dancehall, where many students were celebrating the end of the school year, also collapsed in ruins. Most of the buildings had been put up in the 1960s and were constructed mainly from prefabricated concrete panels, with little or no additional reinforcement.

A little to the north of Neftegorsk, the earthquake damaged an oil pipeline and some oil installations, causing an unknown quantity of the fluid to leak out into the surrounding area. Details about the damage that this caused to the environment have never been made public.

Difficult rescue operation

The next day, rescue work was hampered by thick fog. Thousands of residents lay under the rubble. Of these, it was possible to save only a few hundred. The region was hit by several aftershocks. The Russian authorities immediately sent emergency-relief supplies to the region, but the closest airfield with the capac-

ity for such large cargo planes was separated from Neftegorsk by over 400 miles (650 km). Due to the fog and the poor condition of the roads, it took a relatively long time before supplies and aid could reach the town.

By the end of the first day after the quake, more rescue workers and medical teams had arrived in Neftegorsk either by road or helicopter. A special search team was flown in from Moscow. Neighboring towns provided cranes and other heavy equipment to enable the weighty slabs of concrete to be hoisted out of the ruins. On Sunday evening, 224 injured survivors were transferred to the hospital in Okha and to hospitals on the Russian mainland.

Approximately 500 rescue workers arrived in Neftegorsk on Monday. By the end of the day, a total of 938 survivors had been pulled from the rubble. Doctors were caring for the wounded at the scene: many had crushed limbs that had to be amputated. Dazed survivors searched through the ruins or scanned lists for missing family

members and friends. According to the local authorities, it was largely people who lived in brick-built dwellings three or four stories high who had managed to reach safety.

Icebreaker

An icebreaker was sent to Neftegorsk from the mainland to clear a passage through the 3-ft- (1 m-) thick sea ice for a hospital ship. Some wounded casualties were even transported to hospitals in Vladivostok, approximately 920 miles (1,475 km) away. Neighboring countries offered emergency supplies and food; South Korea donated $1 million, partly because of the relatively large Korean community living in Sakhalin.

On Tuesday, the third day after the quake, a further 32 people were pulled alive from the rubble. Many survivors refused to leave their town, staying huddled around campfires next to the ruins of their homes. Several looters were arrested amid the devastation and the police cordoned off Neftegorsk. The small airfield at Okha was a hive of activity: airplanes brought in food supplies, as well as wood for coffins. The wounded and evacuees left for the mainland by air. In the suburbs of Okha, many fled their homes in fear of aftershocks, moving into garages or summerhouses as temporary shelters with blankets to keep them from the cold. They were only too aware that their homes were of the same type as those in Neftegorsk, which had collapsed so overwhelmingly and with such ease.

At the beginning of July, approximately 400 people were still living in Neftegorsk in holiday cabins on the edge of the town, mostly without running water, electricity, or central heating.

In August 1995, the then president, Boris Yeltsin, decided that the local government of Sakhalin could use all its revenue from oil for the rest of that year for repairs and reconstruction following the earthquake. The focus of recovery was largely on the oil industry and hardly at all on private housing and public facilities.

ВИ ЛЕНИН
1870 – 1924

The El Niño meteorological phenomenon

This phenomenon, whose causes are unknown, is repeated every six or seven years.

During the winter of 1997–1998, pictures of flooded villages, rain beating down on various parts of the globe, and news of abnormal temperatures in the United States and South America were commonplace on television and in newspapers throughout the world. Such events were associated with a phenomenon called El Niño.

A new look at El Niño

The visit of El Niño in 1997 and 1998 was not unfamiliar to meteorologists and the people it affected. It has been studied constantly since 1923. Its name, meaning "Little Boy," comes from the fishermen of South America, as its arrival coincides with Christmas and the coming of the infant Jesus. El Niño consists of an abnormal warming of the equatorial waters of the Pacific Ocean, whose temperature is normally some 33 °F (0.5°C). These temperature changes are associated with changes in the pressure system and therefore the winds that blow in those areas are also subject to change. Due to this warming of the waters, storms arise more frequently, especially throughout the Pacific, on both its east and its west coasts.

In South America, the effects of the phenomenon are greater than in other parts of the world. Summers become hot and wet, with torrential rain on the coasts of Peru and Ecuador. From December 1997 through February 1998, the floods caused by the rains were especially serious.

The same thing happened three months later in northern Argentina and southern Brazil, with severe consequences in the latter country from which the Rio de Janeiro region has not yet recovered.

Conversely, Chile and the Bolivian Altiplano experienced an extremely harsh winter with snowstorms and lower temperatures than normal. In northern Amazonas, Colombia, and Central America, the summer was extremely dry.

The other side of the Pacific Ocean experienced very similar effects, although on a smaller scale. In Indonesia, the Philippines, and Australia, the weather was drier than in recent decades.

The United States and Canada experienced alternating rises and falls in temperatures. The Midwest and Canada had a warm winter, while southern California, northwestern Mexico, and several of the southern states of the U.S.A. suffered abnormal, persistent rain.

Africa also experienced remarkable climatic variations due to El Niño. December through February was very wet for equatorial Africa and the southern Sahara. Conversely, Zambia, Zimbabwe, Mozambique, and Botswana were surprised by hot, dry weather. The torrential rainfall in the countries of the American continent produced floods and frequent landslides that caused massive material damage and nearly 800 deaths.

The El Niño phenomenon also reached the United States. The picture shows floods in California in March 1998.

Along with the floods, California suffered several mudslides that destroyed homes and cars.

The climate changes in South America promote the spread of diseases such as cholera, dengue fever, malaria, encephalitis, and leptospirosis, which, combined with the poor health facilities in the developing world, frequently cause high death tolls, especially the cholera breakout of in 1991, during the period of El Niño, which has since caused more than 12,000 deaths.

The fishing industry is the worst affected by the weather changes. All along the west coast of South America, El Niño drastically reduces the cold currents that are rich in the nutrients that support fish and seabirds. The decline in those populations on the coast is very damaging for the fertilizer industry, as the excrement of seabirds is used in the latter. The situation of hundreds of fishermen and factories was endangered by El Niño. Curiously, while the fishing industry suffered a severe recession, life in the countryside improved. The warm climate favored harvests and local farmers could relax a little.

The future of El Niño

Unfortunately, the causes of El Niño are still unknown today, as are its possible effects on global climate change. The phenomenon is repeated every six or seven years and its duration depends on a series of factors that meteorologists are now discussing.

The 1997–1998 episode brought La Niña with it. This other natural phenomenon accompanies El Niño when the climatic conditions El Niño brings with it are especially harsh. La Niña is the opposite of El Niño. Where one brings warm temperatures, the other causes them to fall. If El Niño has caused rain, La Niña will cause dry weather.

On the South American coast, La Niña is greeted with joy, as the temperature of the currents falls, favoring the passage of fish so that catches increase. Conversely, in the agricultural world La Niña is not popular: the decline in temperatures destroys harvests.

In recent years, and especially since El Niño of 1982–1983, the most serious episode, and 1990–1994, the longest, the coun-

tries affected by the phenomenon are relying on forecasts. Doubtless, an accurate forecast helps with planning harvests and the movements of fishing fleets. Governments can also plan their policy on financial aid to the various sectors of the economy.

Unfortunately, however, only a small part of the phenomenon can be predicted and it is not possible entirely to prevent floods or landslides and the destruction of homes caused by the rains. The fact that El Niño mainly affects poor countries is a serious misfortune. Poor infrastructure, adverse living conditions, and, sometimes, the disdain of governments themselves certainly make it hard to establish preventive measures against the storms or droughts caused by El Niño.

Houses destroyed by the swollen river Nido in California.

Floods in Moravia

The 1997 floods were among the most devastating natural disasters ever to hit Czech lands.

The river Morava, Czech Republic

July 4–21, 1997

50 dead

Floods are the most dangerous natural phenomenon to affect the territory of the Czech Republic and they have helped shape the landscape. The people used to respect the natural flooding, constructing their settlements in places beyond its reach and reserving the valley beds—the flood plains—only for buildings that harnessed water power, such as flour-mills, saw-mills and iron-mills. There was no stopping urban sprawl, however, and during the twentieth century even the historically threatened flood plains were gradually developed. A long period without serious flooding, coupled with a sense of security due to constantly improved flood defenses, led people to turn a blind eye to the risk of floods.

Catastrophic rains

The first warning that the Czech Republic was not protected against natural disasters was the flood of 1997. This hit the entire eastern part of the country—Moravia and East Bohemia, i.e., the entire course of the rivers Morava, Dyje, and Odra (Oder) and also the upper part of the Labe (Elbe). These areas were actually hit by two waves of floods, in the periods July 4–8 and July 17–21. Although the rainfall of the second flooding was mostly only 30–50 percent that of the first, when 81 billion cubic feet (2.3 billion cubic meters) of water fell on an area of 3,860 square miles (10,000 square km), the second flood wave was just as destructive because the ground was already waterlogged. The exceptional nature of these floods is underlined by the fact that all 34 official rain gauges of the area recorded 8 inches (203 mm) of precipitation in the course of two days, the highest measured rainfall during the whole month being 32 inches (812 mm), four times the average. This suggests a period of cumulative rainfall that happens perhaps once in a thousand years.

The floods were caused by two deep troughs of low pressure. The first low over the Czech Republic and southern Poland moved in from northern Italy, its further progress being blocked by an area of high pressure from the Azores that settled over southern Scandinavia. This meant that the rain accompanying the low pressure all fell in one place, the highest levels being recorded on July 6. The second low, which produced the heavy rains from July 17 through 21, differed from the first only in being caused by a merging of two weather fronts. Otherwise, its further development was identical, confirming that atmospheric circulation processes have an immediate repetitive tendency.

Flood waves

The two distinct episodes of rain in July 1997 produced two separate flood waves. During the first of these, upper-course river flows peaked on July 7 and middle-course flows culminated July 8–10. During the second, both the upper- and middle-course flows mainly peaked on July 19. In the lower reaches of the Morava, the second wave of rainfall considerably prolonged the flooding and the first and second flood waves merged, culminating on July 22. Watercourses were flowing at 800-year flood levels, i.e., a flood whose peak flow is attained or exceeded only once every 800 years.

Around 4,250 square miles (11,000 square km) were inundated.

The July floods of 1997 wreaked considerable damage on the river network itself, leading to extreme erosion and an enormous accumulation of flood sediment in the lower parts of the river systems. For example, some 400,000 tons of silt were deposited between the towns of Kroměříž and Strážnice. Moreover, 405 extensive landslips were produced or activated, particularly in the Beskyd mountain area, where buildings and infrastructure were frequently imperiled.

Fifty people died in the July floods. Some 29,000 homes were inundated in 536 towns and villages, more than 1,400 houses were totally destroyed, and a further 4,000 suffered serious structural damage. Previously unheard-of villages such as Troubky nad Bečvou and Bochoř, where subsidence due to flooding caused one house after another to collapse, drew headlines in the mass media. Total direct material damage was put at 62.6 billion CZK, i.e., 3.5 percent of the country's GDP. Mere figures, however, are not enough to express the extent of the destruction, since the affected area is a culturally important region of Central Europe. The

The customarily peaceful streets of Olomouc transformed into a wild, swollen riverbed.

floods struck Olomouc, historically the second most significant city of the Czech Republic, and Kroměříž with its famous castle and gardens, listed by UNESCO as a World Heritage Site. In addition, the floods knocked out a whole series of waste-water treatment plants, leading to leakage of hazardous industrial waste into the rivers. Wells were contaminated in many places, so that people had to rely on water supplies distributed in tankers. The produce in flooded fields had to be plowed in, and emerging lagoons around flooded areas became breeding grounds for mosquitoes.

The disaster revealed just how unprepared were the weather forecasters, water management authorities and state administration for an event on this scale. Even the flood crisis emergency team at Olomouc had to be evacuated as the Morava burst its banks. Despite all this, however, the flooding sounded a positive note too. People began taking account of flood risks, and not only in the areas directly hit by those floods. Measures were taken that would limit the damage caused by the next floods in 2002, which this time affected the western part of the Czech Republic. Yet another positive sign was the solidarity with

suffering fellow-citizens shown by people throughout the country, be it in the form of help in clearing flood damage or in material or financial donations. A number of charitable foundations and humanitarian organizations were set up immediately after the floods, to help restore the affected towns and villages.

Floods in China

In the summer of 1998, an estimated 240,000,000 Chinese were affected either directly or indirectly by the flooding of the Yangtze River.

Yangtze, China

August 1998

3,600 dead

During the summer months, central China is well accustomed to an excess of water. The monsoon at that time is responsible for severe downpours. In 1998, however, rainfall levels were much higher than normal. After a wet spring with a great deal of melt water, there followed two brief, but severe, bouts of rain. All this water proved too much for the 3,960-mile (6,380-km) Yangtze River in the first week of August. The dikes were breached in several places, and a huge area was inundated with floodwater.

Nearly six million homes were washed away by the water; seven million others were seriously damaged. This forced fourteen million people to seek new dwellings. For weeks, millions of evacuees bivouacked in small, makeshift tents along the tops of muddy dikes. Diseases such as typhus and dysentery broke out in some of the refugee camps. All in all, some 3,600 people died as a result of this flood disaster.

In order to relieve the pressure, dikes were broken upstream, near the 7-million-strong city of Wuhan. Elsewhere, too, thousands of agricultural laborers had to abandon their land, which was sacrificed by the authorities in order to save the cities. Hundreds of thousands of soldiers and citizens were deployed to reinforce the existing dikes and build emergency ones to deal with

In 1998, the hugely swollen waters of the Yangtze River took thousands of lives

Agricultural workers try to close the gaps in a dam at Dongting Lake

the rising waters. More than 260,000 were involved in the attempt to save the city of Harbin—a city of 9,000,000 people.

In a few cases, ships were sunk to fill breaches in the dikes. Close to the city of Jiujiang, the local population became so panicked by a 120-ft (36-m) hole in the dike that they tried to seal it using a truck and a small ship. Both were carried off by the water. Partly using sandbags, it took an army unit four days to close the breach.

The financial losses caused by the disaster were enormous. Estimates vary from 20–30 billion dollars. Agriculture was not the only sector to be dealt a heavy blow; so, too, was the oil industry. The oil fields of Daqing were awash. In 1997, these oil fields accounted for one-third of crude oil production in China. To release funds for fighting the disaster, the Chinese government announced a number of measures. In the end, however, the fast-growing Chinese economy found itself well able to absorb the costs of the disaster.

146

Public outcry

Although the catchment basin of the Yangtze has for centuries been subject to flooding, in recent times many citizens have begun to feel that proper measures should be taken against it. Some refugees of the 1998 disaster had even had to save themselves from the rising waters 44 years before. Many Chinese openly questioned the reasons for the disaster. Criticism of the government can be dangerous in China, but it was in fact the Chinese premier, Zhu Rongji, who brought matters to a head, by voicing his explicit opinion in public. "Some of the dikes would seem to be made of tofu," he shouted angrily during an inspection.

He certainly had a point. "In recent years, the population has been paying a heavy price for decades of neglect regarding the rivers and dikes," explained a hydraulic engineer. "Local government is responsible for the greater part of these projects, and that is where it has been going wrong." In fact, local administrators had been embezzling on a grand scale funds intended for dike maintenance. As a result, the maintenance program for many dikes was well behind schedule.

Apart from overdue repairs to the embankments, deforestation as a result of large-scale tree felling was another significant cause of these floods, and many others besides. Little is now left of the forests that once covered great swathes of the Yangtze basin. During the Great Leap Forward at the end of the 1950s, many forests were felled to fuel the small-scale furnaces in the communes. Later, they were cleared for agriculture, because more grain and cotton had to be produced to sustain the burgeoning population. Many trees were also sacrificed in the construction of the Three Gorges Dam. As a result of this deforestation, not only is the soil able to retain less water, but the Yangtze also carries off more mud and sand than in the past. This reduces its discharge capacity, which increases the danger of flooding.

Overflow zones

Additionally, in the decades preceding the disaster, the number of overflow zones had seen a sharp reduction. Countless lakes and marshes had been drained in the 1960s to allow grain to be grown on the reclaimed land. Partly because of this, the buffering capacities of the Dongting Lake and the Poyang Lake had declined from over 1,000 to 530 billion cubic feet (29 to 15 billion cubic meters). Farmers had created fields on the fertile silt, as well as building houses and dikes there. At the time of the disaster, six million people were living in these areas. After the disaster, the government initiated a project to restore thousands of the lost lakes and natural drainage systems so that the river could be better managed during periods of prolonged, heavy rainfall.

Since the floods of 1998, the government has also been attempting to halt tree felling. The province of Sichuan has announced an outright ban on the procedure. Furthermore, even the axes used by lumberjacks were to be requisitioned.

The vehemence of the waters affected the region surrounding Wuhan, a densely populated city of 7 million inhabitants

Ice Storm in Ontario

For more than 80 hours, a series of hailstorms fell, doubling the average annual precipitation in Ontario.

Eastern Ontario
Southeastern Quebec
(Canada)

January 4–10, 1998

40 dead

The courtyard of the University of Vermont, totally frozen.

The hailstorm in Canada in January 1998 was the worst natural catastrophe that peaceful country has suffered in its history. Although Canada is extremely well prepared to withstand cold storms, the 1998 phenomenon exceeded all forecasts, causing severe material damage and several deaths. The prompt action of the authorities and volunteers prevented the disaster being even greater.

A commonplace event

Hail, or frozen rain, is commonplace in Canada and the northeastern states of the U.S.A. The winters of these regions usually bring cold air from the west and moist air from the east. In turn, the east contributes with rainfall and the west with snowfalls. The mixture of the two produces hail. In the neighborhood of Montreal, hailstorms are recorded 12 to 17 times throughout the year, totaling some 65 hours of hail.

On January 4, 1998, a series of meteorological circumstances, and particularly a warm, damp front from the Gulf of Mexico and high pressure from the Atlantic Ocean, projected frozen air between Kingston, Ottawa and the city of Quebec for three days, until the cold front dissipated in the Atlantic. Between January 4 and January 10, 1998, for more than 80 hours, hail fell on an area of thousands of square miles in eastern Ontario and southwestern Quebec. South of Ontario, ordinary precipitation was considerable, while on the coast, snowfalls were intense. Meteorologists announced a fall in temperatures in the area affected by the hailstorm. They were right. The marked fall, recorded by thermometers, exacerbated the situation.

Before the 1998 phenomenon, Canada had experienced several hailstorms. In 1986, Montreal received 2.36 inches (60 mm) of hail. The 1998 storm was much worse, however. The thickness of the hailstones approached 5 ft (1.5 m). The hail destroyed electricity pylons and trees and blocked dozens of streets and communication routes. Days after the disaster, scientists investigating the event reported the amount of hail that had fallen in three days: twice the annual average for the area. Hence, the collapse that occurred.

The ice storm caused great material damage. More than four million residents of the region were left without electricity, especially in southern Quebec, New Brunswick, and eastern Ontario. The lack of electricity adversely affected daily life. Combining that

with the marked drop in temperatures shows us the reason for most of the nearly 40 deaths caused by the storm – hypothermia. Some of the deaths were due to traffic accidents. Roads became unpassable and driving on ice was highly risky. Accidents soon occurred. South of Montreal lie the communities of Saint-Hyacinth, Granby, and Saint-Jean-sur-Richelieu. That area was one of the worst affected by the storm. It was nicknamed the "triangle of darkness." A state of emergency was declared in several cities: Ottawa, Smiths Falls, Ontario, and New Brunswick. On January 7, the situation was unbearable. Quebec, Ontario and New Brunswick were obliged to ask the armed forces for help, which was not long in coming. More than 15,000 soldiers came to the area worst affected by the brutal phenomenon.

Calm is restored

When the storm ended and after electricity was restored in various places, the scene was macabre. Traffic was prohibited in the streets and avenues of Montreal, and some districts and areas with large amounts of ice were even cordoned off by the police because of the risks involved in entering them. Almost a month after the storm, 700,000 residents were still without electricity.

The tragedy caused some 5 billion dollars' worth of material damage. The cultivation of fruit and other products was seriously disrupted, as the ice had destroyed harvests and farm installations. In the barns, livestock suffered the effects of the storm. With no heating, they died of cold. The hundreds of animal deaths caused their owners serious losses.

The recovery operation was conducted by the Canadian army.

It was the first time in Canada's history that the army had been deployed in a natural disaster. Previously, the country's emergency services had sufficed. This time, the deployment of armed forces within the country was the greatest since the Korean War. Most of the troops went to Quebec, Ontario, and New Brunswick and were enthusiastically received by the suffering population. Other rescue teams also helped with the clearance operations. They worked to clear the roads of fallen posts and trees, restore electricity and telephones to houses and buildings, and provide shelter for more than 100,000 people who were suffering the rigors of the cold, as they had no adequate way of heating their homes. More than 6,200 civilians, including the Red Cross and unnamed volunteers, took

part in the rescue and reconstruction work.

Millions of trees collapsed under the weight of the ice, as did 1,000 metal electricity substations and more than 25,000 electricity and telephone poles. Humanitarian aid also came from the United States, which, a few days later, suffered a big hailstorm on its own territory, linked to the one in Canada.

In spite of the beauty of the pictures that were shown on television and in the printed media, ice storms such as the one in 1998 are highly dangerous, and insufficient attention has been paid to them.

Road in Vermont. The ice caused multiple accidents throughout the state, as it did in Canada.

Trees frozen by the hailstorm in Orange County, Vermont. Ninety percent of the trees in the region were severely damaged by the weight of the ice.

Aitape Tsunami

It was impossible to foresee this tsunami: the early warning system works for disasters that affect large regions, but not for such small areas.

PACIFIC

PAPUA-NEW GUINEA
Port Moresby●

Papua New Guinea

July 17, 1998

2,200 dead

One of the Sissano mission buildings in ruins. The mission was the hospital and educational center, and fulfilled other vital community functions.

The terrible tsunami that devastated the north coast of Papua New Guinea in 1998 shows how the absence of precautionary measures regarding natural disasters can have highly negative consequences. If the people of the affected region had received any kind of preparation, the effect of the gigantic waves would have been less severe.

In a seismic zone

Aitape is in northern Papua New Guinea. On July 17, 1998 it was devastated by three giant waves, as were other places nearby. It was not the first time a phenomenon of that kind had reached the island's coasts, although it is true that some time had passed since the last visit by a highly destructive tsunami.

There are reports of the arrival of three different tsunamis, in 1930, 1952, and 1957, so this one was not unusual.

New Guinea lies in a highly active seismic zone. Tectonic plates converge beneath the surface, causing earthquakes that devastate the region. The island and its neighbors have numerous volcanoes. Tremors precede the formation of a tsunami. Violent movements in the seabed cause enough agitation to create waves of great height that advance at high speed, a factor which affects their destructive power.

In the early evening of July 17, a tremor measuring 7 on the Richter scale shook New Guinea. Its epicenter was nearly 400 miles (640 km) out to sea, opposite the small town of Aitape. The tremor caused barely any damage on the large island's surface. It woke a few residents and others who, although taken by surprise, did not pay much attention to it. At that point, reports become somewhat

confused. It is believed that, between 15 and 20 minutes later, the first of the three gigantic waves arrived. As with other tsunamis, witnesses affirmed that they heard a strange sound minutes before the wave arrived. Most described it as the sharp buzz of a fast, low-flying jet. The same was said of the famous Indian Ocean tsunami. The first wave ran parallel to the coast, between the river Bliri and Aitape, in northern New Guinea. A few seconds later, it surged on to the coast, devastating everything in its path. The second and third waves arrived minutes later. Along a coastal fringe of over 25 miles (40 km) the result was devastating.

The worst affected area was the Sissano lagoon. The four villages around it were devastated. The waves were some 40 feet (12 m) high. About 15,000 people lived in the affected area. Some 2,200 of

them died and 4,000 lost their homes. The waves caused most of the deaths when they withdrew from the coast and the inland area. Their force was so great that they dragged away the unfortunate people who had tried to escape. The initial tsunami destroyed several dwellings. The weak buildings of the region could not withstand the enormous strength of the waves. Only those that had been raised on posts remained standing. The water carried off the rest. The Sissano mission church, built on strong concrete foundations and with room for 500 souls, was swept away by the tsunami, only its solid foundations remaining. Not even the small mission hospital withstood the thrust of the three waves. Fifteen days later, corpses were still being found many miles from the affected region, returned by the sea.

Errors

A few hours after the magnitude of the disaster was known, criticisms began to be leveled at the PTWC (Pacific Tsunami Warning Center) set up in 1949. Why had the alarm signal not been given? The entity's management could not have done much to help New Guinea. The alert system works for large-scale tsunamis that threaten large inhabited areas, but not in the case of such a local phenomenon as the Aitape tsunami. Moreover, the brief time between the earthquake and the formation of the wave did not allow enough time to set the required action protocols in motion. As if that were not enough, the possibility of communicating between the nearest station and the affected area was almost non-existent.

The experts who traveled to the devastated villages harshly criticized the authorities and residents of the zone for their extremely poor preparation in the event of a tsunami, an even more serious lapse considering the island's exposure to that danger. The people of the affected coast had had no preventive training. They did not know what to do if a tsunami arrived. The order to run and take refuge in high places was almost unknown – regrettably, as the time between the earthquake and the first wave, 15 to 20 minutes, would have given a sufficient margin to save a good number of people.

Although most of the residents were aware that an earthquake

could be followed by a large wave, most of them did not move, even when they heard the infamous noise announcing the arrival of the phenomenon, a fact which many affirmed that they knew. Some people went down to the beaches to ascertain the source of the noise. Unfortunately, the affected zone had no system for issuing the alarm to neighboring places.

The authorities' pitiful management of the disaster exacerbated the situation. It was hours before the injured were attended to, leading in many cases to amputations and, sadly, deaths resulting from infection. As if that were not enough, in many nearby places it was a public holiday, so the emergency services that came to the

scene of the tragedy were few. It is sad to note that, months after the disaster, when a team of researchers conducted a series of surveys and interviews with survivors and asked the reason for the unleashing of the tsunami, more than 40 percent said that it was a punishment from God, against which nothing could be done.

The Sissano mission church, before (top) and after (bottom) the tsunami.

Hurricane Georges

This hurricane, gusting at 125 miles (200 km) per hour, was so intense that it left hundreds of thousands of people homeless.

Puerto Rico
Dominican Republic
Haiti

September 15–29, 1998

602 dead

A family from Toa Baja, Puerto Rico, in front of the remains of their former home. Georges struck the island severely.

1998 was especially hard for the islands of the Caribbean. Two of the storms in that year produced a level of destruction comparable to that of several hurricane seasons combined. Two storms were the principal cause of the disasters. They were the worst of the twentieth century in the zone and the biggest since the hurricane that struck the Caribbean in 1780.

From Cape Verde to the Caribbean

In 1998, two phenomena were outstanding in that harsh season: hurricanes Mitch and Georges. The latter was the sixth storm to touch North America that year, as well as visiting six other countries. Until then, and since, no other hurricane has made such a tour.

On September 14, meteorologists detected the formation of a tropical depression in the Cape Verde islands. It was to become the only hurricane of 1998 with that point of origin. With unusual speed, 17 hours later, the depression had developed into a tropical storm. It was named Georges. On September 17, its size and speed increased. Georges became a hurricane, the fourth that season after Bonnie, Danielle, and Earl. The rise in temperature in the Atlantic

Ocean favored its growth and rapid movement. On the afternoon of September 18, its winds were in excess of 105 miles (170 km) per hour and moving west. The next day, the winds inside the storm reached 125 miles (200 km) per hour and it continued to advance. When it was positioned over the Leeward Islands on September 19, its winds and speeds decreased considerably, and people in the weather stations breathed sighs of relief. It was a false alarm. A day later, a sudden change of direction sent Georges toward Puerto Rico and Cuba, when it had previously seemed unlikely to touch any island.

Puerto Rico was severely damaged by the passage of the hurricane. Then, it moved toward the mountainous region of Hispaniola. There, its winds again fell to some 70 mph (115 kph). On September 24, it left the island, where it had caused much damage, and moved toward the Florida Keys. In Florida, Miami and Key Biscayne suffered the worst damage. In a new movement that surprised the meteorologists who were tracking its progress, it veered northwest toward the town of Biloxi, Mississippi. That state received the rainfall from the storm, which

caused severe floods. The communities on Dauphin Island, and other places on the south coast of the United States, suffered serious damage to beaches and natural reefs that will take decades to restore. Changing position again, hurricane Georges moved to Alabama and Georgia, where is slowly dissipated on September 29.

The devastation of Georges

In just nine days, hurricane Georges visited the United States, Antigua, Barbuda, St. Kitts, the Virgin Islands, Puerto Rico, the Dominican Republic, Haiti, Cuba, and the Bahamas. A record, especially in that the hurricane's passage caused severe problems in all those territories. The worst affected places were Puerto Rico, the Dominican Republic, Cuba, and Haiti.

In Puerto Rico it caused 12 deaths. Water and electricity supplies were suspended for more than three and a half million inhabitants. About 34,000 homes were destroyed and 50,000 more were severely damaged. Economically, the storm caused the loss of 75 percent of the coffee plantations and 70 percent of the barns where poultry were raised, the staple food of Puerto Rico. The da-

mage was assessed at some two billion dollars. Fortunately, the victims received generous help from the United States.

The story was somewhat worse in the Dominican Republic, with 210 deaths, 500 people missing, and 100,000 people rendered homeless. Infrastructure was severely affected, with 70 percent of bridges were destroyed. The airport was unusable for weeks because of damage to the runways, control tower, and terminals. The amount of stones and trees that fell onto roads because of landslides made 80 percent of communication routes unpassable. For six days, the capital Santo Domingo remained under the influence of the powerful storm. No building escaped at least some damage. For a couple of days, there was no electricity supply or telephone service in most of the country.

On one of the poorest islands of the region, Haiti, 94 people died and 60 disappeared. Floods were severe all over the island. The few bridges its residents had were on the point of collapse. Eighty percent of the banana harvest was destroyed. Days after the hurricane, some 8,000 people were living in temporary shelters.

The winds showed no mercy in Cuba either, especially in the eastern part, which suffered severe floods. Evacuees numbered 340,000; 5 deaths were recorded; more than 2,000 houses were destroyed and 40,000 damaged; and the sugar-cane harvests were devastated.

The islands of St. Kitts and Nevis were severely hit. Three people died and 85 percent of the buildings were damaged. For some hours, damage to the airport prevented the arrival of emergency teams and humanitarian aid.

By the time the storm reached the United States, it had weakened, but it nevertheless caused large floods in Florida and Alabama, leaving some 700,000 residents without electricity and killing two people. In the Florida Keys, in the south of the state, the consequences of the hurricane were the most severe: it destroyed 150 homes, damaged some 900, and seriously affected the reefs of some islands. Georges' devastating tour of the Caribbean and the southern United States cost over 9 billion dollars and 602 lives. Worse, however, was yet to come — hurricane Mitch was to make its appearance only a few weeks later.

A neighborhood of Puerto Rico. In the wake of the strong wind and floods, nothing recognizable remains, except for the fragment of wall behind the group of people in the picture.

Sand buries this mobile home on the coast of Alabama. The remains of the flood are still visible under the building to its right.

October 22 through
November 5, 1998

10,000 dead

Hurricane Mitch

This hurricane, which generated winds of 200 miles (198.84 km) per hour, maintained a score of 5 – the maximum on the Saffir-Simpson scale – for longer than any other hurricane on record.

In Tegucigalpa, Honduras, Mitch swooped down on constructions that were considered resistant. Part of the asphalt from this street disappeared.

A common occurrence

Hurricanes are by no means alien to Central America. These violent storms, which form at sea and often whip up winds of over 70 miles (110 km) per hour form an important part of the atmospheric circulation system that moves heat from the regions close to the Equator to higher latitudes. In fact, Central Americans are so accustomed to hurricanes that the very word originated in one of their ancient cultures: that of the Mayans. Hurakan was the name of the God who breathed across the turbulent waters at the beginning of time, thereby creating the Earth. Unfortunately, however, this close familiarity with hurricanes has done nothing to lessen their devastating impact when they reach the shores of the region.

In 1998, special circumstances made Mitch especially powerful and destructive. The hurricane seasons from 1994 through 1998 had been the most active on record since reliable statistics became available. After the disappearance of El Niño – a meteorological phenomenon that tends to repress hurricanes in the Atlantic – ten hurricanes and five tropical storms occurred in 1998. For the first time since 1893, four hurricanes struck the Atlantic simultaneously in 1998: Georges, Ivan, Jeanne, and Karl.

On October 21, a tropical depression formed in the southern Caribbean; 24 hours later, it turned into a tropical storm, which meteorologists named "Mitch." For a few days the storm barely moved, but then it veered slightly toward the northeast and gathered strength. Between the evenings of October 23 and 26, its intensity heightened so much that it became a hurricane registering 5 on the Saffir-Simpson scale – the highest reading on this scale measuring the strength of a hurricane's winds – with air currents of over 180 miles (290 km) per hour and gusts of up to 200 miles (320 km) per hour. Mitch is the hurricane that has stayed longest in category 5, as well as being the most intense to appear throughout the entire twentieth century and the second most destructive of all time, after the one that battered Martinique in 1780. Even today we do not know exactly how many deaths Mitch caused, but it is somewhere between 10,000 and 16,000.

Mitch over Central America

On October 27, the eye of the storm stopped off the coasts of Honduras and Nicaragua, where it remained for a couple of days, losing some of its strength in the meantime. On October 29, the storm reached the mainland and unleashed rain on the two countries, as well as on Guatemala and El Salvador, on an unprecedented scale.

On October 31 the hurricane gradually left Guatemala and headed toward the Yucatan Peninsula and Gulf of Mexico, where it arrived as a moderate tropical storm on the shores of Florida. It then continued northeastward and on November 9 its last vestiges, now deprived of all destructive

potential, were recorded close to the British Isles. The scenes it left behind in Honduras, Nicaragua, El Salvador, and Guatemala beggar description.

No corner of Honduras escaped the effects of the hurricane. It is estimated that 5,000 people were killed, with 12,000 more injured and 8,000 unaccounted for. The hurricane led to severe food shortages, as well as a lack of medicines and – as is often the case with tropical storms of this intensity – drinking water. Hunger was the order of the day in a great many towns, along with the appearance or aggravation of malaria, dengue fever, cholera, and respiratory diseases. The country's infrastructure was almost entirely destroyed – 70–80 percent of roads and bridges were obliterated and the airports were wrecked. Whole towns were engulfed by water, but attempts to rescue the survivors were severely hindered by the lack of helicopters and reliable boats. Approximately 70 percent of crops were destroyed: large coffee warehouses were flooded and cornfields were devastated. Material losses were calculated at almost 1 billion dollars.

Nicaragua was also ravaged, particularly in the north and northeast. Three thousand people died and almost 20 percent of the country's population was affected by the calamity. On October 30 the heavy rains caused the lake in the Casita Volcano to overflow, setting off an avalanche of mud that swallowed up entire villages, killing over 2,000 people. In some places near the volcano, the local people had to wait until the mud dried before it was safe to walk on it. As in Honduras, Nicaragua lacked drinking water and disease ran rampant in its worst hit regions. Food was also in very short supply, as the harvest that year was devastated. More than 700,000 people were thought to have lost their homes.

El Salvador and Guatemala were also severely affected, although to a lesser degree. In El Salvador the death toll was 374,

Parking lots near the River Choluteca, on the outskirts of Tegucigalpa; most of the vehicles were only good for scrap afterwards.

Swollen rivers resulting from the torrential rain had fatal consequences. Here, the left bank has been pummeled by the water

Devastated houses next to the River Choluteca, destroyed by the advancing mud. Its path into the buildings can be clearly seen.

with around 60,000 evacuated on account of the rain. Most of the corn, coffee, and sugar crops were spoilt. Guatemala lost 268 people, with a further 100,000 transferred by the emergency services. The coffee and banana crops were damaged, but survived better than those of the neighboring countries.

Unfortunately, Mitch was not detected in time, despite all the technological resources available, and many meteorologists were surprised by its intensity. It should be stressed, however, that, over and above the strength of the winds, this hurricane was particularly devastating because it struck a part of the world with little infrastructure capable of withstanding its effects.

Earthquake in Colombia

Amplification of the seismic waves and inappropriate construction methods meant that this disaster had a particularly strong impact on Armenia and Pereira.

Armenia and Pereira (Colombia)

January 25, 1999

1,000 dead

A heavily damaged police station in Armenia, Colombia. Eighteen policemen lost their lives inside.

Rufin School in the neighborhood of Berlin, Armenia. Over 80 years old, it was unable to resist the power of the earthquake.

A church in Barcelona, Colombia. The building collapsed immediately, leaving only reinforced elements like the steel beams and bell tower in place.

The cities of Armenia and Pereira were two oases of prosperity in a Colombia torn apart by undeclared civil war and plunged into serious problems by drug trafficking. The earthquake of January 1999 snatched away their promising future, although international aid and the determination of their inhabitants smoothed the road to recovery.

Double tragedy

The cities of Armenia and Pereira were the capitals of the departments of Quindío and Risaralda, respectively. Armenia had a population of 290,000, while Pereira was bigger, with 700,000 inhabitants. The economies of both cities were based on agriculture, with their main crops being bananas and coffee. Pereira was also an important industrial and commercial center that benefited from close links with Colombia's three foremost cities: Bogotá, Cali, and Medellín.

The epicenter of the earthquake of January 25, 1999 – which registered 6 on the Richter scale – was about 12 miles (20 km) from Armenia and 30 miles (50 km) from Pereira. The tremor struck at 1.19 p.m., but four hours later it was echoed by another of a magnitude of 5.4, which considerably worsened the situation caused by the first one. The epicenter of both tremors occurred deep below the Earth's surface.

This type of tremor is caused by the subduction of the Nazca Plate, although virtually no vertical movement was detected on the fault line (in contrast to the earthquakes on the San Andreas Fault in California).

Even though the earthquake was of only moderate intensity, it wreaked tremendous destruction. According to the experts, there were two main causes for the extent of the devastation: amplification and the construction methods used in the two cities. Amplification is a geological phenomenon that causes thick alluvial layers of subsoil to act as resonators of seismic waves, thereby intensifying their strength.

As for the buildings in Armenia and Pereira, these were very similar. Three main techniques were predominant: *bahareque*, brick, and reinforced cement. *Bahareque* is a traditional building system based on the use of strips of *guadua* – a type of bamboo – adobe walls, and roofs made with mud and plant fibers. In Pereira, many of the brick buildings had no reinforcement whatsoever, as they predated the 1940s. Armenia was a city that had expanded enormously in the last 15 years – it was nicknamed "Miracle City" – albeit with a chaotic lack of planning or building controls. Pereira had had extensive experience of earthquakes, as it had endured four over the course of the nineteenth century. The most recent earthquake – the Calima-Darien – had occurred only four years previously, causing losses to the value of 50 million dollars.

The damage done

More than thirty municipalities were hit by the 1999 earthquake, with Armenia and Pereira bearing the brunt of the damage. The death toll in Armenia was 543, along with 1,700 serious injuries, and 60 percent of its buildings were severely damaged. In Pereira, there were fewer dead (44) and injured (650), but some 400 buildings were destroyed.

The damage in Armenia was concentrated in the south and the city center. These were the oldest parts and most of their buildings lacked the earthquake-resistance measures that the Columbian government had made compulsory in 1984. Approximately 90 percent of the buildings in these areas collapsed, as was also the case in other neighborhoods like Cónica and Brasilia. The alleyways of Armenia were invaded by debris, human suffering, and serious health problems, as almost the entire city was deprived of drinking water within minutes. Both the police station and the fire station were severely hit by the earthquake, with dozens of people dying inside them – with a subsequent lack of public employees trained for rescue missions or in humanitarian aid.

In Pereira, the destruction was also concentrated in the oldest area, the historic center. Experts from various countries arrived on the scene a few days after the earthquake; in all, it is reckoned that some 520 buildings had to be demolished to guarantee safety.

The emergency services in Quindío were completely overwhelmed. Their disorganization and lack of coordination became apparent over the course of the rescue operation, along with their almost total lack of material resources to confront the disaster. Little heavy machinery was available and, furthermore, many roads had been left in a deplorable state and become impassable. Hospitals were unable to cope with the patients who flocked to their doors. The situation became so acute that it was finally decided to evacuate 400 of the injured to other nearby cities.

The response of volunteers, firemen, police, and other organizations was more efficient in Pereira, despite even more crushing blows to its infrastructure – perhaps its

experience in this type of crisis stood the city and its inhabitants in good stead.

The day after the earthquake, the Columbian government announced a series of financial measures to assist those affected by the disaster, and also declared its intention to formulate action plans in the event of an earthquake to tighten up building regulations.

Volunteers arrived from all over the country to collaborate in the rescue operation in Pereira, and

this show of solidarity was all the more heartwarming in the light of Colombia's dire social and economic problems. Despite the country's difficulties, the authorities generally proved to be a match for the situation and earned the esteem of the population.

Earthquake in Izmit

The geological structure of Anatolia makes it the European region most vulnerable to earthquakes.

Anatolia
(Turkey)

August 17, 1999

17,000 dead

This building in the city of Sakarya caved in on account of lique-faction, although its walls, like those of its neighbors, remained standing.

In 1999, the Turkish region of Anatolia grabbed the headlines. It was not its architectural treasures or beautiful landscapes that had attracted attention but one of the earthquakes to which it is frequently subjected. It was not the first, nor will it be the last, but it was the worst one for decades.

Anatolia, land of earthquakes

If there is one area in Europe particularly vulnerable to earthquakes, it is Anatolia. Its unusual geological structure has meant that earthquakes have become part of life here.

The 1999 earthquake was caused by movements of the Anatolia Fault against the plates of Africa, Eurasia, and Arabia. More than 300 miles (500 km) of the Anatolia Fault are in constant movement toward the north, and this has caused frequent tremors for many years. Seismologists estimate that over 20,000 earthquakes have taken place in this area since 1964. Its inhabitants know only too well that they are at risk, but, however accustomed they are to this fact, events like that of August cannot fail to leave a deep mark.

It was 3:02 a.m. when a tremor of 7.4 on the Richter scale brutally rocked Anatolia. Its epicenter was in the city of Gölcük, from where it extended along a radius of over 12 miles (20 km), leaving behind it a trail of death and destruction that few of the locals had ever witnessed.

The tremor gave rise to fissures in the ground over 75 miles (125 km) long and lateral movements of up to 16 ft (5 m), which is rarely the case in a European earthquake. The cities most affected were Gölcük, Kocaeli, Sakarya, Yalova, and Istanbul. Minutes after the tremor, a gigantic wave in the Bay of Izmir crashed into various ports, destroying cranes, boats, and containers. It proved impossible to prevent the Tupras refinery from exploding fiercely several times, causing a conflagration that lasted two days, but fortunately did not reach any populated areas. A whole section of Gölcük was flooded as a result of the tsunami. The Istambul–Ankara railroad line was heavily damaged and remained out of action for two days. The buildings in the affected cities toppled like houses of cards, crushing thousands of their occupants.

In the following hours, the rescue teams' hardest task was to free the children and elderly people trapped under the rubble. Some succeeded in surviving for up to nine days, but the overall reckoning was desolate: 17,000 dead — although some sources raise this figure to 45,000 — and over 40,000 injured.

Unfortunately, the Turkish government's handling of the disaster proved hopelessly inadequate and the NGOs that arrived on the scene denounced cases of corruption. The material losses were also very severe, with 15,400 buildings destroyed and nearly 120,000 suffering extensive damage. One of the problems associated with housing in earthquake situations is people's tendency to return home before even minimal repairs have been made. These houses are in great danger of collapsing, even if no new earthquake occurs. In this respect, however, the Turkish government did rise to the occasion, by providing over 112,250 tents and 25,000 prefabricated homes.

Foreign aid arrived almost immediately. Spain, France, Greece, Russia, and Germany sent their top rescue teams, along with heavy machinery to clear the debris and dogs trained to sniff out buried survivors. The portable hospitals provided by various countries also proved invaluable, as the Turkish medical services were unable to offer adequate treatment to the many thousands of wounded. The material losses are difficult to quantify even today. It has been suggested that they could amount to 20 billion

dollars, although some commentators have come up with the marginally more optimistic estimate of 10 billion.

Months after the disaster, Anatolia was hit by another earthquake, in Duzce, 90 miles

(150 km) from Istanbul. The experts think that this was one of a series of reactions to the first tremor on August 17. Despite being an earthquake of similar intensity – 7.2 – the death count was much lower as the afflicted area was far less densely populated.

A gloomy future

Even before the catastrophe, Anatolia had been closely monitored by geologists. A major earthquake like that of 1999 was foreseeable, although not inevitable. It is now a top priority for Turkey to prevent another disaster of this scale, particularly in Anatolia, which contains 25 percent of the country's population and much of its industry.

Another factor to be taken into account is the enormous appeal of this region to foreign visitors. The income generated by tourism is a precious asset, and its loss due to calamities like the so-called Kocaeli earthquake or the Anatolia Fault would

deliver the country a further heavy blow.

After this appalling disaster, state-of-the-art monitoring systems have increasingly been installed, particularly with respect to the fault under the Marmara Sea. Geologists believe that this fault could snap in one go, giving rise to a single big earthquake, or could splinter into various pieces, producing various earthquakes of less intensity. In either case, the main target will undoubtedly be Istanbul, which could even be wiped off the map. Both the country's authorities and its scientific community are trying to avoid this by equipping this major capital city with the best possible earthquake detection systems.

Apartment block in the city of Golcuk. Fortunately, it was in the process of being built so nobody was inside at the time of the earthquake.

A store in the city of Sakarya. Its ground floor barely resisted the tremor, giving it this bizarre appearance.

Earthquake in Taiwan

The area's topographical conditions and inaccessibility meant that it was several days before the outside world appreciated the full magnitude of this disaster.

Taiwan

September 21, 1999

2,400 dead

The lack of a reinforced structure saw the portico and part of the garage of this house giving way.

This unfortunate car was trapped under the weight of an apartment building in Dongshi.

The earthquake that hit Taiwan in 1999 was the worst this island experienced in the whole of the twentieth century. Despite all the preventive measures that had been in force for years, the damage was extremely extensive. Nature was the chief culprit, obviously, but many local property developers had put thousands of lives at risk purely for their own financial benefit.

Taiwan, a high-risk area

Taiwan is one of the most seismologically active regions in Asia, lying as it does at the meeting point of the small Philippines Plate and the huge Eurasian Plate. The collisions and subductions of these two plates pose a threat to the former Nationalist China. These phenomena lead to earthquakes, mainly in Taiwan, but also in the Philippines, Japan, and Indonesia, with disturbances from the Eurasian Plate being the main culprit.

When the tremor struck, Taiwan had experienced more than six decades without any earthquakes measuring over 7 on the Richter scale. Geologists believe that the cycles for earthquakes of this scale last 15 years in a seismological zone of this kind, so this long respite was an anomaly. In March 1999, however, scientists from Taiwan's meteorological stations began warning of the possibility of a substantial

earthquake – and with good reason, as on September 21, at 1:47 a.m., a dramatic tremor of 7.6 on the Richter scale rocked the island. Its epicenter lay at a depth of 4 miles (7 km) on the outskirts of the city of Ji-Ji – hence the popular name of the Ji-Ji earthquake – in the district of Nantou, some 95 miles (160 km) to the southeast of the capital, Taipei.

In the next few hours, Taiwan was further shaken by dozens of strong aftershocks, which greatly hindered the rescue operation and finally destroyed many of the buildings left standing after the initial tremor. The earthquake severely affected the districts of Nantou and Taichung, which were vacation spots for thousands of the island's inhabitants. Nearby regions on the Chinese mainland, such as Fujian and Zhejian, were also hit, though fortunately suffered no casualties. Electricity and water supplies were cut off in the disaster areas, along with all means of communication – even cell phones were rendered useless.

Furthermore, the rugged, mountainous landscape of Nantou and Taichung prevented the full extent of the disaster from being known for several days. The roads were gashed by fissures of various depths, or their asphalt was twisted out of recognition, so the region's towns

and cities could only be reached by air, but the rescue helicopters only flew out once, as it proved too risky for their crews to venture into the area – it must not be forgotten that tremors were still constantly occurring and could happen anywhere at any time.

The survivors of the catastrophe set about looking for their loved ones under the rubble, even after the first emergency teams arrived. Almost a week later, the situation was still chaotic. International aid had arrived – 14 countries helped clear the debris and provide healthcare – and the Taiwanese rescue services and army had both reached the scene. The effects of the disaster were so far-reaching that they proved very difficult to alleviate. Homeless people were living as best they could in the streets or in shelters supplied by the government, but some of these stood next to piles of decomposing corpses, which increased the danger of epidemics. The morgues were also out of action, due to the lack of electricity, which made the situation even more hazardous. The material losses amounted to 9 billion dollars.

Construction practices in Taiwan

It has been reckoned that over 44,000 buildings were damaged, and in many cases completely destroyed, leaving over 100,000

people without a home. This took many architects and experts by surprise. Even though the instability of Taiwan's soil was no secret, these results were still not normal. In 1997, Taiwan had introduced regulations for construction and safety that took into account the risk of earthquakes. This legislation was based on American and Japanese models, and was therefore extremely coherent. In fact, when it was unveiled it was hailed as one of the most advanced of its kind in the world, and it remains so to this day. As far as many property developers and architects were concerned, however, the regulations were not worth the paper they were written on, and they ignored them to save money on construction materials.

In Nantou and Taichung, most of the buildings had been built to take into account only earthquakes of 6 on the Richter scale, in blatant disregard of the law. In the city of Douliu, five of the apartment buildings that collapsed had been built by the same company; plastic bottles and cans had been used to insulate and reinforce the walls, instead of bricks. In Taipei, a modern, 12-story building that toppled over as a result of the earthquake turned out to have been built with cheap, illegal cement.

These are just some of the examples of the construction practices that led the Taiwanese government to investigate the dealings of over a thousand architects and property developers. The penalties for non-

compliance with the building regulations went up to five years in prison, as well as heavy fines. Regrettably, it transpired that some of the guilty firms had contacts with government institutions; to damper the flames of scandal, it was decided to offer generous subsidies to those affected by the disaster – a gesture that could do nothing to bring back to life the 2,400 people who had perished.

A great many people had been injured, too – somewhere in the region of 10,000. To cap it all, there

was an enduring sense of insecurity and defenselessness on the part of the Taiwanese population, which remains exposed to the possibility of future earthquakes, without knowing whether its houses are sufficiently prepared to withstand them.

Tornado in Oklahoma

This tornado, which caused material losses in excess of 1.1 billion dollars, is the worst ever to affect the United States.

Oklahoma, Kansas, and Texas

May 3–6, 1999

53 dead

The tornado that devastated Oklahoma in 1999 had an enormous destructive power; 42 of its citizens were killed by the disaster.

The interior of what was once a kitchen in a house ravaged by the tornado.

Tornadoes can occur anywhere in the world, but the United States has proved particularly susceptible to these meteorological phenomena. In 1999, one of the worst tornadoes on record buffeted Oklahoma for three whole days.

Tornado country

Tornadoes are violent windstorms typical of the American Midwest and South, but they can occur anywhere from Britain to Asia. The tornado season in the United States generally stretches from March through October, although a tornado can spring up at any time of the year. (They usually strike in the evening.) Around one thousand tornadoes hit American soil every year, causing about fifty deaths and millions of dollars' worth of damage.

The strength of a tornado is measured by means of the Fujita-Pearson scale, which classifies it from F0 to F5 according to the readings of a Doppler impulse radar or the extent of the devastation. F5 tornadoes are very rare; only 1 percent of those that strike the United States reach this level, but they do occur – and the tornado that pounded Oklahoma in May 1999 was one of them. To be more exact, no less than 66 tornadoes swept through various parts of Oklahoma and Kansas – which

are well accustomed to tornadoes, as we know from *The Wizard of Oz* – the biggest cluster ever known in these states.

May 3, 1999 seemed to be just like any other day: it was warm and sunny, but this fine weather was not to last. The state meteorological bureaus announced a brusque change in the weather around mid-morning and forecast the possibility of thunderstorms and tornadoes. The experts agreed that the conditions were ideal for the appearance of more than a few tornadoes. In the afternoon, the skies started to darken, and before long thunderclaps were heard up and down Oklahoma. The tornadoes did not wait long before making their dramatic entrance.

At 7:00 p.m. on May 3, strategically situated radars detected a tornado of over 250 miles (400 km) per hour heading for Moore, Oklahoma. This speed automatically classified it as an F5 tornado. The strong winds ran amok in Moore before turning their attention to nearby towns like Newcastle, Bridge Creek, Midwest City, and Del City. Other smaller tornadoes formed elsewhere in the state: Stroud was particularly hard hit, as a Class F4 tornado descended on it and completely destroyed its shopping center. Another F4 ravaged Mulhall, shattering even

strong structures like water towers. For three whole days, storms in the form of a tornado battered not only Oklahoma and Kansas, but also parts of Texas, leaving in its wake six dead in Kansas, five in Texas, and forty-two in Oklahoma. A huge amount of data was recorded during this time, and hopefully these will serve in the future to make more reliable predictions about these phenomena. At present, despite our extensive knowledge of tornadoes, it is difficult to anticipate how they will behave and how long they will last. Technological progress has enhanced this research, but much work still remains to be done.

After the storm

The tornadoes caused a huge amount of damage. Apart from the 53 casualties, they destroyed around 10,500 homes and 47 business premises, such as office blocks, small factories, shopping malls, etc. The material damages amounted to over 1.1 billion dollars, making it the most costly tornado in the history of the United States. It was also the most deadly since the Wichita Falls tornado in Texas, which killed 42 people in 1979. Fortunately, a battery of warnings prior to the catastrophe saved many lives. Radio and television programs were interrupted to warn of the arrival of the tornadoes, and some local TV stations even dared to follow the story at close hand to provide regular information of their exact whereabouts, creating a cocktail of professional newsgathering and sensationalism.

Some of the deaths were the result of misguided attempts to seek shelter. Faced with the arrival of the tornado in Oklahoma City, many terror-struck people took refuge under the bridges of the Interstate highways, or at the intersections of their overpasses with the streets of the city, such as the junction of 16th Street and Interstate 44.

One of the recommendations in the event of a tornado is to search for refuge. The ideal is an underground shelter, like a basement, but, in its absence, the best alter-

native is a windowless room in the center of a building with no access to air currents. Seeking shelter under a bridge is extremely risky, as the structure covers anybody underneath, and is exposed to air on the sides. This imprudence – highly understandable, as it is difficult to react rationally in such circumstances – cost three people their lives and resulted in injuries to several dozens more. The strong winds of the tornado swept along debris that crashed against these improvised shelters, sometimes causing injury.

Tornadoes are undoubtedly spectacular, but they are also highly dangerous. The case presented here is not an isolated incident and could easily be repeated. States like Oklahoma and Kansas are well aware of this and will surely be fully prepared when the next tornado season comes around.

Hundreds of vehicles like the one in this photograph were wrecked, along with over 1,500 buildings.

Caracas and the state
of Vargas, Venezuela

December 15–16,
1999

30,000 dead

Mudslides in Venezuela

An estimated 30,000 dead, 20,000 wounded, thousands made homeless, and 100,000 homes destroyed or damaged: these were the sorry statistics the Venezuelan authorities had to compile following the winter of 1999, when avalanches of rubble and mudslides hit the north of the country.

The mudslides swept entire slums from the hillsides in the vicinity of Caracas. The coastal area to the north of the capital city, Caracas, was overwhelmed beneath avalanches of rubble, gigantic boulders, and rivers of mud coming from the El Ávila massif, a mountain range that separates Caracas from the Caribbean Sea. The mudslides and avalanches of rubble on December 15 and 16, 1999 were the result of extreme rainfall, which caused landslides in the high mountains. The rocky debris strewing the slopes became saturated and unstable, and slid down the steep inclines. The amount of rain that Venezuela received over a two-week period was 24 times more than the monthly average. Rivers of mud and debris carried away houses, trees, cars, and people on their downward rush from Ávila, ultimately coming to rest at a depth of several feet or flowing into the Caribbean. Pictures of the landscape and satellite images still show where boulders, debris, and mud ended up in the sea and at the foot of the mountain range.

Ghost towns

In the northern state of Vargas, which was worst hit, over 20,000 people met their deaths and 20,000 houses were destroyed. The airport and harbor were badly damaged. The university campus was buried under a blanket of mud. The damage caused proved largely irreparable. Other states located further west, such as Falcón, Yaracuy, Zulia, and Táchira, also sustained heavy losses.

Like many other coastal settlements, the resort of Caraballeda to the north of Caracas turned into a ghost town. Boulders the size of cars rolled down the mountainside, flattening the houses in their path. Victims were buried alive in mud.

In the capital, losses were "limited" to 40 dead, with the complete destruction of 1,500 homes and damage to 4,500 others. It was, however, the slums in the immediate vicinity of Caracas, built on spurs of the El Ávila range, which took the full brunt of the disaster, the flimsy dwellings being no match for the force of the rockslides and mudflows. A dam failed in the state of Miranda to the east of Caracas. In other parts of the country, airports suffered damage. Around 750,000 acres (300,000 hectares) of agricultural land were laid waste, and major blows sustained by the tourism and fishing sectors. Afterward, economists calculated the total financial loss at two percent of Venezuela's gross national product.

Migration

Dozens of countries provided relief supplies and loans, but not all this aid succeeded in getting to the right destination at the time of the catastrophe. The authorities, which initially underestimated the scale of the disaster, had been largely concerned with political issues arising from the new constitution that had been approved by a referendum during the same period. President Chávez, who had been in office for exactly one year when the calamity occurred and was extremely popular among the poorer sections of the population, traveled through the country to raise the spirits of his people. At least 130,000 were evacuated to safety in the first week of the disaster, but many of the homeless were still sheltering six months afterward in tents or temporary relief facilities, such as sport centers, schools and military barracks.

Politicians blamed the large number of victims caused by the natural disaster on the haphazard proliferation of slums on the slopes of the El Ávila range. The Chávez government wanted to prevent the slums from being rebuilt and, immediately after the disaster, started to implement a previously drafted emigration plan, the intention of which was to initiate a flow of migrants from the overpopulated north to the more sparsely inhabited interior further south. This was not, however, a popular move among many Venezuelans, three-quarters of whom live in poverty.

La Niña

The extreme rainfall in 1999 is connected with the climatological phenomenon known as "La Niña:" a cold period in the eastern and central regions of the Pacific Ocean cau-

Buildings in La Guaira, Venezuela, about 12 miles (20 km) north of the capital city, Caracas, cut off by rivers of mud

sed by disturbance of the ocean currents as a result of strong trade winds. La Niña is the meteorological "sibling" of the far more powerful, and more frequent, phenomenon of El Niño: a period in which, conversely, the equatorial ocean is warmer than average. El Niño owes its name to the fact that the temperature change usually reaches its peak just before Christmas: thus El Niño refers to the Christ child.

For many Venezuelans, however, the natural disaster that had overwhelmed them was explicable neither by meteorology nor climatology. They saw the mudslides as a punishment from God. Even the Mayor of Caracas was convinced that a divine hand was punishing the country. According to the beliefs of some, the sin lay in the verbal battle engaged in by politicians who opposed the position of the Roman Catholic Church against the new constitution.

Man removing mud from his devastated home in Caracas

Water streams through the slums of Los Erasos, on the outskirts of Caracas, carrying off shanty dwellings, rubble, and mud

Heat waves in the United States

Two heat waves across large parts of the United States in 1995 and 1999 were responsible for serious agricultural losses and took hundreds of people's lives in major cities such as Chicago and St. Louis.

USA Chicago
Washington D.C. ●
St. Louis

PACIFIC   ATLANTIC

The Midwest and
northeastern US

July 1995 and July
1999

Estimated 1,300 dead

A spurting fire
hydrant provides both
drinking water and
respite from the heat
in Chicago, Illinois

One of a total of over
100 victims of the
heat wave in Chicago

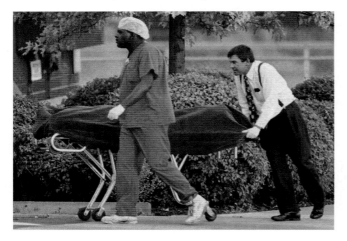

The months from April through July 1999 were the driest on record in the states of New Jersey, Delaware, Maryland, and Rhode Island in the northeast of America. On top of the drought was the heat, which took on an extreme character throughout the month of July, not only in those four states, but also in other states in the Midwest and eastern US. In several states during the final two weeks of that month, temperatures soared above 89.6 °F (32 °C) for more than ten consecutive days. On the night of July 29, the city of Chicago had to contend with an all-time temperature record: just before dawn the following day, generally the coolest time in any 24-hour period, it was 82 °F (27.8 °C). During the day, temperatures of (104 °F) 40 °C were recorded.

Over the course of July, stringent measures were announced in a large number of states to restrict the use of domestic water. Spraying the lawn or hosing down the car with water was forbidden, subject to fines of up to $1,000 or jail terms of up to six months. Water reserves slumped so drastically that in some places freshwater springs became contaminated with salt water, and water mains had to be shut down.

The effect this had on agriculture in the northeastern states was disastrous. Entire harvests of corn, wheat, and soya were lost, and many farmers were forced to sell their dairy herds at reduced prices because they could no longer feed them. The total loss to agriculture was estimated at some $10 billion.

The drought in these states came to an abrupt end when Hurricane

Floyd raced across the country on September 16. This hurricane was accompanied by profuse rainfall, which in some places broke records for the highest amount of precipitation in one day. Thus in the state of Delaware, for example, the drought alert was converted into a flood alert within the space of one day. Hurricane Floyd was responsible for 40 fatalities and caused an estimated billion dollars' worth of damage, largely as a result of flooding.

Death in the cities

Particularly in the larger cities, the 1999 heat wave claimed the lives of many people through dehydration and hyperthermia (excessive heat). This was notably the case in Chicago (Illinois) and St. Louis (Missouri). Both cities had also had to deal with a heat wave in 1995 whose death toll had been extremely high. Although this heat wave was shorter in dura-

tion, it had been somewhat more extreme and had been responsible, in Chicago in particular, for a far greater number of deaths than in 1999. In 1995, 739 people died in Chicago as a result of the heat; in 1999, this figure was 114. In St. Louis, which has a much smaller population than Chicago, there were fewer deaths in 1995 (27) than in 1999 (36). The explanation for this is that the heat wave in Missouri in 1999 was more intense than it had been in 1995.

The large number of deaths in Chicago during the 1995 heat wave can be largely explained by the fact that there had been little preparation for such an event, and that the authorities did too little, too late, in response to it. On July 13, 1995, the first day of the heat wave, the temperature gauge recorded a maximum of 105.8 °F (41 °C). In the days that followed, through to July 20, temperatures remained sweltering. Only

on July 15 did the municipality of Chicago issue a heat warning, and it was some time before emergency measures to protect the citizens were put in place. On the day the heat warning was issued, the mortuary of the Cook County Hospital was already overwhelmed with bodies that the police had found in dwellings and on the street. On any normal day, an average of 17 corpses might be delivered to the hospital, but that day the figure ran into hundreds. During the period of the heat wave, the emergency rooms of the various Chicago hospitals became increasingly unable to cope with the demands of overheated and dehydrated people. Ambulances sometimes had to drive round the city with patients for hours before they could find a place for them. By then, it was sometimes too late.

At times, even the city's inhabitants did not seem fully to appreciate how dangerous the situation could be. There were those who claimed they could stay cool with just an electric fan and an open window, but who were found the next day on the verge of total exhaustion. Many of the fatalities were among elderly people, on whom no one had taken the time to check: they died isolated and alone in their homes.

Emergency measures

The fact that there were fewer victims in Chicago in 1999 was due to the measures and emergency plans put in place following the 1995 heat wave. "Cooling centers" were set up in public buildings and schools for people who did not have air conditioning at home. Transport to these centers was free of charge, with buses being sent to collect people from their homes. Through a network of social organizations, calls were made everywhere on the elderly and people living alone to see whether they needed help. There was also a special subsidy scheme to compensate poorer residents for higher utility costs as a result of using air conditioning.

Chicago in 1999 did, however, have to contend with power outages due to greater demands being placed on the electricity supply. On July 30, the power from two substations failed, leaving 72,000 people electricity—a situation that was to last for 3 days for approximately 10,000 of them. Various electrified trains came to a standstill during the rush hour, packed full of commuters on their way home. They were trapped in their seats, unable to leave overheating cars, and some had to endure waits of over an hour before the police and fire department could free them.

In St. Louis, three highways around the city had to be closed because the road surface had buckled and split open. There were also problems and fatalities as a result of the heat in Kansas City (Missouri), Cincinnati (Ohio), and Milwaukee (Wisconsin).

Since 1999, the United States has had to deal with heat waves on several occasions. The most recent, in the summer of 2006, claimed a number of lives, particularly in California. It was not, however, as extreme as the heat wave of 1999. Nevertheless, weather experts anticipate that, partly due to global climate change, the United States will have to manage more of such heat waves in the near future.

Parched land in Loudon County, Virginia, a state declared a disaster zone, like parts of Kentucky, Ohio, Maryland, and Pennsylvania

Tropical storm Allison

The floods occasioned by this storm were the worst Houston experienced in its entire history.

Houston
(United States)

June 5–19, 2001

41 dead

Tropical storms have frequently reached the coasts of the United States. On many occasions they take on their most powerful form, i.e., that of a hurricane, and on others they remain tropical storms forewarning a hurricane, but without growing into this dreaded phenomenon. Even if they are not full-fledged hurricanes however, they can still spell danger for any region in their path. In fact, the 2001 tropical storm known as Allison displayed behavior more typical of a hurricane.

Erroneous predictions

The year 2001 was marked by hurricanes Iris and Michelle, which both caused substantial damage, but the most significant and problematic meteorological phenomenon was not a hurricane – it was tropical storm Allison. The storm initially emerged in early June in the Gulf of Mexico, a few hundred miles off the coast of Texas, where meteorologists watched its every move.

They accorded it little importance, however, as its winds did not exceed 60 miles (100 km) per hour and there was no sign of it turning into a hurricane. Two days later it reached the Texan coastline, bringing torrential rain that caused flooding in Kemah. Neighboring Galveston was also heavily hit by rain. In the end, it proved to be the storm that has reaped the greatest loss of life in the United States: some 6,000 people were killed. Galveston, now a popular vacation resort, was hastily evacuated.

Let us not forget that Galveston had been devastated by an infamous hurricane in 1900 (see pp 30–31), but the area struck by the waves caused by Allison was not protected by the levees put up after that fateful event. Waves of over 7 ft (2 m) high and constantly pounding rain led to serious flooding along the seafront, as well as washing away its lovingly tended beaches. As the waves and rain intensified, the coastal roads began to take a battering. On June 7, the storm arrived in Houston, though the rain caused only minor flooding as the waters receded as Allison headed toward Lufkin. Everything happened more or less

according to the forecasts of the experts, apart from the surprising drama of events in Galveston. On June 8, however, the storm suddenly veered in the direction of Houston once again. The second coming proved calamitous, as the torrential rain created a whole host of problems. The bayous – the wetlands typical of Texas and the southern states – around Houston could not absorb the rain and overflowed. The city center registered downpours of over 10 inches (250 mm) per hour, while the rainfall in the Port of Houston broke all state records, with over 36 inches (920 mm) per hour on the morning of June 9. The floods overwhelmed the city authorities.

After pummeling Houston, Allison went on its way toward eastern Texas and southern Louisiana, flooding the cities of Beaumont, Baton Rouge, and New Orleans, despite the fact that it was now a subtropical system. Days later, it would cause significant damage in the distant state of Pennsylvania, before blowing itself out in the North Atlantic on June 19. During its stay in American territory, Allison helped spark off 23 tornadoes, from June 11 through 16: ten in South Carolina, four in Mississippi, three in Florida, two in Alabama, another two in Georgia, and one each in Louisiana and Virginia. As was to be expected, they left a trail of destruction in their wake.

Houston under water

The flooding caused by tropical storm Allison in Houston was without precedent in the city. Over 70,000 buildings were damaged and almost 200,000 lost their electricity supply. The Texas Medical Center had to evacuate most of its patients in the dark, in appalling sanitary conditions. The water destroyed the hospital's emergency generators, as was the case with the local universities. Houston is one of the most important centers for scientific

This house was dragged by the floodwaters to the banks of a small river. Its structure remained remarkably intact.

Tropical storm Allison over Louisiana and part of Texas. It was directly responsible for 20 deaths and material losses of a billion dollars.

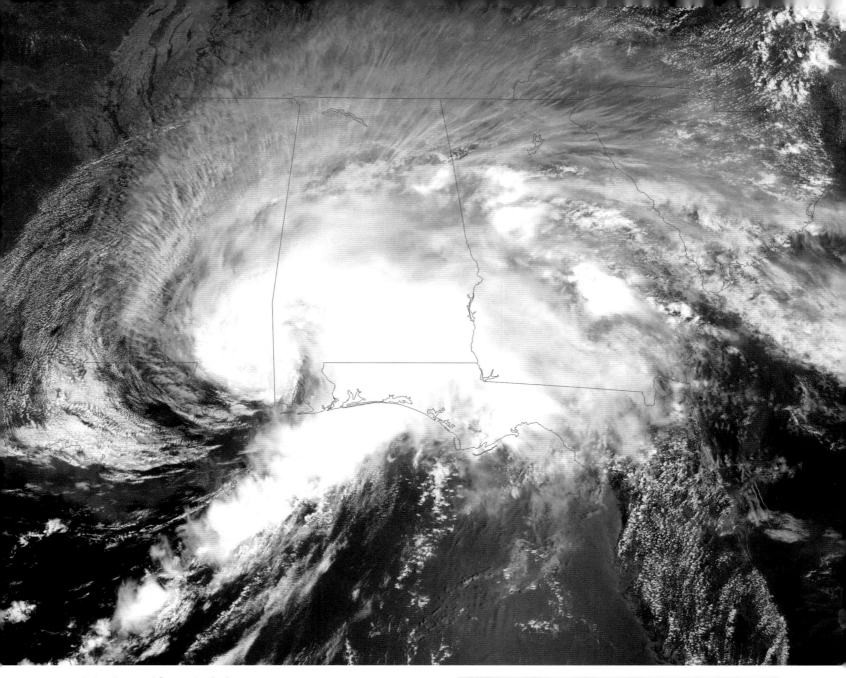

research in the world, particularly with respect to medicine, but many laboratories were paralyzed by the lack of electricity and the extreme conditions, and some projects suffered serious setbacks as a result. In the city center, underground tunnels and garages, as well as entire streets, were flooded, destroying a large number of cars and properties. The television studios in the area had to stop broadcasting, on account of power cuts and equipment failure. Normal service was resumed after a few hours, however; a timely satellite connection allowed those residents still with electricity to follow the progress of the storm.

Tropical storm Allison left 41 dead in its wake; half of these died in the floods, the remainder from tornadoes, outsize waves, or accidents caused by the heavy rainfall.

Once the storm had lulled and reconstruction work had begun in Houston, a recovery program was set into motion for those afflicted by the disaster; this is still in force today, and has allowed many people to benefit from healthcare and a new home.

Dozens of trucks, like the one in the photo, took days to clear and transport the debris left by Allison.

Flooding in La Paz, Bolivia

The floods on "Black Tuesday" in the Bolivian capital of La Paz were the fault, in part, of both the government and the citizens. Drainage channels had been blocked, and areas that should have been left as open space had been densely developed.

La Paz, Bolivia

February 19, 2002
69 dead

On February 19, 2002, La Paz was struck by exceptionally bad weather that featured intense deluges of rain and hailstones together with thunderstorms. In just one hour, 1.5 inches (39.4 mm) of rain fell— a record amount in the history of the city. As a result of the severe rainfall, the Choqueyapu and Irpavi Rivers burst their banks.

La Paz is extremely vulnerable to flooding because of its geographical position. The city lies in a valley in the Andes at a height of around 11,800 ft (3,600 m), while the peaks of the surrounding mountain range rise to over 21,000 ft (6,400 m). The ground is hard and dry, so that precipitation is not easily absorbed; surface water therefore seeks the shortest route downhill instead. Although even La Paz is accustomed to the rain and hail storms typically occurring throughout the Andes mountains, the downpours on "Black Tuesday," as Bolivians were later to name that day, were unparalleled in their extent.

The floods created swirling rivers through the streets of the city. The water carried off everything in its path: sidewalk paving, street cobbles, streetlamps, trees,

cars, and people. Many residents sought refuge in their homes, attempting to reach the topmost floor or roof to escape the torrents of water. The hailstorms alone caused a great deal of damage and suffering, particularly outside the city. Whole harvests were devastated and, in the small town of Capinota to the south of La Paz, considerable numbers of livestock perished. By the time the storm had run its course, the ground in some places had been covered in a layer of hailstones over 4 inches (10 cm) deep.

The poor suffered most

The poorer inhabitants of La Paz bore the brunt of the floods. Self-erected and with poor foundations, their humble homes were no match for the violence of the water. Many street vendors also became casualties. Some 2,000 small shops and stalls were destroyed. The waters also invaded a warehouse at the Plaza Eguino, where 246 market traders and street vendors had stored their goods.

Yolanda León, a woman who sold candy on the street, had by chance left her children at home that day. Normally, she would have

taken her five little ones with her, but it would seem that she must have had a premonition. At her usual place on Avenida Ismael Montes, she was standing next to her friend and colleague, Filomena, when a massive hailstorm broke out. They both went to shelter under an awning, but soon noticed that the street was filling with more and more water. They were able to save themselves only by crossing the street to higher ground, but to do so they had to wade through the seething tumult. They decided to risk it, but the force of the water was so strong they lost their bearings. A stranger grabbed Yolanda's hand and pulled her to dry land, but she saw Filomena being swept away. She was never to see her again.

Elena Ticona Aguilar lived with her daughter, son, and seven grandchildren in a humble mud-built house on land close to the river. When the thunderstorm began, the river water rose within only a few minutes to reach her home. Her daughter, Justina, sensed danger immediately gathered the grandchildren together, and sent them off to higher ground. But Elena wanted to stay and save as many things as

Bolivian firemen rescue people after a hailstorm in downtown La Paz

Clearing up the havoc wrought by the violent storms and flooding in La Paz

A fireman in La Paz inspects wooden supports preventing houses from collapse

she could from the house. As she was doing this, the walls of the house collapsed inward under the pressure from the water. Elena managed to get at foothold on a ledge. Her son, Hernán, threw her a garden hose, which she was only just able to catch hold of. In the meantime, water was churning straight through the house. With the help of Justina and a few neighbors, Elena was finally hauled to safety. The whole house with all its contents had by then entirely disappeared.

Many people were rescued from their cars or from the water through the swift actions of citizens, policemen, and firemen. Though national and international assistance geared up relatively quickly, it was not without its problems. Over five hundred homeless people were accommodated in the Coliseo Cerrado, a covered sports stadium. They were still there one week after the disaster, dressed in the same clothing they were wearing when the floods first began, and with little to eat or drink. Witnesses said that poor migrants from the country had abused the situation, by registering as victims with the aid organization working there in order to get food and clothing that was intended for the refugees.

Criticisms

The authorities in La Paz came down for a great deal of criticism following the flooding. Scientists and environmental activists pointed to the fact that, over the years, large plots of land designated for parks or agricultural use had been illegally built upon. It was precisely these zones that would have been of such importance during the heavy rainfall, as they would have absorbed a great deal of the water. Furthermore, attention was drawn to the fact that La Paz had far too few deep bore drainage wells to its sewerage system. Also, in many places, the road surface was too high in relation to the sidewalks. According to experts, the difference should be at least 10 inches (25 cm) in order to ensure the efficient discharge of water but, due to constant new road works and additional layers of asphalt, this measurement had slumped to barely 2 inches (5 cm) in many spots. The authorities were not alone in taking criticism, however. The residents of La Paz themselves were held responsible for unnecessarily clogging the streets with trash, causing drains to become blocked, and

felling trees illegally.

Nevertheless, it does not seem that many lessons have been learnt from the disaster. Scarcely a year later, on January 22, 2003, La Paz was again assailed by an intense thunderstorm and flooding occurred once more. This time the number of fatalities was limited to three. Immediately after the flooding, municipal workers set to work on cleaning out blocked drains and gutters.

In January 2006, floods again ravaged large areas of Bolivia, destroying houses, roads, schools, and bridges. Twenty people lost their lives. It is estimated that nearly 400 square miles (100,000 hectares) of agricultural land were washed away; there were severe food shortages and 34,000 families lost their homes.

Colorado forest fires

Nearly 613,000 acres (248,000 hectares) of woodland were destroyed by fire in the United States in 2002. The federal government's response to this disaster was exemplary.

Inferno in Colorado

When a fire goes out of control in a woodland setting, there is always a possibility that it will lead to death and major material damage. Unfortunately, the frontier between Nature and civilization is becoming increasingly smaller, so nowadays a forest fire often springs up close to urban areas. There are a number of causes for these fires. An electric storm can shoot down rays of lightning that set light to trees, but most of these blazes are of human origin. A cigarette butt or the smoldering remains of a barbecue can spark off veritable disasters, quite unintentionally; on top of that, there are arsonists – individuals moved by unfathomable reasons to ignite centuries-old forests, with no apparent benefit to themselves.

Drought also plays an important role in forest fires, as most occur in periods of little rainfall. If a wood is dry, it burns more easily and more quickly, so there is a greater likelihood of far-reaching consequences.

Forest fires occur in all parts of the world, but there are some regions with extensive woodland that are particularly vulnerable to this phenomenon, such as whole swathes of Australia, the United States, and Canada. Their climate favors the growth of trees on a large scale, but long, dry periods in which leaves and branches fall can create veritable tinderboxes. The wind is another factor to be taken into account, especially with respect to a fire's propagation and subsequent extinction. If the wind fans the flames, little can be down to put them out. On the contrary, a lack of wind plays into the hands of fire fighters – at least in theory.

It is now agreed that forests have their own survival mechanisms and that these even facilitate the work of the flames. Fire serves as a means of balancing an ecosystem. Some trees, such as eucalyptus, even contain substances that help to propagate fire, in order to eliminate competition from other species.

In the United States, fires burn an average of 6,560 sq. miles (17,000 km²) of woodland every year. In 2002, the country experienced its worst season ever, with fierce blazes in Arizona, California, Oregon, and, above all, Colorado.

A fateful season

The fires in the western state of Colorado usually start in June. They tend to be minor and well within the capacities of the fire service. In 2002, however, a significant drought put the authorities on high alert. Experts in various government agencies warned of the enormous potential danger and, in April, the governor of Colorado requested extra funds to combat possible fires. The worst fears were soon confirmed.

The first big fires sprang up on June 8, in Hayman, Coal Seam, and Miracle Complex. In Hayman, the blaze began in Park County, 3½ miles (6 km) to the northeast of Lake George in the Pike National Forest. It then spread to the counties of Jefferson, Douglas, and Teller, but the high temperatures and strong winds made it extremely difficult to control. More than 135,000 acres (55,000 hectares) of woodland went up in smoke, with 133 houses destroyed and three people injured. Much infrastructure, including bridges, roads, and mountain refuges, was seriously damaged.

The Coal Seam fire was less extensive, but wreaked similar havoc. It started on June 8 in an old cold deposit to the west of Glenwood Springs and went on to devastate around 12,400 acres (5,000 hectares) of woodland, as well as 40 buildings.

Miracle Complex was the last of the big forest fires sparked off that day. This was in fact a conjunction of two separate blazes – in Dierich Creek and Long Canyon – both originating in Mesa County. The first was unfortunately started by a barbecue that was not put out correctly, while the other was caused by lightning hitting dry trees. Between the two, they accounted for 3,900 acres (1,580 hectares). Three people were injured in the efforts to extinguish them.

To complete this desolate picture, the forest rangers were confronted with another fire on June 9 to the northeast of Durango, on the Missionary Ridge Path. This proved to rival Hayman as the most significant fire of this fateful season; over 69,000 acres (28,000 hectares) raged for days, destroying around a hundred houses, provoking dozens of injuries, and killing a fireman. Soon after, it was discovered that this blaze was the work of an arsonist.

There were more fires to come, but luckily these were less extensive and virulent. For weeks, volunteers joined forces with professional firefighters supported by airplanes.

The final toll for this season was awesome, with a total of over 4,000 fires, 612,820 acres (248,000 hectares) reduced to ashes, 9 people dead, and a further 80,000 evacuated. The value of property destroyed amounted to over 300 million dollars.

The reaction of the federal government was exemplary, as it issued generous subsidies and strengthened even further the services devoted to detecting and extinguishing fires. Despite all such precautions, however, the unpredictable nature of a forest fire can require extraordinary

The flames had not died down, so another fire was started to act as a firebreak on Horse Mountain.

Evacuation underway in West Glenwood. In the background, the sky has turned red with the flames.

resources that sometimes prove insufficient. Fire prevention is not the sole responsibility of firemen and forest rangers; it also depends on the responsibility of ordinary citizens.

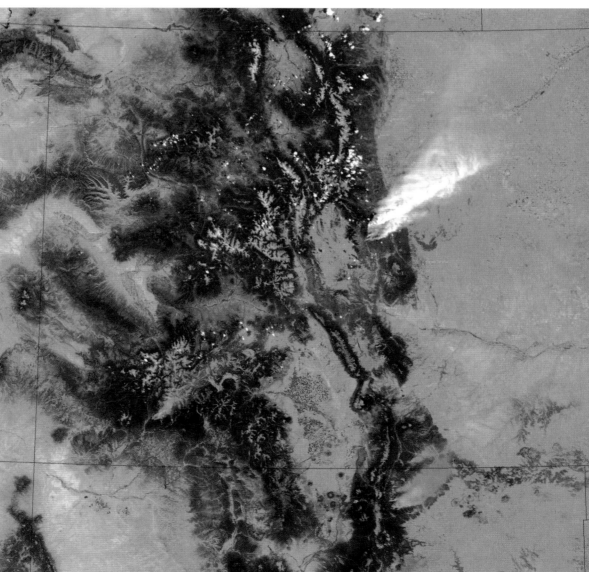

Satellite image of various fires that devastated thousands of acres in the state of Colorado.

Disastrous floods in Prague

Berlin
GERMANY
CZECH REP.
Prague
Vienna
AUSTRIA

Prague, Vltava, Czech Republic

August 6–19, 2002

19 dead

The flood barriers held, but parts of the historic quarter were under water nonetheless.

In August 2002, the swollen Vltava river flooded Prague, paralyzing a major part of the city center and causing immense damage to precious historic buildings.

In August 2002, great swathes of Bohemia were hit by floods. Unrelenting rains raised the levels of the rivers, particularly in southern and western Bohemia, and within a few days there was extensive flooding along the Malše, Lužnice, and Otava. The water swept rapidly from the upper and middle reaches of these tributary rivers and into the Vltava, where a massive flood surge began advancing inexorably to the north. Nothing in its path could stop it—not even the sequence of seven reservoir dams, whose original purpose included protecting the capital city against flooding. In Prague, the Vltava attained the highest flow rate ever recorded, and when the river then fed into the Labe (Elbe) there was even more extensive flooding in the middle and lower reaches of that great European waterway.

Historic floods

This was not the first time Prague had been flooded. The earliest recorded floods were in about 932, when the Rokytka, a tributary stream that joins the Vltava in Prague, overflowed. Full records of all the Vltava floods have been preserved since the end of the eleventh century, the biggest of these occurring in 1118, 1272, 1342, 1432, 1501, 1784, 1845, 1872, and 1890. The great flood of September 1118 was mentioned in the chronicle of Cosmo, the February flood of 1342 washed away Prague's great stone-built Judith Bridge, and in 1432 even the Old Town Square was submerged. The biggest flood was in 1784, followed in the nineteenth century by three, hundred-year floods: in 1845 the Vltava in Prague attained a rate of flow which was not exceeded again until 2002; the May flood of 1872 took the greatest toll (240 lives), while the September flood of 1890 severely damaged the Charles Bridge and flooded the Old Town. Not once in the following century did the Vltava match those hundred-year highs, and flood levels remained exceptionally low throughout the second half of the twentieth century. All the more surprising then, were the events of the summer of 2002.

Heavy summer rains

Like the Moravian floods in 1997, the Vltava flood disaster was caused by heavy rains associated with deep troughs of low pressure moving from northern Italy to central Europe, where their progress was slowed. The result was two waves of heavy rainfall, especially in South Bohemia. The first occurred August 6–8, with local falls of 4 inches (100 mm) that thoroughly waterlogged the soil. The next wave of rains fell August 11–13, when all of South Bohemia had a further 4 inches (100 mm) that ran straight off the surface and into the watercourses, causing floods.

In total it is estimated that the Vltava river basin received 175 billion cubic feet (4.98 billion cubic meters) of rain, 16,775 million cubic feet (475 million cubic meters) more than the total in the Odra and Morava basins in 1997. Whereas the rains of 1997 produced two floods that flowed into two different seas, however, the flooding of 2002 all came at once, and mostly drained through the Vltava alone. This also meant that all the water went through Prague. At the culmination of the flood on August 14, 2002, the Vltava in Prague was flowing at an unprecedented 182,230 cubic feet (5,160 cubic meters) per second, compared with an average August rate of just 1,765 (50). According to historical records, this was Prague's greatest flood since 1432, on the kind of scale that repeats just once in 500 years. Most rivers in the Vltava basin were estimated as flowing at levels seen once in 500–1,000 years.

The 2002 flood

The progress of the flooding in Prague was affected by the sequence of reservoir dams on the Vltava, which swallowed up part of the first flood wave and thus granted time for anti-flood measures. Threatened districts of the city were evacuated, major transport routes closed, and the banks of the Vltava secured with mobile barriers designed to prevent flooding of the historic city center. The second wave of rains, however, could no longer be contained by the now overflowing reservoirs. The ensuing surge of water burst through the barriers on the left bank of the Vltava in the city center and flooded a substantial part of Malá Strana (the Lesser Town), submerging listed buildings to second-story level, inundating the metro station, and, at its highest level, reaching the Valdštejn palace garden below Prague Castle. On the right bank of the Vltava the flood barriers held, so preventing more substantial damage to the Old Town. A large proportion of tenement buildings and other premises in the districts of Karlín, Holešovice, and Libeň suffered severe damage, however, and dozens of them later had to be demolished. The flooding was also disastrous for the Prague Zoo in the city's Troja district and for a large part of Podbaba, where a wastewater treatment plant was put out of action for several months.

In spite of the anti-flood measures introduced in Bohemia after the floods of 1997, the August flood of 2002 caused 73 billion CZK of direct material losses (i.e., 3.2 percent of GDP), 11 billion more than the floods of 1997. The extent of the damage was due particularly to the devastation in the center of Prague, which, as well as its historic buildings, also has a major concentration of businesses. The flood was considerably larger than in 1997 in terms of its geographical extent (6,560 square miles/17,000 square kilometers, as against 4,250/11,000) and the number of municipalities affected (968, as against 558). It hit around 3,200,000 people in the Czech Republic. Warning systems and the cooperation between flood emergency and government crisis teams had markedly improved since 1997. This is also borne out by the lower death toll (19) compared with the number of lives lost in the floods five years before.

The stone Bridge in Písek is the oldest bridge in the Czech Republic, dating from the 13th century. It resisted the turbulent water of the Otava River. Repairs were made to this valuable heirloom in the Spring of 2003.

Ústí nad Labem on alert. Residents from endangered streets did battle with the surging water.

Hurricane Lili

This hurricane is one of the disasters to be most closely surveyed by meteorologists in the last few years.

The Caribbean and southern United States

September 21 through October 6, 2002

13 dead

Prefabricated houses and trailers damaged by the passing of Lili in Point-Aux-Chenes.

Rain pouring on Point-Aux-Chenes, Louisiana, where it reached a height of 7 ft (2 m).

The 2002 hurricane season was a quiet one, at least in the United States. The storms that arose in the Atlantic and Caribbean only attained the status of hurricane on three occasions; of these, hurricane Lili created the most problems in the region of the Caribbean and the United States.

A visit announced

The hurricanes of 2002 were few and far between. Apart from Lili, only two other storms qualified as hurricanes – Kyle and Isodore. In the Pacific, however, it was a very different matter. The Chata'an typhoon slammed the island of Guam in July before heading toward Micronesia and the Marian Islands. In December, Guam was battered once again by super-typhoon Pongsona. The damage caused by these two storms was immense.

On September 21, a tropical depression was detected 750 miles (1,200 km) to the east of the Windward Islands. Meteorological observatories went on the alert. The season was nearly over, but this did not mean that a new storm would necessarily be subdued. A close watch was needed. The depression moved quickly westward and turned into a tropical storm, passing over the Windward Islands on September 24. The experts breathed a sigh of relief as, once it left the islands, it abated and became a tropical wave. This made what was to come even harder for the meteorologists to believe. On September 27, this wave gathered new strength to become a tropical storm, which was named Lili. On September 28, it passed over northern Jamaica, unleashing heavy rain both there and in Haiti.

After leaving Jamaica, Lili moved in the direction of Cuba, rising in intensity all the while. By the time it reached western Cuba, the storm was a full-fledged hurricane of class 2 on the Saffir-Simpson scale. On October 1, it veered away from Cuba, but still continued to increase in both size and speed. By October 3, it was a class 4 hurricane a few hundred miles off the coast of Louisiana, an area with a long and doleful experience of such storms. To the delight of its inhabitants, however, 12 hours before Lili was due to reach American soil, it had weakened to such an extent that it was now classified as class 1.

Most meteorologists in the American National Hurricane Center had predicted the arrival of a class 3 hurricane. In the event, Lili did bring to Louisiana torrential rain that caused serious damage and flooding, but not the grave disaster anticipated by the meteorologists and government. On October 4, the hurricane gradually started to fade, before blowing itself out a few days later in the North Atlantic.

Hurricane Lili was one of the most closely scrutinized meteorological phenomena of recent years. Despite the fact that its winds reached speeds of 100 miles (160 km) per hour, it proved possible to set up three mobile radar stations after its arrival on Louisianan soil, as well as extremely portable monitoring units along the lines of those used by tornado hunters, which provided a wealth of invaluable data. The radar stations were manned by employees of NOAA and other meteorological agencies from Louisiana State, although volunteers also made a significant contribution.

The arrival of hurricane Lili

The second most important storm of 2002 left behind it a trail of death and destruction, despite its continuous fluctuations in size and intensity. The brunt of its fury was felt in the Caribbean. In St. Vincent, the heavy rains caused landslides that cost the life of four people; flooding in St. Lucia resulted in the loss of banana crops; in Barbados, more than 400 buildings were damaged by the onslaught of Lili's gusting winds. Jamaica and Cuba, however, were the countries that suffered most. Four people were killed in floods, including a three-year old child, and the waters damaged houses, bridges, and roads, as well as devastating crops and food stores.

Barely a month before, Jamaica had played host to hurricane Isidore and the ground had hardly dried when Lili struck. As for Cuba, the damage was especially severe on the western part of the island, as the torrential rain left hundreds of families without electricity or telephone, destroyed crops, and caused serious damage to buildings, bridges, and trans-

port networks. Over 360,000 people were evacuated from their homes, though fortunately there was only 1 fatality.

In the United States, Louisiana was the worst hit. Most of the sugar crops in the south of the state had to be written off and the flood waters left almost half a million people without electricity. Hundreds of trees and telephone and electricity posts were knocked to the ground, blocking the way of the few cars that had ventured out. The coastal areas experienced significant damage as a result of the strong waves whipped up by the winds of over 90 miles (150 km) per hour. The beaches were totally washed away and required weeks of work to restore their former appearance. The total sum of material losses was 900 million dollars and 13 people lost their lives during Lili's frenetic tour.

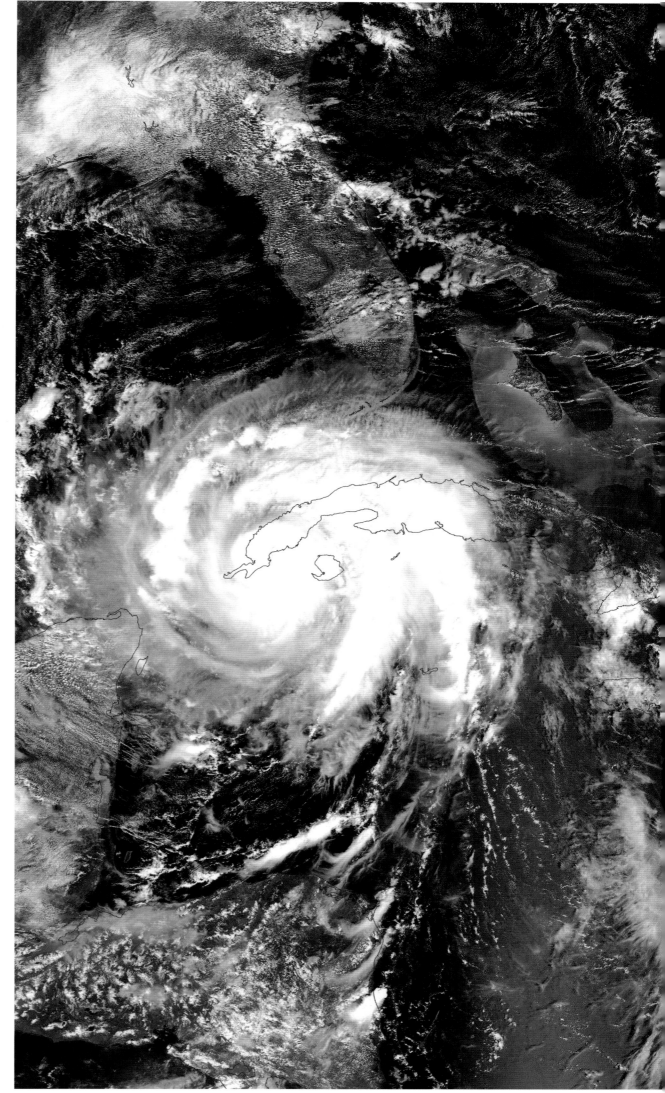

Hurricane Lili over Cuba, where it raised the level of the tides and caused serious damage.

Hurricane Isabel

ATLANTIC

North Atlantic

September 14–19, 2003

50 dead

The eye of the hurricane seen from the International Space Station.

This class five hurricane, which covered an area of 275,000 square miles (712,000 km²), was one of the most virulent of all to have buffeted the region in the last few decades.

Hurricanes from the Atlantic reach the coasts of Caribbean countries and frequently strike the southern part of the United States, particularly Florida and Alabama. One of the most powerful hurricanes of the 2003 season, however, stayed clear of the Caribbean to penetrate the northern portion of the United States – something that had not occurred since 1999. This hurricane was named Isabel.

An unusual storm

Hurricane Isabel was the big surprise to emerge from the 2003 hurricane season. The last storm of this kind to hit the northeastern United States was the class 2 hurricane Floyd, which left 56 dead and severe material damages amounting to over 4 billion dollars. In early September 2003, meteorologists in the northeast of the country and their Canadian colleagues warned of a storm that was forming in the northern Atlantic. In a certain set of circumstances, it could approach both countries. In the following days, the depression grew until it turned into a hurricane.

By September 14, it had become clear that Isabel, as the hurricane had been named, was one of the strongest storms to have formed in that area in the last few decades. On the 16th, the forecast went out that Isabel was heading close to Cape Hatteras. From there, it could strike North Carolina before turning to Chesapeake Bay, which straddles Virginia and Maryland, and then descending on the capital, Washington D.C. Once the storm had subsided, the experts thought it could go on to Buffalo, New York, and the Great Lakes, by which time it would still be a major tropical storm, albeit one weakened by its long journey.

Before touching American soil, Isabel whipped up a speed of almost 160 miles (260 km) per hour. The clouds formed by the gigantic hurricane covered an area of 275,000 square miles (712,000 km²), almost double that of Texas. As a result, before long it was endowed with the status of a class five hurricane on the Saffir-Simpson scale. In view of this situation, the authorities began to take measures to confront the storm. The Air Force and Navy evacuated their airplanes and ships to faraway bases, although their personnel were retained to provide assistance in the event of any serious calamities caused by this hurricane.

The inhabitants of the small Outer Banks Islands in North Carolina were all evacuated on September 15. That same day, the governor of Virginia declared a state of emergency, as the hurricane was expected to pass over its territory. In the northeastern United States, the inhabitants stockpiled food and reinforced the structures of their homes as best they could. Hospitals brought in extra emergency generators and medical supplies. Days before Isabel hit dry land, schools and businesses in North Carolina, Virginia, Maryland, and the other implicated states closed their doors to prepare themselves for the possible catastrophe. In Washington D.C., the federal bureaus closed, leaving only a skeleton staff – the first time that such drastic measures had been taken. Hours before the arrival of Isabel, the streets of the capital were deserted.

Isabel finally reached American soil in the mid-afternoon of September 18; by now, it was a class 2 hurricane with winds of up to 94 miles (150 km) per hour. The storm followed a route similar to the one that had been forecast, but fortunately it was weaker than predicted. In the early stages, Isabel caused serious damage and heavy flooding on the coasts, with rainfall of 6–10 inches (150-250 mm) per hour. The worst floods were seen in Virginia, where they rivaled those created by hurricane Agnes in 1972.

Following the trail of Isabel

On September 18 and 19, Isabel passed over the territory of the United States, before turning northward at the end of the second day, all the while gradually fading in intensity until it became a tropical depression and finally disappeared. It still found time, however, to unleash substantial rainfall on Ontario and nearby areas. Furthermore, in those two days, more than 5,700 flights were cancelled from airports in the eastern United States, with all the inherent financial repercussions; trains were out of operation for even longer, as repairs had to be made to tracks damaged by the hurricane.

The damage resulting from Isabel was particularly substantial in South Carolina, central Ontario, and the valleys of the Rivers Ohio and Hudson. It was estimated that over 4.5 million inhabitants in these regions were left without electricity. More than half of Maryland was plunged into darkness, and it was the same story in Virginia – not to mention the roads and freeways that were put out of action in both states for weeks. Sadly, 50 people lost their lives during the two days in which Isabel ravaged the northeastern United States, while the material damages occasioned by the storm

amounted to 3.5 billion dollars. Shortly afterwards, aid programs were set up for those affected by the hurricane.

As a result of the distinctive meteorological conditions that Isabel left in its wake, a series of tornadoes occurred in New Jersey, creating even more headaches for the authorities. Ever since 2003, the local meteorologists have stepped up their vigilance, con-

scious of the fact that, if a class two hurricane could wreak such havoc, then a class five hurricane like Andrew would have a devastating effect on the eastern seaboard of the United States.

Hurricane Isabel approaching North Carolina.

Hurricane Isabel caused floods that went on to undermine the foundations of hundreds of homes, as in this photo of Hatteras Village, North Carolina.

Heat wave in France

Western Europe

August 2003

22,000–35,000 dead

Heat waves are a regularly recurring phenomenon in the south of Europe in particular. Now and then, heat waves occur in northwestern Europe as well; but, whatever the case, the heat wave of 2003 was a record as far as average temperatures were concerned for France, Germany, and Switzerland. A herald of the heat to come was the exceptionally heavy rainfall in West Africa in the month of July. This caused an anticyclone system to arise, which traveled via North Africa, where it

was heated up by air from the Sahara Desert, to Western Europe, where it remained, blanketing the continent with an area of high pressure. Meteorologists refer to persistent high-pressure areas such as these as "summer blockades," as they can sometimes hold back low-pressure areas containing rain and cooler air for weeks. Thus, in the first two weeks of August, record after record was broken across Europe. The town of Auxerre in northern France recorded seven days with maximum tem-

peratures in excess of 104 ° F (40 °C); in Switzerland, temperatures above 104 °F (40 °C) were recorded for the first time in history, and in England, the town of Faversham, Kent, broke all British temperature records by registering a temperature of 101.3 °F (38.5 °C). Between August 1 and 5, 2003, maximum daytime temperatures in France rose from 77 °F (25 °C) to 98.6 °F (37 °C). At that time, nobody was especially concerned about the possible risks to public health. The French newspapers devoted their attention largely to the negative impact of the heat wave on agriculture and the dangers of air pollution, forest fires, and electricity outages due to a lack of cooling water for nuclear power stations. On August 6 and 7, average temperatures rose a further 3.6 degrees Fahrenheit (2 degrees Celsius). On August 8, the Ministry of Health issued a moderate warning, which, in the main, was directed toward people in outdoor and physical occupations and not toward the elderly, the largest risk group.

Death rate rises

By August 10, the death rate in France as a result of the heat had already increased by 300 percent. The heat continued unabated on August 11 and 12, with the highest temperatures of all being recorded on August 12. In the meantime, the hospitals were unable to handle the deluge of patients showing acute symptoms of hyperthermia (overheating), while the mortuaries were filled to capacity with dead bodies. Tents with temporary air conditioning and empty auction halls had to be used to keep the corpses from decomposing.

On Monday, August 11, the Minister of Health issued a press statement from his vacation residence, appealing for calm and insisting that the problem was not acute. The minister was not the only one to be on vacation; Prime Minister Raffarin and President Chirac were also absent, as were a great many other French men and women: in France, almost everyone takes their vacation in August, including many hospital staff as well. In some hospitals, the first-aid stations had been closed for as much as a whole month due to a lack of staff—and, under normal circumstances—a lack of patients as well. No contingency plans had been made for an extreme period of heat

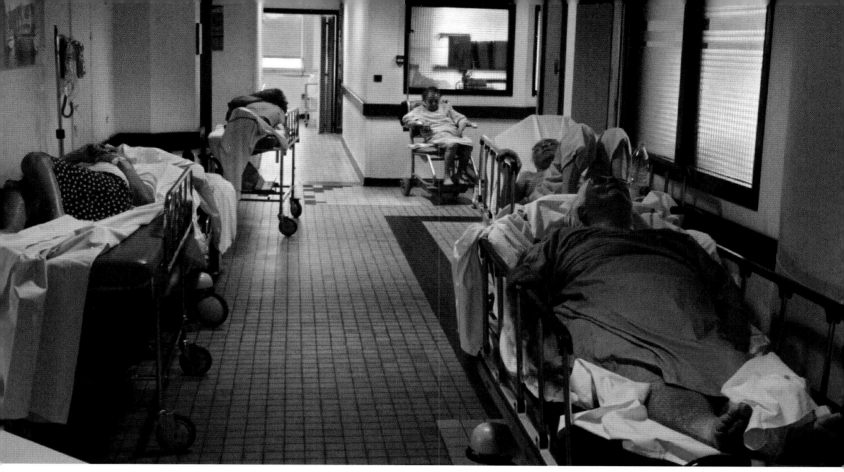

and its associated health problems for the elderly, young children, and people with respiratory difficulties. Almost none of the hospitals and nursing homes in France had air conditioning; neither did most people in their homes. France lagged well behind other European countries in that respect, not only in comparison with southern countries, such as Greece and Spain, where the heat is taken more generally into account, but also with many northern European countries.

The "White Plan"

It was only on August 13 that the French government responded to the situation. Prime Minister Raffarin announced the "Plan Blanc," (White Plan) which included the recall of hospital staff from their vacations, the opening of military hospitals for citizens requiring help, and the deployment of cooling trucks in which people could "shelter" from the heat. It was, however, too late. Not only had many people died by then, but also the worst of the heat wave was over by Friday, August 15. In all that time, President Chirac had not voiced a single word—he had taken three weeks' vacation in Canada. After his return on August 21, he delivered an address in which he regretted the loss of the victims and stated that the French had paid too little attention to their isolated, elderly neighbors.

It was announced in September that, during the heat wave, a total of 14,802 people had died in France above the norm for the period. The French government was overwhelmed with a wave of criticism.

Although the problems experienced in France were the most pronounced, other countries suffered human losses to the heat as well. Most of these occurred in Germany, Spain, and Italy. In the Netherlands, it was calculated that there had been approximately 1,400 more deaths than the average for the first two weeks of August. The total number of fatalities for the whole of Western Europe varied in differing estimates from 22,000 to over 35,000. The financial losses, caused above all by crop failures, were estimated at approximately 10 billion.

More heat waves

In July 2006, Western Europe was once again faced with a heat wave. From a meteorological point of view, it actually involved two heat waves, one following the other in quick succession. In France, emer-

gency measures were taken, and teams of volunteers were deployed to make daily checks on the situation of the elderly. In the interim, air conditioning had also been installed in many more hospitals and nursing homes.

Global climate change appears to be causing a direct increase in the number of heat waves in Europe. There were 32 heat waves in the whole of the 20th century, while there have already been 6 in the 21st. At the same time, all Western Europe is having to cope with an ageing population and an increasing shortage of nursing staff. Experts are therefore warning that additional measures are needed to prevent unnecessary deaths during future heat waves.

The Eiffel Tower wreathed in the thick smog caused by continual heat and lack of wind

People suffering heat-related sickness are treated in a hospital in Versailles

August, 2003: parched sunflower field in the neighborhood of Toulouse

Bam earthquake

This disaster deprived thousands of people of their livelihood. Two years later, there is still much work to be done and the city's inhabitants are draining away.

Bam (Iran)

December 26, 2003

26,000 dead

Iran has endured several major earthquakes in the last 40 years, the last of which was particularly heartbreaking for a number of reasons. The death count was extremely high – as is to be expected in a city as ill-prepared as this one – and, what is more, Bam's greatest architectural treasure, its citadel, was reduced to rubble, taking with it centuries of history.

An oasis lost in time

Bam, a city that dates back centuries, is situated in the northeast of the province of Kerman. At the time of the disaster, it was one of Iran's most prosperous cities. It was once an important stopover on the Silk Road – hence the need for its adobe citadel. In more recent years, it has become a magnet for tourists attracted not only by the fortress, but also the architectural remains of a variety of millenarian civilizations. Bam's other main source of income was agriculture. The fertile soils around Bam yielded exquisite dates and citrus fruits that were renowned throughout the country. All the efforts made to boost tourism and modernize cultivation techniques were undermined by the violent earthquake that rocked the city in 2003. At 5:26 a.m. on December 26, a tremor of 6.6 on the Richter scale decimated the city; although it lasted only a few seconds, its effects were devastating.

For years, the Iranian authorities had turned a deaf ear to international seismological organizations, with the country's buildings still generally being erected without any heed to advice. This policy of denial exacted a high price. Bam's humble stone and adobe buildings offered no resistance at all and the city was turned into a smoking pile of debris within minutes. The historic Arg-é Bam citadel was reduced to rubble. The houses fared no better. When the earthquake struck, most people were still asleep, and thousands were buried under their own homes. The fragility of the construction materials left little possibility for the formation of pockets of air that would increase the chances of survival of those trapped in wreckage. Nobody was taken out alive from the rubble, and 70 percent of the city's buildings were destroyed. Months after the tragedy, the Iranian government announced an official death toll of 26,271. Western sources were more pessimistic, however, and suggested a figure closer to 30,000, or even more.

The situation in Bam was appalling. There was no drinking water available, electricity was cut off, and telephones were not working. Healthcare was rudimentary to the extreme, at least until the arrival of volunteers from nearby cities, Iranian soldiers, and international aid organizations. The earthquake destroyed two of the city's hospitals, killing hundreds of doctors and nurses. In just a few hours, however, help came from the Iranian interior, and a few days later international aid was at hand, with Russia, Germany, the United Kingdom, and Spain the first on the scene.

International rescue teams took charge of looking for residents still unaccounted for and clearing the debris, while priority was also given to providing tents to shelter the 90,000 people who had lost their homes. The cold of the desert nights only made matters worse, as did the abundance of scorpions and poisonous snakes. Lack of clean water was another serious problem. Many of the wells had been damaged and some were totally irreparable. Not only was there a danger of epidemics of cholera or dysentery, but also the thousands of uncollected corpses were highly propitious to the spread of infectious diseases. Although health workers had arrived from all over the world, they were hard pressed to control

A specialized rescue team from Fairfax County, America, examines the desolate scene in Bam.

A group of women observe the remains of their old house. The adobe buildings were incapable of resisting the enormous tremor that destroyed the historic city of Bam.

the situation. Fortunately, however, they were able to avert any fatal outbreaks of disease.

The earthquake deprived thousands of people of their livelihood. Their carefully tended fields and irrigation channels were swallowed up by the earthquake. It was obvious that it would be a slow, laborious task to recover this land for agricultural purposes. As well as that year's crops being ruined, the lack of electricity meant that the refrigerated stores stopped working and tons of dates and other fruit were lost. The earthquake ruined thousands of families, who were left without jobs or homes.

Popular discontent

Bam's recovery has been slow and fraught with problems. For-eign volunteers complained of the lack of cooperation by the Iranian authorities, as well as their obscurantist approach to Westerners. They were not the only ones to show dissent, however. In the month of March, the inhabitants of Bam, disgusted with bureaucratic incompetence, burned official vehicles and stoned government buildings. The police even fired on the angry protestors, and the Iranian government went onto riot footing.

It cannot be disputed that the government was completely overwhelmed by the catastrophe. Furthermore, when it was announced that Bam would be granted special subsidies, thousands of underprivileged people flocked to the city from other parts of the country. Obviously, there was not enough to go round for everyone, and discontent simmered even more.

Two years later, the reconstruction work is still in progress. Much still remains to be done, as the schools and hospitals vital to society have yet to be completed.

This satellite photograph shows the extent of the damage to Bam. Particularly striking is the destruction of the monumental adobe citadel, top right.

Fires in California

This fire claimed 24 lives, destroyed more than 4,500 homes and burned 692,000 acres of land.

California
(United States)

October 25 through
November 3, 2003

24 dead

The charred remains
of a pick-up and
a house in Waterman
Canyon, San Bernardino.

The California fires
as seen from one
of NASA's satellites.
Note the multiple
fronts.

This prefabricated
metal house in San
Bernardino, California, melted completely.

Fire on too many fronts

The year 2003 proved especially hot. Europe experienced one of the worst heat waves in living memory, particularly in France and Spain where hospitals were overwhelmed by patients suffering from the hot weather. In all, tens of thousands of people died, many of them elderly, unable to withstand the onslaught of temperatures in excess of 104 °F (40 °C) for weeks on end. The situation provoked both expert and public opinion: while some claimed the weather was a sign of climatic change, others underplayed its importance, arguing that it was nothing more than an isolated spell of unusually high temperatures. What is certain is that neither argument held complete sway, nor were people fully reassured by their respective governments' handling of the crisis.

The situation was similar in North America. The climate was very strange for summer. While the eastern United States experienced some hot months, it was suddenly subjected to heavy rainfall unusual for this period. On the West Coast, such rain would have provided a welcome respite, particularly in California, where the summer was particularly hot. The lack of rain was preoccupying ecologists and local authorities, as they knew that the woodlands were extremely dry and therefore very vulnerable to fire. The slightest mishap could prove fatal, as trees, branches, shrubs, and even garbage left by tourists could act as powerful combustible material for any sparks.

The summer came to a close, but October was the eighth hottest month on record since 1895. (On the East Coast, in contrast, the temperatures were lower than normal.) California's weather stations monitored the situation intensely, fearful of the emergence of a forest fire.

In the last week of the month, a front of low pressure on the frontier with Mexico whipped up the so-called Santa Ana Winds, fanning them rapidly toward California. These winds were viewed with alarm throughout the state, as they formed a warm current that would stoke any fire and help it spread. On October 25, the dreaded flames made their first appearance and in just a few days the situation was out of hand, as various forest fires took hold across a large part of California. There were over 12 focal points, the most important being in Piru, Verdale, Simi Valley, Gran Prix, Otay, and, above all, Cedar, the site of the most devastating fire ever seen in California. The fires were concentrated around the San Bernardino Mountains and the cities of Julian and San Diego, where a large number of historic buildings succumbed to the blaze.

The schools and universities in the region suspended their activities and groups of students showed their solidarity by serving as volunteer firefighters and offering humanitarian aid to those in need. Right from the start, the local airports cancelled a large number of flights, as the radar systems for air traffic control were not working properly on account of the climatic conditions created by the fires. Meanwhile, the organizational difficulties were further complicated by the need to evacuate an increasing number of people helpless in the face of the fires inexorably approaching their homes.

The Santa Ana Winds only helped propagate the flames still further, which in some cases reached heights of 115ft (35 m). The fire service immediately attended the scene, their trucks and 10,000-man force supplemented by the National Guard and hundreds of volunteers. There was also significant backup from the air, with the National Guard contributing four C-130s converted into firefighting planes, along with eight high-capacity UH-60 helicopters, similarly transformed for the occasion. Airplanes from neighboring states also provided support. The work of all the courageous pilots involved was magnificent, but they were powerless to stop the continuous spread of the fires, which raged until the end of October, the strong, warm winds only adding fuel to the blaze.

Suddenly, however, the firefighters had a stroke of luck, as the wind changed direction. The firemen, soldiers, and volunteers worked unstintingly to take advantage of this opportunity and were finally able to declare the battle won on November 3. They had defeated the fire, but at a high cost.

Controversy ensues

After ten days of intense struggle, the situation was back under control. The citizens of California could go back to their homes (if they still had them) or start long bureaucratic procedures to obtain help.

Days after the disaster, it was discovered that three of the fires had been sparked off by human hands. One of these, in Cedar, was

caused by a young huntsman who had lit a warning flare that had fallen into dry leaves. After being identified by various witnesses, he was arrested by the County Sheriff and eventually sent to prison for five years. This sentence did not meet the approval of either the media or public opinion, which considered it far too lenient.

In two other blazes, Old Fire and Grand Prix, there were somewhat confused descriptions of possible culprits, but no arrests were made; ever since then, there have been campaigns for tougher sentences for arsonists as well as closer vigilance of risk areas.

Large parts of
Portugal

August 2003

18 dead

Semi-charred woods
in the vicinity of
Seia, central Portu-
gal

Forest Fires in Portugal

In 2003, forest fires in Portugal destroyed some 750,000 acres (300,000 hectares) of woodland. For over two weeks, an all-out effort was made to fight a total of 72 fires

The forest fires in Portugal arose during the heat wave that plagued large parts of Western Europe at the beginning of August 2003. To some extent, the Portuguese are used to forest fires during the summer. There are many pine and cork forests. These become tinder-dry throughout the summer and are thus highly inflammable. The 2003 forest fires spread so quickly and to such an extent, however, that a state of emergency had to be declared and assistance requested from abroad.

It began with a few fires in the center and north of the country, which, though initially minor, fanned out extremely rapidly due to a combination of extremely dry, hot weather and strong winds. On August 5, the prime minister of Portugal, Durao Barroso, declared a state of emergency and appealed to the European Union for help in fighting the fires. At that time, 72 fires were blazing simultaneously, still mainly in the center and north of the country. Around 135,000 acres (54,000 hectares) of forest had already gone up in smoke, and dozens of houses in small villages had burned to the ground. The death toll stood at nine, including a number of firefighters who had died while tackling the blazes. The appeal by Barroso generated criticism among residents in towns and villages at the heart of the disaster, who said they had been waiting for days for the fire service to arrive, but that their appeals had gone unheeded. Nevertheless, assistance soon arrived from abroad. At the height of the fires, nearly 3,000 firemen and 1,400 military personnel were involved in fighting them, with a total of 650 vehicles and 44 firefighting aircraft and helicopters being deployed.

Hell

In the vicinity of the town of Semideiro, some 62 miles (100 km) to the northeast of Lisbon, firemen had been fighting a blaze in an area of pine forest for days. There was palpable relief among the 1,500 residents of the town at the eventual appearance of the firefighting airplanes, which finally halted the conflagration.

As August progressed, the fires in the north were brought increasingly under control; in the interim, however, the danger had shifted to the center and south of the country. By mid-August, two major fires were

blazing in the vicinity of Lisbon, one of which was particularly close, in the neighborhood of Loures, some 9 miles (15 km) to the north of the capital. Thick palls of smoke hung above the city and many of its residents began to suffer breathing problems, exacerbated by an air temperature that was already high. Measurements revealed that the persistent forest fires had also had a serious effect on air quality beyond the borders of the country. Increased levels of carbon monoxide were recorded even in France, hundreds of miles to the north.

The fires reached the Algarve, on the south coast of Portugal, where tens of thousands of Europeans vacation every summer. Every effort was made to fight the blazes and thus prevent them from reaching the most popular beach resorts. Several villages in the hills and mountains had to be evacuated. In the end, the sea of flame was halted just 15 miles (25 km) from the coast.

On August 18, most of the fires had been brought under control, and the damage could be assessed. The fires had raged across almost 890,000 acres (360,000 hectares) of land. Around 750,000 acres (300,000 hectares) of this had been forested, and 110,000 acres (44,000 hectares) agricultural land. Some 2,000 homes and buildings had gone up in flames, and 18 people had lost their lives, more than half of these being firefighters. The total financial loss was estimated at approximately one billion euros.

Arson

Meanwhile, forest fires were also being tackled elsewhere in Europe. Dozens of forest fires had raged in the south of Spain, with various towns and villages having to be evacuated. By the end of July, some 75,000 acres (30,000 hectares) of forest had gone up in smoke in France, with some fatalities. The authorities in the countries affected claimed that a great many of the fires had been set deliberately. "It becomes very difficult to combat the fires when new ones are lit simultaneously by a criminal element," commented Barroso.

American and French experts on forest fires subsequently pointed out, however, that global statistics show that no more than 15 percent of forest fires are started maliciously. According to them, it is usually a case of unfortunate accidents from discarded cigarettes, a piece of glass lying in the sun, a spark from a power cable, or an overheated chainsaw. Even more frequently, they involve people who light a campfire or barbecue in an area of tinder-dry woodland. Experts also point to the fact that many forest fires rage every year in large parts of the United States, Canada, and Russia, but that they burn themselves out naturally without human intervention.

Nevertheless, deliberate fire starting did prove to have been a contributory factor in Portugal, where over 50 people were arrested. Some arsonists had taken this course of action in an attempt to change the officially designated land use in their area, to enable them to build on it. Here and there, pyromaniacs were also shown to have been involved; there were also freelance firefighters, who wanted to create more work for themselves.

A firefighting aircraft discharges its cargo of water above a burning forest

The sun sets behind thick smoke from a forest fire

Hurricane Frances

The material damages resulting from this hurricane were calculated at 9 billion dollars, making it one of the most destructive of all time.

USA
Washington D.C.
ATLANTIC
PACIFIC
Caribbean Sea

August 24–
September 4, 2004

50 dead

The 2004 hurricane season was one of the worst in history. Just when it seemed that the last hurricane had visited the Caribbean islands and part of the southern United States, a new storm arrived in the form of hurricane Frances. After the havoc caused by hurricane Charley, Frances posed a new and extremely serious problem for the inhabitants of the region.

Another onslaught

Hurricane Frances was the third big hurricane of 2004, reaching speeds in excess of 140 miles (230 km) per hour and level 4 on the Saffir-Simpson scale. It affected central Florida, which was still recovering from the visit just three weeks before of Charley, one of the strongest storms to hit the area in living memory. The inhabitants of the region were incredulous and desperate when they heard that a new torment was heading their way.

Frances started as a tropical depression on August 24, 2004 to the west-southwest of the Cape Verde Islands. By the next day, it had qualified as a tropical storm, going by the name of Frances. On August 26, the storm acquired the status of a hurricane. It went on to the northern Caribbean, unleashing rain on the Virgin Islands and the Dominican Republic. On September 1, it headed toward the Turks and Caicos Islands, but finally passed them by. On September 2, the eye of the hurricane moved over the island of San Salvador, very close to Cat Island in the Bahamas. At dawn on the 3rd, it descended on Great Bahama and Nassau, where the strong rain and gusting wind took the life of a man who was trying to repair some electric generators. The airports in these islands were put out of operation, due both to the fierce winds and the amount of water on the runways, which prevented any airplane from landing or taking off.

After a short flurry between the Bahamas and Florida, where it dropped speed dramatically and fell into class 2, it arrived in central Florida on September 4, between Fort Pierce and West Palm Beach. A few hours later, it veered abruptly to the Gulf of Mexico, before returning to Florida, close to Tampa. St. Marks was the next stop, but by then Frances had lost strength and become a tropical storm once again. It then turned inland, as a tropical depression that caused rain in Georgia. It had almost run out of steam by now, but refused to surrender and continued on its way, reaching as far as the outskirts of Quebec City in Canada, where it found time to release substantial rainfall before disappearing for good. Over the course of its wanderings, Frances had proved an aggressive, devious storm that meteorologists had found particularly hard to monitor, especially after its arrival in the Gulf of Mexico. The hurricane's formidable powers of destruction made it one of the five most devastating on record, but efficient damage limitation measures and the prior visit of Charley mitigated its effects to some degree. If Charley had not come beforehand, Frances would have wreaked even greater havoc.

Counting the cost and rebuilding

On September 1, in the face of the events in the Caribbean, the governor of Florida declared a state of emergency. The Kennedy space center was closed. The hurricane's journey through the Caribbean and the United States left 37 dead in Florida, 2 in the

Many boats were either sunk by the hurricane or run aground, like this yacht in Fort Pierce.

Hurricane Frances approaches Florida and Cuba. The photo shows the scale of the storm, with an eye measuring over 180 miles (290 km) across.

In South Carolina, Frances lost its status as a hurricane to become a strong tropical storm that battered buildings and caused extensive flooding.

Bahamas, 1 in Ohio, and 8 in Georgia. The overall death count is still unclear, but it is thought to be around 50.

The material damages amounted to 9 billion dollars, making Frances the fifth most expensive hurricane of all times. The NASA premises in Cape Canaveral suffered significant damage, assessed at over 100 million dollars; fortunately, most of the facilities for space missions were not seriously affected, although both the hangar housing the launcher and auxiliary rockets was struck by violent gusts of wind, along with some of the warehouses.

In Florida, the citrus crops were devastated, creating enormous difficulties for local farmers; these were alleviated, at least partially, by aid programs launched by the US government immediately after the disaster.

Once Frances had turned into a tropical storm, its rains caused severe flooding in Alabama, North and South Carolina, the Appalachian Mountains, and the eastern part of Lake Ontario. The losses sustained through these floods in Canada and America were calculated at 45 million dollars.

In the southern United States, more than 20 airports had to cancel all their flights, and even Disneyland closed its doors to the public. More than six million people had their electricity supply cut off, obliging hundreds of schools and universities to cancel their classes. Healthcare facilities were generally more fortunate, however, as in most cases their back-up generators saw them through the crisis. Last but not least, Frances generated 123 tornadoes from Florida to Virginia – beating the previous record of 115 established by Beulah in 1967. These figures are cold and impersonal, but they nevertheless give some idea of the human tragedy created by the ferocity of Frances.

Regrettably, Frances proved not to be the last of the major storms to hit the southern United States and the Caribbean that year, so the inhabitants could only hold their breath and brace themselves for further surprises.

Hurricane Ivan

The passage of this hurricane through the United States caused damage assessed at over 13 billion dollars.

USA
Washington D.C. ●
ATLANTIC
PACIFIC
Caribbean Sea

The Caribbean
and United States

September 2–23, 2004

84 dead

The flimsy beach houses in Florida, such as this one in Pensacola, could not withstand the strong winds unleashed by Ivan.

An excavator tries to clear rubble in a neighborhood in Pensacola, Florida.

Hurricane Ivan plowing through the Caribbean on its way to ravage the coasts of Florida.

The 2004 hurricane season has gone down in history as one of the most devastating in recent decades, if not of all time. Hurricane Ivan, which hammered the Caribbean and a good part of the United States, was the fourth most significant storm of that year and one of the most powerful on record.

A newcomer on the scene

As we have already seen, the 2004 hurricane season was particularly agitated. The formation of a new scourge for the Caribbean was greeted with desperation by the meteorologists in the region, who were fearful of new disasters in places already ravaged by the previous hurricanes. On September 2, a tropical depression formed to the southwest of the Cape Verde Islands. By the next day, it had evolved into a tropical storm moving north-northwest at 15 miles (25 km) per hour. That same day, it was named Ivan. On September 5, when it had reached the Lesser Antilles, Ivan grew sufficiently to be considered a hurricane of class 3, almost 4, on the Saffir-Simpson scale. This intensification of the storm at low latitudes was almost incredible, and totally unexpected by the experts who were tracking its every movement. Moreover, it did not bode well for the future. On September 7, Ivan arrived in Grenada with winds of around 125 miles (200 km) per hour. The island's capital, St. George, was severely hit, and many of its historic buildings, including the Prime Minister's residence, were wrecked. The city's jail was so badly damaged that hundreds of convicts were able to escape. In all, 85 percent of the island was devastated, and its newfound economic boom was brought to an abrupt end. Furthermore, 39 islanders died as a result of Ivan's visit. On the 9th, the hurricane, with gales now approaching 138 miles (220 km) per hour, passed close to the Dutch Antilles and Aruba.

By the time Ivan struck Jamaica, its classification had gone from 4 to 5 on the Saffir-Simpson scale (the maximum score possible) and the winds were raging at 162 miles (260 km) per hour. Half a million Jamaicans needed to be evacuated, but only 5,000 managed to escape the danger zone. Most of the tourists on the island were transferred to Isla Mujeres, on the Yucatan Peninsula. Twenty people were killed in the chaos caused by Ivan in Jamaica.

There was massive destruction on Great Cayman Island, with 80 percent of its buildings affected. After pummeling these two islands, the hurricane, Ivan, now moving at 168 miles (270 km) per hour, set off for the Gulf of Mexico. On September 16, it turned up in Gulf Shores, Alabama, but its speed had dropped to just over 130 miles (210 km) per hour and it was now a class 3 hurricane. Ivan surged inland, reaching the center of the state; by the end of the day, it had turned into a tropical depression. On September 18, it crossed the state of Virginia and reached the coast of New Jersey, where it caused heavy rain. On the 21st, the remains of the storm, along with a low-pressure system and gusty winds, caused flooding and material damage, indicating that new changes were in store. The next day, it was confirmed that the tropical storm had taken form once again. It moved in a circular motion through the southeastern United States, creating heavy flooding. By the 23rd, it had reached Louisiana, considerably weakened, and went on to penetrate Texas before gradually fading away.

Picking up the pieces once again

Ivan's passage through the United States not only cost 25 lives, but also resulted in losses of over 13 billion dollars, making it the fourth most expensive hurricane to hit American soil. The greatest impact was felt in Alabama, particularly in Baldwin County, as well as Pensacola and Fort Walton, both in Florida. Not only were many houses destroyed, but the surfaces of Interstate 10 and Highway 90 were also severely damaged, and had to be closed to traffic. In addition, the bridges on Interstate 10 in Pensacola partially collapsed, causing a large number of casualties. Further inland, Ivan caused serious flooding when its torrential rains overflowed the Rivers Delaware and Chattahoochee, near Atlanta, to levels the like of which had not been seen for a century.

In North Carolina, floods also caused major problems, as the River Pigeon broke its banks, dam-

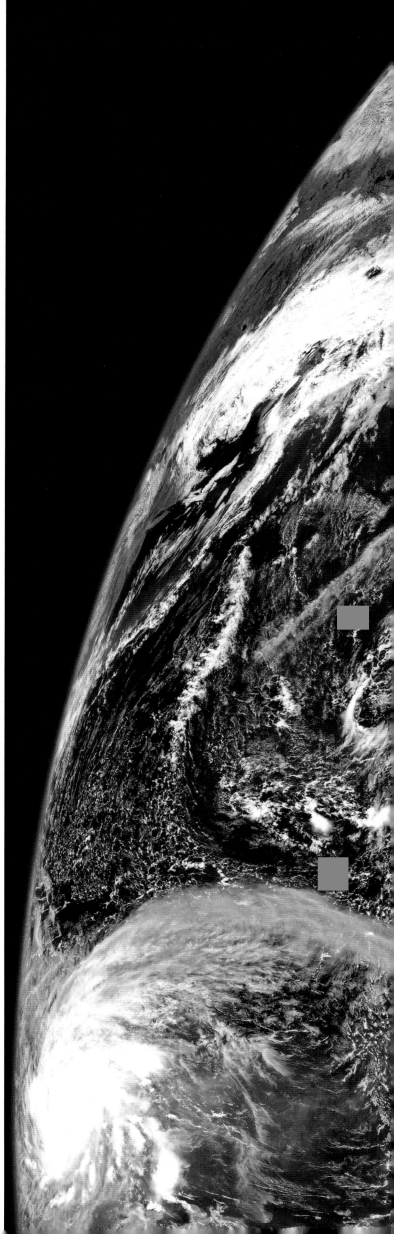

aging the Interstate 40. Finally, hurricane Ivan gave rise to a series of tornadoes in Maryland, the combination of these two meteorological phenomena destroying seven oilrigs in the Gulf of Mexico.

In the Caribbean, the material damage caused by Ivan was assessed at over 3 billion dollars; 59 people were killed. On most of the islands hit by the hurricane, the infrastructure was so thoroughly decimated that their economic activity was paralyzed for weeks. Roads, farms, fishing ports, and lucrative tourist boats were all out put of action for days. As for the rest of the tourist industry – so vital to this area – the big hotels stood up to the storm well, but this was not true of the beach facilities, which were torn apart by the strong winds in Grand Cayman Island, Tobago, and Jamaica. As always, however, it was the modest homes of local residents that bore the brunt of the damage. Between them, pounding rain, winds, and avalanches of mud triggered by the flooding snatched away the homes of thousands of people, forcing them to restart their lives from scratch. Another statistic worth mentioning among Ivan's doleful achievements is the wave it set in motion on its way through the Gulf of Mexico at 88 ft (27 m), it was the highest ever recorded. It is best not to imagine what would have happened if it had hit the coastline, as it would certainly have been capable of swamping a ten-story building.

Hurricane Jeanne

The constant metamorphoses displayed by hurricane Jeanne made it a veritable nightmare for meteorologists in the countries in its path.

The Caribbean (especially Haiti) and southern United States

September 14–28, 2004

3,000 victims

The year 2004 will be remembered by the inhabitants of the small countries in the Caribbean and the southern United States as a meteorological torment, with hurricanes striking one after another in fateful sequence. Some were distinguished by extensive damage, others by their high death toll. Jeanne scored high on both accounts, causing massive destruction and claiming thousands of lives.

A season not to be forgotten

The 2004 hurricane season was the worst on record since 1885. The season lasts from June 1 through November 30, and the inhabitants of the danger zone are accustomed to being on the alert during this period. The citizens of some countries can rest assured that their governments have taken all the necessary precautions, and so both the population and the emergency services know what to do in all circumstances. In contrast, other countries – such as most of the Caribbean nations – are unable to take such measures on account of their precarious socioeconomic situation. It is in these places that most lives are lost.

In 2004, four extremely powerful hurricanes visited the Caribbean and the United States: Charley, Frances, Ivan, and Jeanne. Of all these, the most devastating was Jeanne. It not only caused severe damage, but proved particularly deadly, claiming over 3,000 lives.

Jeanne came to life on September 13 as a tropical wave to the southeast of Guadalupe. At first, it seemed harmless, but by the next day it had already earned the status of a tropical storm. Two days later, it was in Puerto Rico, leaving there as a full-fledged hurricane en route to the Dominican Republic. For a couple of days, however, it lost steam, to the point of being reclassified as a tropical storm once more. On September 18, by now a tropical depression, it passed over northwestern Haiti, where it caused irreparable damage. On the 20th, the center of the storm was a reconstituted hurricane heading for the Bahamas and Florida. On September 25 and 26, it measured 3 on the Saffir-Simpson scale and struck the Bahamas and various parts of Flori-

A striking image of the roof of a small gas station in Vero Beach, Florida. The strong wind left it in a vertical position.

Vero Beach was severely hit, as can be seen from this photo. It was out of bounds to swimmers for weeks.

da, such as Stuart and Port Saint Lucie. On the 27th, it turned north, skirting Georgia before arriving in Virginia, where its strength began to dissipate. Its last vestiges – still a storm of considerable power – touched New Jersey and New York City, before disappearing into the Atlantic.

Jeanne was a veritable nightmare for the meteorological services of the countries through which it passed, as its constant metamorphoses made it an elusive and unpredictable prey. It is normal, however, for a hurricane to present a series of structural changes, but the season had been a hard one and maybe the observers and experts were in need of a rest.

The phenomenon struck several countries in its frenetic rush. The most affected were the Virgin Islands, the Bahamas, Puerto Rico, the Dominican Republic, Haiti, and the United States, especially the

state of Florida, a regular host of hurricanes.

Not all these areas were disrupted to the same extent. In Puerto Rico, the authorities followed the advice of American experts and cut off the island's electricity supply to minimize the impact. The operation was only partially successful, as seven people were killed and many cities sustained damage. The island's nature reserves were seriously affected by landslides triggered by the hurricane.

The damage was less heavy in the Dominican Republic, although 18 of its citizens died, most of them under their own roofs, after their houses had been flattened by the strong winds.

In the United States, the material damage was more striking than the number of casualties: the losses amounted to seven billion dollars, with five people killed. The winds

192

reached speeds of 120 miles (190 km) in Florida, with more than five million residents being left without electricity.

Downpour in Haiti

Haiti was the country most devastated by Jeanne. Although it had not yet obtained hurricane status when it reached Haiti, the storm released torrential rain that proved extraordinarily deadly. The downpour caused floods and huge avalanches of mud, for which the population was totally unprepared.

In Gonaives, the city most affected by the disaster, more than 80,000 people (i.e., 80 percent of the total population) had their lives turned upside down by Jeanne. The only refuge available to the inhabitants was the roofs of their houses or, barring that, any telephone or electricity post that had remained standing.

Haiti was plunged into chaos overnight, as flooding cut the supplies of electricity and drinking water. More than 3,000 people were killed and double that number sustained serious injuries, which were impossible to treat in such circumstances. The floods and unhygienic conditions quickly became apparent in the form of polluted water, causing infection and disease that foreign aid workers struggled to combat.

The health situation was further jeopardized by decomposing bodies lying in the streets. The efforts to bury them were often in vain, as the graves filled with water and swept the corpses out to sea. The arrival of United Nations troops eased the problems to some degree, although, when they distributed food and medicines, they often encountered physical aggression from the desperate local people.

Jeanne stands out as one of the worst natural disasters so far in this new century. If the long-term weather forecasts are anything to go by, however, it could well be surpassed by even more intense hurricane seasons in this area.

Hurricane Jeanne seen from a satellite of NASA. It is undoubtedly a spectacular sight, but also one that inspires awe.

Indian Ocean tsunami

Scientists from all over the world are convinced that the Earth itself vibrated.

Bay of Bengal

INDIAN OCEAN

Indian Ocean

December 26, 2004

283,000 dead

The photos on the right show Gleebruk in Indonesia, before and after the arrival of the devastating wave.

These two photos show part of the Meulaboh Peninsula, before and after the tsunami that devastated Indonesia in December 2004.

If any natural disaster has made a powerful impact on world public opinion, it is the tsunami that ravaged the Indian Ocean in December 2004. This phenomenon constituted one of the biggest natural catastrophes in history, and its ultimate consequences are yet to be understood. If the tsunami can be said to have had a positive side, it was the enthusiastic show of solidarity by ordinary citizens everywhere who contributed whatever they could to relieve the suffering.

Making history

The fateful tsunami was triggered off by an underwater earthquake, which took place at 00:58 a.m. on December 26. At first, experts reckoned that the tremor measured 6.5 or 6.8 on the Richter scale, but information collated after the event confirmed the worst fears of pessimists: the earthquake had had a magnitude of 9. Since 1900, only three earthquakes have surpassed this register on the Richter scale: that of Chile in 1960, with 9.5; the Good Friday earthquake in Alaska in 1964, with 9.2; and that of the Andrean Islands in 1957, with 9.1. All these mega-earthquakes claimed

far fewer victims, however.

Three days before the tremor, a sub-Arctic region of New Zealand recorded a tremor of 8.1 on the Richter scale. Although it has never been proven, many seismologists have speculated that this earthquake and the one that caused the tsunami were related. The violent tremor resulted in a drift of over 33 ft (10 m) along a fault of 750 miles (1,200 km), which set off underwater movements that gave rise to new hills and rock formations on the ocean bed, as well as sinking and shattering older ones.

The earthquake that caused the tsunami lasted a full ten minutes, whereas most are over after only a few seconds. Scientists from all over the world insist that the Earth itself vibrated; nobody had ever experienced the like of it before. The tremor originated at a depth of 20 miles (30 km), in the Indian Ocean, to the north of the island of Simeulue, which in turn lies to the north of Sumatra in Indonesia.

The earthquake unleashed the most deadly tsunami ever known. It battered the shores of Indonesia, Sri Lanka, southern India, Thai-

land, and other countries with waves of up to 100 ft (30 m) in height. Two of the victims of the giant waves lost their lives in Port Elizabeth, South Africa, 5,000 miles (8,000 km) from the epicenter. The time taken by the deadly waves to reach their various destinations ranged from just a few minutes to seven hours in the case of Somalia, where 250 died.

Northern Indonesia suffered the brunt of the blow. Between 90 minutes and 2 hours later, it was the turn of Sri Lanka and southern India. Two hours after that, the next port of call was Thailand, even though it was closer to the epicenter of the earthquake. In South Africa, the waves reached heights of 7 ft (2 m), 16 hours after the first ones hit the shores of Sumatra.

An apocalyptic disaster

In the Indian Ocean, unlike the Pacific, there is no tsunami warning system, as this type of phenomenon is unusual here; in any case, nobody could have predicted the mayhem wreaked by this tsunami. Although the earthquake itself claimed only a few victims, the gigantic waves and subsequent

flooding created havoc. The USGS (United States Geological Survey) has issued approximate data on the aftermath. It is believed that a total of 283,100 people were killed, with a further 14,100 unaccounted for and over a million left without a home. We shall probably never know for sure, however, exactly how many people died in this catastrophe. In February 2005, around 500 corpses were still being recovered every day, with NGOs on the scene opining that the mopping-up operation could continue until late 2005 or early 2006.

The tsunami plunged the entire region into a pitiful socio-economic situation. Famine was rife and diseases such as cholera, typhus, and dysentery threatened. It was not unreasonable to suppose that a further 300,000 people would die from the effects of the tsunami in the twelve months following the disaster. Nine thousand of the direct victims of the tsunami were tourists from Europe, particularly Scandinavia.

The tsunami was one of the worst natural disasters of all times. In terms of fatalities, it was only surpassed by the Tangshan earthquake in 1976, which officially killed 255,000 people, but almost certainly took many more, and the 1556 Shaanxi earthquake in China, which history records as claiming 830,000 lives (although this cannot b proven). Days after the disaster struck, some theories were put forward to explain why this tsunami had been so extraordinarily devastating. Months later, some of these hypotheses have stood the test of time. Sadly, human ecological mismanagement had much to answer for with respect to the mind-boggling effects of this tragic event. According to experts, the destruction of coral reefs, coastal mangrove swamps, and sand dunes had proved decisive. These coastal formations around Sumatra, Thailand, Sri Lanka, and other countries had previously served as natural barriers against the sea; if they had still been in place at the time of the tsunami, the death toll would undoubtedly have been lower.

USA
Washington D.C. ●
New Orleans
PACIFIC
ATLANTIC
Caribbean Sea

United States

August 24–31, 2005

1,000 dead

The devastating hurricane Katrina over the southern states. Its eye is set on New Orleans.

A group of boats sailing along the flooded streets of New Orleans in search of survivors – a typical sight in the days after Katrina.

Hurricane Katrina

With its surface area of over 88,800 sq. miles (230,000 km²), winds of up to 175 miles (280 km) per hour, and its devastating effects, Katrina proved to be one of the cruelest hurricanes ever to afflict the Atlantic Basin.

Louisiana in the eye of the hurricane

The 2005 hurricane season had been fairly normal until the appearance of Katrina. This storm totally altered the scenario and left scars that will take years to heal. Unlike other extremely destructive hurricanes, Katrina was not formed in the Atlantic, but instead emerged near the Bahamas on August 24; it touched land for the first time close to North Miami, Florida, as a class 1 hurricane on the Saffir-Simpson scale, where it caused serious flooding, power cuts for a million people, and 11 deaths. During this first foray, it weakened and turned into a tropical storm, but this proved only a brief respite. Katrina gathered strength more quickly than expected in the warm waters of the Gulf of Mexico, where it grew into a class 5 hurricane and so rang alarm bells in all the monitoring stations. Katrina was by now displaying features – including winds of 175 miles (280 km) per hour – that made it the fourth strongest storm ever to strike the Atlantic Basin.

Katrina headed back north, wavering slightly before brushing Grand Isle, Louisiana, on August 29 as a class 4 hurricane with winds of 150 miles (241 km) per hour. It briefly pounced again to the south of Buras-Triumph, Louisiana, at around 6.10 a.m., before finally establishing itself on dry land at 10.00 a.m. on the borders of Louisiana and Mississippi.

Apart from its winds, which had already broken many of the region's all-time records, Katrina was also remarkable for its enormous size, which wreaked unprecedented destruction on an area of over 88,800 sq. miles (230,000 km²). A few hours after its arrival on dry land, however, it started to weaken, and by the time it hit Clarksville, Tennessee, it had been reclassified as a tropical depression. It continued northward, and on August 31 was seen for the last time in the region of the Great Lakes.

Katrina's journey over American soil sparked the formation of tornadoes – 36 in all, half in the state of Georgia. Most were relatively harmless, but one in Carroll County, Georgia – one of the few of class F2 – led to one death, as well as dozens of injuries and the loss of half a million chickens on a local farm.

A disaster marked by controversy

The statistics for Katrina speak for themselves. The heavy downpours in Mississippi and Louisiana pounded several cities, especially Biloxi and New Orleans. The rain caused the levees of Lake Pontchartrain to break, causing terrible flooding in New Orleans, the jewel of the South. The wind and rain also lashed other states, such as Florida, Alabama, and Georgia, as well as parts of Tennessee, the Great Lakes, the Appalachians, and even parts of Canada, when Katrina was a tropical depression.

It is believed that the material damages will amount to over 200 billion dollars. The death count was thought to be over 10,000 or even more, thus rivaling hurricane Mitch in this grim respect.

Katrina reached New Orleans, which had been at risk from previous hurricanes, but had always emerged miraculously unscathed from such threats. As many experts feared, the city was not prepared for a storm of this magnitude. Once Katrina had blown itself out, humanitarian aid was the first priority, but unfortunately the response on this occasion was not as good as in other disasters. The attempts at evacuations were distinguished by their incompetence and thoughtlessness. Furthermore, there was large-scale looting, not only in New Orleans, but also in other cities, and the police resorted to force.

The sheer scale of the disaster overwhelmed the authorities. The refuges they set up, such as the Super Dome in New Orleans proved to be hellish for those inside. Help began to arrive, however, particularly food and medical care. Volunteers poured in from all over the United States, and a wide range of countries sent medical teams, emergency equipment, firefighters, and heavy machinery to clear the debris. Even countries with severe financial constraints, such as Bangladesh, made a contribution to the recovery process, which promises to be slow and laborious.

This tragedy also had a major long-term environmental impact, as the pollution resulting from damage to reservoirs and oil pipes seeped into the water supply. It is too early to assess the extent of this problem, but it is undoubtedly one

of the chief concerns of the authorities. Outbreaks of dysentery, typhus, stomach disorders, and food poisoning were possible in isolated sections of New Orleans.

It is obvious that we are dealing with a natural disaster of gigantic proportions – possibly, as observed earlier, the biggest in the history of the United States. Only days afterward, hurricane Rita hovered over the territory previously devastated by Katrina. This time, however, luck was on the side of the beleaguered inhabitants of the South, as the faltering Rita did not cause further damage.

New Orleans flooded, with its streets turned into veritable canals.

Hurricane Dennis

Dennis proved extremely difficult to handle, not only because of its destructive power, but also on account of its constant changes in speed, position, and size.

USA
Washington D.C. ●
ATLANTIC
PACIFIC
Caribbean Sea

The Caribbean
and United States

July 5–13, 2005

71 dead

Meteorologically speaking, 2005 will be marked by the disaster of hurricane Katrina, which alone made that year's hurricane season the worst in recent decades, and even, in the opinion of many experts, the most devastating in history. Before that, however, the first hurricane of the season – Dennis – put the meteorologists of the Uni-

ted States and the Caribbean on the alert.

A run-up to Katrina

Hurricane Dennis was the first phenomenon of this type to enter on the scene in 2005. From the onset, it displayed two features that warned of the arduous season in store: never had a storm of this size

appeared in the Caribbean so early in the year, and never had a hurricane wreaked so much destruction before August. In 2004, for example, hurricanes similar to Dennis – such as Alex and Charley – did not make their presence felt until the middle of that month.

Dennis originated as a class 4 tropical depression in the south-

In the foreground, a staircase leading to a house; in the background, the house to which it once belonged. In Nokomis, Alabama, the wind reached high speeds, creating damage like that shown here.

As usually occurs when hurricanes strike Florida, thousands of trailers were severely damaged, as can be seen from this photo taken in Pensacola.

In Navarre Beach, Florida, as in other parts of the state, gusting winds spread sand from the beaches everywhere, creating a host of problems.

east Caribbean, in the early hours of July 4. The following morning, it had turned into a tropical storm that was starting to look threatening for the east Caribbean – and it was building up speed. On July 6, confirming the fears of meteorological observers, Dennis turned into a class 1 hurricane on the Saffir-Simpson scale; at this point it lay above the Dominican Republic. By July 7, Dennis was a class 4 hurricane. No storm of this kind had intensified so dramatically since 1957. It headed north, toward Jamaica and Haiti, then approached Cuba as a fully fledged class 5 hurricane. When it left Cuba, on July 8, its classification had dropped back to class 1.

The following day, Dennis found new energy to regain its category of class 4, and on July 10 it reached the United States, where the states of Florida and Alabama had received hurricane Ivan only ten months before. Dennis honed in on Santa Rosa Island, Florida, one of the places where Ivan had left its mark. Fortunately, before touching down on American soil, its speed had dropped from the 145 miles (235 km) per hour it had flaunted in the Gulf of Mexico to a more modest 120 miles (195 km) per hour. On July 11, meteorologists declared Dennis a tropical storm. For two long days, it hovered over Illinois, regaling it with heavy rain, before disappearing on the 13th.

The weather stations on the southern coast of the United States and the relevant Caribbean countries had found Dennis extremely hard to handle, not only because of its enormous destructive power, but also because of its constant changes in speed, position, and size. Once it was gone, it was time to take stock of the damage it had caused.

Better than expected

Both the Caribbean countries involved and the United States had been quick to respond to the alert, and the first evacuations were organized on July 9. In Cuba, the government transferred over 600,000 citizens to different parts of the island; in Haiti, despite similar orders to evacuate many of the inhabitants to safe areas, the operation was more limited; in the United States, the governors of Alabama, Florida, Mississippi, and Louisiana all declared a state of emergency. Florida was the quickest to react to the impending hurricane, but Mississippi and Alabama soon followed its lead. Extensive traffic jams hindered the operation, however, and it was finally cancelled, due to both lack of time and the weakening of Dennis. Those who had remained at home had had sufficient time to prepare for the onslaught. Prior precautionary measures and the hurricane's unpredictable metamorphoses meant that the damage, although severe, was not as serious as might be expected for a storm of this class.

During its sojourn in the Caribbean and the United States, Dennis caused 71 deaths and material losses of around 9 billion dollars. In Haiti alone, there were 44 dead and nearly 100 people unaccounted for, but the damage was less substantial (although a large number of houses were destroyed). Cuba took the worst that Dennis had to give: 16 deaths and almost two billion dollars' worth of devastation. The winds and rains destroyed countless buildings, as well as hundreds of trees and electricity posts; 85 percent of Cuba was plunged into darkness.

Dennis was the worst hurricane that Cuba had endured since Flora, back in 1963. The United States also experienced widespread power cuts, affecting almost 700,000 inhabitants of Alabama, Florida, Mississippi, and Louisiana. Most buildings in these states were left intact, however, as were the bridges and roads, which emerged virtually unscathed. Nevertheless, the hurricane cost four billion dollars in damages and ten people lost their lives.

The storm's reduction in speed and virulence, combined with effective preparations in the danger areas, resulted in a largely satisfactory post-hurricane scenario. The worst was yet to come, however: Katrina would descend on the American coast only weeks later.

Earthquake in Kashmir

With a destructive force of 7.6 on the Richter scale, the Kashmir earthquake swept whole villages and small towns from the map.

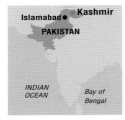

Muzaffarabad, Kashmir, Pakistan

October 8, 2005

75,000 dead

A partially collapsed house, whose debris landed on the car parked alongside

People rendered homeless by the earthquake make improvised shelters amid the rubble

At 5:50 p.m. on Saturday afternoon, October 8, Kashmir was rocked by a powerful earthquake. Residents in the capital cities of India, Pakistan, and Afghanistan felt tremors for several minutes. The earthquake had a devastating effect on the Pakistani part of Kashmir, where far and away the majority of the 75,000 victims died. The Indian part of Kashmir was also affected, however, with the quake there taking hundreds of lives. The earthquake was comparable in its extent and strength with those in San Francisco in 1906, Quetta in 1935, and Gujarat in 2001. According to the Pakistani meteorological service, the earthquake was actually comprised of four severe quakes in succession, which together registered a magnitude of 7.6 on the Richter scale. The first of these lasted for six minutes, with the subsequent three lasting for two-and-a-half, one, and one-and-a-half minutes respectively and occurring at intervals of over ten minutes. The epicenter of the quake was close to Muzaffarabad, the capital of Pakistani Kashmir, where approximately half of all homes, offices, and public buildings collapsed, including among them hospitals and schools. On Saturday, a normal school day in Kashmir, over 500 children were found dead in their school after its roof had fallen in on them. Due to the fact that this occurred during the Islamic month of Ramadan, many people were taken by surprise in their homes while having their first meal following the end of the daytime fast, and had no time to escape outdoors. In consequence, thousands of people were buried beneath their own roofs. In the Pakistani capital of Islamabad, rubble engulfed entire families when two large apartment complexes collapsed. In Kashmir, whole villages and small towns were also largely decimated. Everywhere, survivors scrabbled through the mounds of rubble for their relatives, using only their bare hands. In many places, people spent the night outdoors grouped around fires that were stoked by wood from the ruined buildings. A total of 75,000 died in the earthquake, almost all of them in the Pakistani part of the area. Fourteen hundred people were killed in Indian Kashmir. Over 40,000 people were injured in the earthquake and subsequent landslides, and hundreds of thousands lost everything that they owned. For a long time after the disaster, survivors had to endure the harsh living conditions of encampments.

International emergency relief

The first Pakistani rescue teams arrived in Muzaffarabad the very same Saturday, helped by British relief workers. Their rescue work was made much more difficult by landslides. Many roads had become impassable. Villages along the logistically important Karakoram Highway—the old Silk Road between Pakistan and China—had been completely cut off from the outside world. Contact with the disaster zone was seriously hampered because power and telephone lines were down. Severe aftershocks also impeded the search for survivors, filling people with trepidation as they continued with their mission.

The United Nations sent a team of experts to the region to assist with coordinating the relief efforts. First and foremost, rescue workers were having to deal with shortages: there was a lack of heavy machinery for excavations, and there were too few resources to provide shelter for the large numbers of people made homeless. The United States put military helicopters at the disposal of the relief effort and donated $50 million in emergency aid. The European Commission donated 3 million euros. The United Kingdom, Japan, Turkey, and the United Arab Emirates also offered direct aid to Pakistan. In total, international bodies and governments pledged some $5 billion in aid to the affected region.

The relief workers had to divide their focus between finding survivors and keeping alive the hundreds of thousands of people who no longer had a roof above their heads. Many victims had been deprived of blankets, medicines, and food. The lack of clean water became an increasingly urgent problem. Human corpses, debris, and waste had contaminated the most important source of drinking water for Muzzaffarabad, the River Neelum. The likelihood of a raft of diseases breaking out became greater by the day. Local health services had been completely destroyed, and malaria began to spread almost immediately. There was also great fear of a measles epidemic: the disease could easily spread among people having to live in close proximity with one another in cramped, temporary shelters.

A cold winter

The arrival of winter brought with it additional concerns, given that approximately 2.5 million people were homeless and at least 1 million lacked food. Kashmir usually experiences extremely hard winters, with heavy snowfall from October onward. Thus arctic tents, food, medicines, blankets, and water purification installations were urgently needed. Of the tents that had been hastily erected to house the survivors, 90 percent were unsuitable for winter conditions. Even during the first few days and weeks, hundreds of people had to be treated for symptoms of hypothermia. Through temporary measures, the tents were made as "winter-proof" as possible. They were fitted with extra-thick layers of insulation material and provided with as many additional blankets and stoves as possible. Cold-resistant tents are scarce and extremely expensive; almost all of them had to be imported. Since the earthquake, relief organizations had brought more than 400,000 tents to the affected region. One major problem for the relief effort was that many of the homeless were high up in the mountains and therefore difficult to reach.

The severe winter weather set in later than expected. Heavy rain and snowstorms set in just before New Year, with disastrous results across the whole region. Encampments flooded, and the tents started to leak or collapse. Relief organizations, too, suffered badly from the weather. As a result of landslides, they were no longer able to reach towns and villages. Facilities such as emergency hospitals suffered damage. Helicopters could no longer be used because heavy fog obscured the pilots' vision. Ultimately, the winter turned out not to be as severe as it could have been, considering the region. For the population having to live in the encampments or in isolated areas, however, conditions remained extraordinarily harsh for many more months.

A disputed region

It is almost 60 years since India and Pakistan entered into armed conflict over Kashmir. In the Pakistani-controlled part of Kashmir, over 100,000 military personnel are stationed in bunkers and artillery positions. In the past, the claim of both countries to the region has resulted in two wars and many confrontations. In 2002 came the threat of a third, nuclear confrontation, when India and Pakistan stationed a million soldiers along the border. The earthquake came at a time when India and Pakistan were once again seeking conciliation over the disputed region. The number of casualties it claimed among the armed forces either side of the frontline is still unknown.

Rescue workers search for survivors under the rubble of a ruined building

Earthquake in Indonesia

Three months after the devastating tsunami a severe earthquake occurred in western Indonesia.

PACIFIC

INDONESIA

Sumatra

Jakarta

Aceh, Nias, and Simeulue

March 28, 2005

Estimated 1,000 dead

On the island of Nias, a weekafter the disaster, children gather pieces of metal to sell amid the devastation

Shortly after the tsunami that hit Asia in December 2004, seismologists issued warnings of possible new movements in the floor of the Indian Ocean. The 2004 tsunami was caused by an earthquake of magnitude 9.0 on the Richter scale, just off the coast of northern Sumatra at a depth of around 6 miles (10 km). The quake had made an enormous rift in the sea floor, creating the potential for renewed tremors that, according to experts, could result in a new, major earthquake at any given time. But nobody was able to predict precisely when and where such an event might occur. The earthquake took place in the evening of March 28, 2005, 100 miles (160 km) from the epicenter of the preceding one. This quake had a magnitude of 8.7 and occurred at a depth of over 18 miles (30 km). The earthquake was not only felt on Sumatra and its surrounding islands, but also in Singapore, Malaysia, and even in Bangkok, Thailand. People fled in panic in all the areas where the tsunami had previously hit. Even in large cities, such as Singapore and Kuala Lumpur, people fled their homes onto the streets for fear of the buildings collapsing. Tsunami warnings were issued in all the countries surrounding the Bay of Bengal and,

though a new, major tsunami never appeared, the thinly populated Cocos Islands (belonging to Australia), several hundred miles to the south of Sumatra, were hit by a tidal surge. Seawater had been largely displaced in a southeasterly direction and not, as in December 2004, to the northwest.

Affected islands

Nevertheless, the inhabitants of the islands of Nias and Simeulue, some 62 miles (100 km) off the northwest coast of Sumatra, were still badly hit by the earthquake. On Nias, the two largest towns, Gunung Sitoli and Teluk Dalam, were largely destroyed, and Simeulue was additionally hit by a tidal wave. Insofar as it was still possible, the inhabitants of both islands (populations 440,000 and 78,000, respectively) fled from the coast into the hills. On the other side of the straits, on the coast of Aceh (northern Sumatra), it was the town of Singkilbaru that was most badly affected. The town had been left relatively unscathed at the time of the previous tsunami, but now suffered considerable damage as a result of this new quake. All 10,000 of its residents took flight. At other locations in Aceh, which had already

been devastated by the December tsunami, people fled the encampments where they had been given shelter to seek out safer refuge on higher ground. A situation of major panic ensued among the still traumatized population. In the provincial capital of Banda Aceh, it was days before people felt confident enough to return to the relief centers.

On Nias and Simeulue, the havoc was severe, but help was patchy. Hardly any relief workers managed to reach the islands during the first few days. The Gunung Sitoli airfield was no longer operational, because its control tower had collapsed and the landing strip was damaged; there was no airfield on Simeulue. Thus aid had either to be shipped or airlifted in by helicopter, and it was some time before relief workers, food, medical supplies, and temporary shelters arrived.

People used their bare hands to scrabble through the ruins for survivors, the wounded had to wait for days for help, and large numbers of the population went without food. On April 1, four days after the earthquake, the starving masses stormed and entirely ransacked a government food depot in Gunung Sitoli. For days, many people had been subsisting on nothing more than a few bananas, searching through the rubble for cans or packets of food. There was also a serious shortage of drinking water, as the violence of the earthquake had disrupted the water mains.

By April 5, over a week after the disaster, there were still numerous injured people on Nias who had yet to receive any medical attention. A 25-year-old woman, who had worked as a waitress in a restaurant in Gunung Sitoli, told how she had been in the restaurant when the earthquake struck. She had tried to get outside, but then the lights went out, and she was no longer able to find the exit. Shortly afterward, the building collapsed, and she lost consciousness. She awoke the next day and saw that much of her left leg had been torn away. It took the whole day before she managed to reach a medical station, where, although her bleeding was stopped, nothing else could be done for her.

Now, a week later, she was being transported by helicopter to a hospital in Medan on Sumatra to attempt to save as much of her leg as was still possible.

For many others with injuries, help came too late. On April 12, the head of a relief station in the south of Nias reported that 42 wounded people had died due to a lack of medical assistance, food, and medicines.

Heavy blow to tourism

In the end, the number of fatalities was in the region of a thousand. Amazingly, there were no foreign tourists among these, despite a number of them having been on Nias at the time. Although Nias is a relatively isolated island, it still attracted a considerable number of tourists. This was firstly because of its native, traditional culture, such as the entirely unique architectural style of its houses, and, secondly, because of its surf. Australian surfers, in particular, found the sea ideal for their sport at a variety of beaches on Nias.

As a result of the earthquake, some 17,000 dwellings were completely devastated and a further 60,000 suffered partial or serious damage. Bridges, roads, hospitals, and schools were also destroyed. Tourism—an important source of income for a section of the community—was swept away in an instant. Over 700 aftershocks were recorded in the wake of the earthquake. Later, in May 2005, yet another major quake occurred below the seabed near Padang (West Sumatra), registering a magnitude of 6.9.

Reconstruction on Nias took a

very long time to get underway. One year after the disaster, at end March 2006, thousands of people were still living in encampments and just 1,500 new homes had been constructed. Schools had still to be built, too: children were being given lessons in the open air. A number of roads and bridges had, however, been restored in the interim and the ferry service between Nias and the Sumatran port of Sibolga fully reinstated. It thus became a little easier for relatives to visit each other—since the earthquakes, several thousand islanders have departed for the mainland in search of work and new lives.

Amid the remains of her home, a woman is comforted by her family

A woman walks through devastated streets on Nias

Landslides in Sulawesi

In Indonesia, landslides have become an increasingly recurrent phenomenon over the past few decades. In June 2006, devastating mudflows on the island of Sulawesi were the most serious in years.

South Sulawesi, Indonesia

June 18–22, 2006

226 dead

Survivors try to salvage their possessions from the remains of their house in Sinjai, in the south of Sulawesi

The floods and landslides in the south of Sulawesi were as a result of heavy rainfall that began on June 18, 2006, and lasted for three days. Due to this rainwater, streams turned into raging torrents, large sections of mountainside slumped, and valleys overflowed with water. The floods occurred principally in the southeastern part of the province of South Sulawesi in the districts of Sinjai, Jeneponto, Bulukumba, Bantaeng, Luwu Utara, Bone, Gowa, and Sidenreng Rappang. Several rivers and smaller streams flow from central mountainous areas to the coast in these districts. The district of Sinjai was the worst hit, where it was largely those living in small villages in the hills who were taken by surprise. "We heard a thunderous rumbling and ran for our lives," related a man from the village of Gantarang, which was hit by one of the mudflows. "But not everyone managed to get out of their houses in time, and they were swamped under the mud, buried in their own homes." After the surge of mud had passed, the inhabitants tried to dig out the houses and rescue possible survivors. "But it was next to impossible, because we only had hand tools and it kept raining the whole time." Outside help was late to arrive, because landslides had blocked the roads to these isolated villages. Consequently, heavy machinery such as excavators could not be deployed. Others also fell victim to the floods, particularly people living in houses near to, or alongside, the rivers. "We were sleeping when our house was swept away by a flood wave," explained a despairing father a few days after the disaster. He managed to grab hold of a plank and was carried off by the river toward the sea. Afterward, he was left bobbing around among the waves for six hours before a fishing boat picked him up. At the hospital in the district capital of Sinjai, he waited in vain for news about his wife and two young children. This father's experience was mirrored by many of those living in riverside villages. In the days following the floods, the Indonesian navy found dozens of bodies floating between the coast of Sinjai and the Pulau Sembilan islands, some 18 miles (30 km) away. Progress made by the rescue operations was laborious. Isolated villages in the hills and mountains could not be reached by road. This required relief workers, food, and drinking water to be airlifted in and dropped by helicopter or plane. In other places, attempts were made to reach the stricken areas either on foot or via the rivers, traveling upstream in rubber boats. In total, over 5,000 homes were completely destroyed, and a further 1,300 suffered damage. Approximately 13,000 people were rendered homeless; the death toll was 226. An estimated 7,400 acres (3,000 hectares) of rice fields and 370 acres (150 hectares) devoted to coffee and cloves were devastated, while some 2,500 head of livestock were killed.

Evacuations

Over a week after the disaster, a further 4,300 people were evacuated from five villages in the district of Sinjai, amid fears of a landslide hitting their homes. The relief teams sometimes had great difficulty in convincing people of the need to evacuate their dwellings. Many did not wish to leave their sole possessions to fate; in the end, however, all the villagers were successfully brought to safety.

At the same time as the disaster in South Sulawesi, similar events were taking place in the south of Kalimantan—the Indonesian part of the island of Borneo—where a total of 52 fatalities were recorded and more than 3,600 homes destroyed.

In January and February 2006, various parts of Indonesia had already had to contend with landslides as a result of excessive rainfall. In January,

18 people died in landslides on the islands of Bali, Lombok, Sumbawa, and Flores. In the east of Lombok, thousands of people were cut off from the outside world because floods and landslides had blocked the roads to their villages. Over 3,400 people had to be evacuated. At the village of Ranaka on Flores, traffic on a busy road was overwhelmed by a landslide, burying ten motorbike riders and three passenger-filled buses under the mud. Five people lost their lives.

In February 2006, 33 were killed in North Sulawesi by flooding and landslides, which also hit the major centers of Manado and Bitung. On February 13, heavy rainfall caused more floods and landslides, resulting in four fatalities. Much more rain fell only a week later. Long, heavy rainfall persisted from February 19 through February 21, with Manado being particularly badly affected. Homes in outlying districts of the city were swamped under earth washed down from the neighboring hills. Most of the fatalities were children who had not managed to flee their houses in time. Parts of the city were also devastated by flooding that destroyed houses, bridges, and schools.

Deforestation

These floods and landslides follow a pattern that has been unfolding in Indonesia since the 1990s. The entire archipelago has been subject to increasing deforestation and the large-scale settlement of river

basins. Days after the disaster in South Sulawesi, the Indonesian Minister for Forestry, Kaban, stated that the landslides had been the result of "thirty years of malpractice." According to him, lumber license holders in South Sulawesi were responsible for the deforestation, because they have been felling trees for years without making any efforts to replant. "What happened in Sinjai must be a lesson to all the regions in Indonesia with less than 27 percent forest cover. When it rains hard in these areas for over three consecutive hours, the same problems arise," said the minister.

Indonesia's regions should have a minimum of 30 percent forest cover, enabling the large quantities of rain that can fall to soak away into the soil. However, illegal and quasi-legal lumbering has been going on there for decades, not only by companies wanting to export tropical hardwoods, but also to clear land for agriculture, such as oil palm plantations. According to the forestry minister, Indonesia now faces a huge backlog in terms of its commitment to reforest felled areas of terrain: "6.9 million acres (2.8 million hectares) of forest disappear annually, and we are able to reforest only 1.5 million acres (600,000 hectares) of this. If the situation is allowed to continue at these rates, it will take us 120 years to get back to a proper balance."

Indonesian rescue workers recover the body of a victim from a mudflow in Sinjai

Rescue workers and army units search amid the wreckage for survivors

Tsunami on Java

The tsunami that hit the coast of Java in the summer of 2006 took the local population completely by surprise.

PACIFIC

INDONESIA

Jakarta · Java

Pangandaran, Java, Indonesia

July 17, 2006

660 dead

A child playing on a truck surrounded by ruined buildings and devastation in Pangandaran

The tidal wave hurled a car into a shop in the coastal resort of Pangandaran in western Java

In the afternoon of Monday, July 17, 2006, a tsunami hit the south-western coast of Java following a severe ocean floor earthquake that had earlier taken place over 125 miles (200 km) offshore. A tidal wave tens of feet in height flooded a number of resorts and fishing villages on the Indonesian island of Java. In Pangandaran, a coastal resort popular with tourists, nobody had felt the shock from the earthquake of magnitude 7.7 on the Richter scale. Consequently, everyone was taken completely by surprise by the flood waves. Panic broke out when the sea flooded the coastal road and advanced nearly 2 miles (3 km) inland. The population fled in terror, either to the highest points in their homes or into the branches of trees. Fishing boats disappeared in the high waves and bamboo huts on the beach were washed away. The tsunami completely flooded Pangandaran and houses, hotels, and restaurants lining the coastal road were destroyed. "I saw a house coming toward me, but I couldn't run away. It stopped about 65 ft (20 m) from me," related a tourist. "We weren't warned. People suddenly started running toward us, and a boat was washed into our hotel lobby." Tens of thousands of people fled into the hills. In an area covering a 112-mile (180-km) stretch of coast, thousands of people sought refuge in the neighboring hills or climbed trees to escape the tidal wave. In total, some 53,000 people were driven from their homes.

Early-warning system

In December 2004, 200,000 people died from an enormous tsunami that hit virtually the entire southern coast of Asia and the east of Africa. The ocean floor earthquake that preceded this tsunami had a magnitude of 9.1 on the Richter scale. On that occasion, it was Aceh, the northernmost province of Indonesia, which was most seriously affected. Almost 170,000 people perished in the natural disaster. By and large, Java was miraculously spared the destructive force of the 2004 tsunami.

Since then, Indonesia has implemented a tsunami warning system for inhabitants of the island of Sumatra. Such a system is still lacking on the island of Java, however. The tsunami center in the Indonesian capital of Jakarta is under construction, but it may well be 2008 before the entire country has an operational warning system.

The epicenter of the seaquake on July 17 was at a depth of 6 miles (10 km) below the ocean floor, 150 miles (240 km) to the southwest of Java, according to the United States Geological Survey. The quake took place at 3.19 p.m., local time. Soon after the earthquake was registered, the Pacific Tsunami Warning Center on Hawaii sent warning that a possible tsunami could flood parts of Indonesia and the coast of Australia. The Japanese meteorological service also warned the Indonesian authorities, but there was too little time to alert the local authorities. By then, the tsunami had already reached a large part of the southwestern Java coast.

Several eyewitnesses stated that the first of several waves hit the south coast of Java at 4:15 p.m., local time. The warning came too late for the local population. The majority of those killed by the tsunami, over six hundred in number, died in Pangandaran. These were principally local residents. The bodies of 28 unidentified people were buried the following Wednesday. Four foreigners also died.

In the open air

Over 80,000 survivors in the region had to sleep in the open after the disaster. Many people lost their homes. Some fishing villages were almost completely destroyed, and the few buildings left standing were severely damaged. Thousands of people were frightened to return to their homes, in case of a new tsunami. Food aid began to reach the area only late in the day and, initially, there were not enough tents for the homeless. People who had lost all of their belongings camped out in mosques and government buildings,

Havoc and devastation along the coast at Pangandaran

or under improvised canvas sheets.

Following the severe shock that Monday afternoon, seismologists recorded several dozen aftershocks, which varied in strength from 4.6 to 6.1 on the Richter scale. Although the floodwater soon subsided, people were afraid that subsequent quakes might produce a new tidal wave. On the Wednesday after the disaster, tremors were felt in Pandangaran and rumors about another tsunami caused great anxiety. Parents ran about in panic looking for their children, people leapt into their cars and tore away, and many took flight on foot. Hundreds of residents left their hastily erected emergency shelters and, once again, fled into the hills.

It proved to be a false alarm. A fisherman sitting in his boat alongside the beach believed he saw a wave that was much higher than normal. The wave turned out to have been caused by a gust of wind at sea and had already dissipated by the time it reached the shore. It cost the army and police much time and effort to calm the situation down again.

The relief effort for the affected area was slow to get underway. It took a week before the Indonesian authorities began a major clean-up operation of the southern Java coastline. It was days before the Indonesian government sent in large numbers of troops to the disaster area. At first, these were largely deployed to search for victims lying under the rubble. In total, some 3,000 soldiers, police, local government officials, volunteers, and local residents helped with the rescue operation and clearing the devastation.

Houses and streets in Pangandaran were cleaned up, and debris burned. In the years immediately preceding the disaster, this former fishing village had grown into a very popular tourist destination, particularly feted by surfers and kite flyers owing to the annual kite festival held there. Another tourist attraction was a nature reserve in the immediate vicinity. Restaurants and hotels had sprung out of nowhere. Immediately after the disaster, these and other facilities underwent a period of reconstruction and regeneration, since tourism is an important source of local income and visitors to the island have become part of everyday life.

Ring of Fire

Indonesia lies in what is termed the "Ring of Fire"—a chain of volcanoes and fault lines that almost entirely encircle the Pacific Ocean. As a result, the Indonesian archipelago is under continual assault from earthquakes and volcanic eruptions. The tsunami in the summer of 2006 was the second disaster of seismological origin to affect Java that year. In May 2006, an earthquake occurred on the island that measured 6.3 on the Richter scale and claimed the lives of over 6,000 people.